PREFACE TO THE DOVER EDITION

During the past several years it has become more and more apparent that a need exists for the publication of a new edition of Aitken's *The Binary Stars*. Since the book has been out of print for many years, copies of it are practically unattainable. With the advent of the Space Age, many of the methods presented in this book are applicable to other fields than binary stars, and many of the binary-star astronomers would either like to replace their old worn-out copies, or own one for the first time. It is with the idea of serving these people, as well as libraries, computing centers, and industry, that this edition is presented.

No attempt has been made to bring the material up to date. This has been adequately done elsewhere, as is indicated throughout this book by new references. The book is simply presented as a classic in the field. We have attempted to eliminate all known errors, and to present sufficient additional footnotes and references to start the reader on the right path should he wish to continue his reading and study.

We wish to express our appreciation to the following people for their suggestions and invaluable assistance in listing all known errors, and eliminating them: Dr. George Van Biesbroeck, Yerkes Observatory; Dr. Hamilton M. Jeffers, Lick Observatory; Dr. W. H. van den Bos, Union Observatory, Johannesburg, South Africa; Dr. K. A. Strand, U.S. Naval Observatory; and others.

JACK T. KENT

TEXAS A & M UNIVERSITY
November, 1963

v

PREFACE

The first edition of this book was prepared as a contribution to the *Series of Semi-Centennial Publications* issued in 1918 by the University of California and was included in that series, although published commercially. It has long been out of print and is now also, in large part, out of date, as a result of the great amount of work that has been done in the field of binary star astronomy in the past sixteen years.

In its chapter headings and in the general form of presentation the present edition follows the plan adopted in the original work, but it has been necessary to revise all of the chapters and to rewrite some of them in large part to take account of the work done in recent years. One measure of this later work is given by the tables of orbits in the Appendix. In the first edition 87 orbits of visual binaries and 137 orbits of spectroscopic binaries were listed. In the present edition, the two tables which are based upon all data available to me before September 1933, contain 116 and 326 pairs, respectively, though Cepheids and pseudo-Cepheids are excluded.

It is a pleasure to express my gratitude to my colleague, Dr. J. H. Moore, for his kindness in revising the excellent chapter (V) on The Radial Velocity of a Star, which he prepared for the first edition; to Profs. H. N. Russell and R. S. Dugan for criticisms and suggestions relating to the chapter on Eclipsing Binary Stars, and to Dr. W. H. Van den Bos for placing data relating to the Thiele-Innes method at my disposal, and to acknowledge my indebtedness to other friends. I desire also to express again my thanks to all those who gave generous assistance in the preparation of the first edition.

ROBERT GRANT AITKEN.

UNIVERSITY OF CALIFORNIA,
April, 1935.

PLATE I.—The 36-inch refractor of the Lick Observatory.

THE BINARY STARS

BY

ROBERT GRANT AITKEN

Late Director and Astronomer, Lick Observatory,
University of California

DOVER PUBLICATIONS, INC.

NEW YORK

This Dover edition, first published in 1964, is an unabridged and corrected republication of the second edition, published by the McGraw-Hill Book Company in 1935

The publishers wish to thank Jack T. Kent, Associate Professor of Mathematics and Astronomy at Texas A & M University, for preparing the corrections and supplementary reference materials that have been incorporated into this Dover edition.

Library of Congress Catalog Card Number: 64-13456

Manufactured in the United States of America

Dover Publications, Inc.
180 Varick Street
New York 14, N.Y.

CONTENTS

INTRODUCTION

It is the object of this volume to give a general account of our present knowledge of the binary stars, including such an exposition of the best observing methods and of approved methods of orbit computation as may make it a useful guide for those who wish to undertake the investigation of these systems; and to present some conclusions based upon the author's own researches during the past forty years.

The term *binary star* was first used by Sir William Herschel, in 1802, in his paper "On the Construction of the Universe," to designate "a real double star—the union of two stars, that are formed together in one system, by the laws of attraction."

The term *double star* is of earlier origin; its Greek equivalent was, in fact, used by Ptolemy to describe the appearance of *ν Sagittarii*, two fifth-magnitude stars whose angular separation is about 14′, or a little less than half of the Moon's apparent diameter. It is still occasionally applied to this and other pairs of stars visible to the unaided eye, but is generally used to designate pairs separated by not more than a few seconds of arc and therefore visible as two stars only with the aid of a telescope.

Not every double star is a binary system, for, since all of the stars are apparently mere points of light projected upon the surface of the celestial sphere, two unrelated stars may appear to be closely associated simply as the result of the laws of perspective. Herschel draws the distinction between the two classes of objects in the following words:

. . . if a certain star should be situated at any, perhaps immense, distance behind another, and but little deviating from the line in which we see the first, we should have the appearance of a double star. But these stars being totally unconnected would not form a binary system. If, on the contrary, two stars should really be situated very near each other, and at the same time so far insulated as not to be materially affected by neighboring stars, they will then compose a separate system, and remain united by the bond of their mutual gravitation toward each other. This should be called a real double star.

Within the last half century we have become acquainted with a class of binary systems which are not double stars at all in the ordinary sense of the term, for the two component stars are not separately visible in any telescope. These are the *spectroscopic binary stars*, so named because their existence is demonstrated by a slight periodic shifting to and fro of the lines in their spectra, which, as will be shown, is evidence of a periodic variation in the radial velocity (the velocity in the line of sight, toward or away from the observer) of the star. With the possible exception of factors which may be introduced by the fact that the distance between the two components of a spectroscopic binary is, in general, so small (tidal interactions, for example), there seem to be no dynamical differences between the spectroscopic and the visual binary systems. The two classes will, therefore, be regarded in this volume as members of a single species.

THE BINARY STARS*

CHAPTER I

HISTORICAL SKETCH: THE EARLY PERIOD

The first double star was discovered about the year 1650
by the Italian astronomer, Jean Baptiste Riccioli. This was
ζ *Ursae Majoris* (*Mizar*). It is a remarkable coincidence that
Mizar was also the first double star to be observed photographically, measurable images being secured by G. P. Bond, at the
Harvard College Observatory in 1857; and that its principal
component was the first spectroscopic binary to be discovered,
the announcement being made by E. C. Pickering in 1889.

In 1656, Huygens saw θ *Orionis* resolved into the three principal stars of the group which form the familiar Trapezium,
and, in 1664, Hooke noted that γ *Arietis* consisted of two stars.
At least two additional pairs, one of which proved to be of
more than ordinary interest to astronomers, were discovered
before the close of the seventeenth century. It is worthy
of passing note that these were southern stars, not visible from
European latitudes—α *Crucis*, discovered by the Jesuit mis-
sionary, Father Fontenay, at the Cape of Good Hope, in
1685, and α *Centauri*, discovered by his confrère, Father Richaud,
while observing a comet at Pondicherry, India, in December,
1689.

These discoveries were all accidental, made in the course of
observations taken for other purposes. This is true also of the
double stars found in the first three-quarters of the eighteenth
century. Among these were the discoveries of γ *Virginis*, in
1718, and of *Castor*, in 1719, by Bradley and Pound, and of
α *Cygni*, by Bradley, in 1753.

No suspicion seems to have been entertained by these astronomers or by their contemporaries that the juxtaposition of the
star images in such pairs was other than optical, due to
chance positions of the Earth and the two stars in nearly

G. Van Biesbroeck, in the book review, *Ap. Jour.* **82**, 368, 1935.—

1

a straight line. They were therefore regarded as mere curiosities, and no effort was made to increase their number; nor were observations of the relative positions of the two components recorded except in descriptive terms. Father Feuille, for instance, on July 4, 1709, noted that the fainter star in the double, α *Centauri*, "is the more western and their distance is equal to the diameter of this star," and Bradley and Pound entered in their observing book, on March 30, 1719, that "the direction of the double star α of *Gemini* was so nearly parallel to a line through κ and σ of *Gemini* that, after many trials, we could scarce determine on which side of σ the line from κ parallel to the line of their direction tended; if on either, it was towards β."

Halley's discovery, in 1718, that some of the brighter stars, *Sirius*, *Arcturus*, *Aldebaran*, were in motion, having unmistakably changed their positions in the sky since the time of Ptolemy, unquestionably stimulated the interest of astronomers in precise observations of the stars. These researches and their results, in turn, were probably largely responsible for the philosophical speculations which began to appear shortly after the middle of the eighteenth century as to the possibility of the existence of systems among the stars. Famous among the latter are the *Cosmologische Briefe*,* published in 1761 by Lambert, in which it is maintained that the stars are suns and are accompanied by retinues of planets. Lambert, however, apparently did not connect his speculations with the double stars then known. Six years later, in 1767, John Michell, in a paper read before the Royal Society of London, presented a strong argument, based upon the theory of probabilities, that "such double stars, etc., as appear to consist of two or more stars placed near together, do really consist of stars placed near together, and under the influence of some general law, whenever the probability is very great, that there would not have been any such stars so near together, if all those that are not less bright than themselves had been scattered at random through the whole heavens." Michell thus has the credit of being the first to establish the probability of the existence of physical systems among the stars; but there were no observatio

* *Cosmologische Briefe über die Einrichtung des Weltbaues*, Ausg
von J. H. Lambert, Augsburg, 1761.

Catalogue of Dover
SCIENCE BOOKS

BOOKS THAT EXPLAIN SCIENCE

THE NATURE OF LIGHT AND COLOUR IN THE OPEN AIR, M. Minnaert. Why is falling snow sometimes black? What causes mirages, the fata morgana, multiple suns and moons in the sky; how are shadows formed? Prof. Minnaert of U. of Utrecht answers these and similar questions in optics, light, colour, for non-specialists. Particularly valuable to nature, science students, painters, photographers. "Can best be described in one word—fascinating!" Physics Today. Translated by H. M. Kremer-Priest, K. Jay. 202 illustrations, including 42 photos. xvi + 362pp. 5⅜ x 8. T196 Paperbound **$1.95**

THE RESTLESS UNIVERSE, Max Born. New enlarged version of this remarkably readable account by a Nobel laureate. Moving from sub-atomic particles to universe, the author explains in very simple terms the latest theories of wave mechanics. Partial contents: air and its relatives, electrons and ions, waves and particles, electronic structure of the atom, nuclear physics. Nearly 1000 illustrations, including 7 animated sequences. 325pp. 6 x 9. T412 Paperbound **$2.00**

MATTER AND LIGHT, THE NEW PHYSICS, L. de Broglie. Non-technical papers by a Nobel laureate explain electromagnetic theory, relativity, matter, light, radiation, wave mechanics, quantum physics, philosophy of science. Einstein, Planck, Bohr, others explained so easily that no mathematical training is needed for all but 2 of the 21 chapters. "Easy simplicity and lucidity . . . should make this source-book of modern physcis available to a wide public," Saturday Review. Unabridged. 300pp. 5⅜ x 8. T35 Paperbound **$1.60**

THE COMMON SENSE OF THE EXACT SCIENCES, W. K. Clifford. Introduction by James Newman, edited by Karl Pearson. For 70 years this has been a guide to classical scientific, mathematical thought. Explains with unusual clarity basic concepts such as extension of meaning of symbols, characteristics of surface boundaries, properties of plane figures, vectors, Cartesian method of determining position, etc. Long preface by Bertrand Russell. Bibliography of Clifford. Corrected. 130 diagrams redrawn. 249pp. 5⅜ x 8.
T61 Paperbound **$1.60**

THE EVOLUTION OF SCIENTIFIC THOUGHT FROM NEWTON TO EINSTEIN, A. d'Abro. Einstein's special, general theories of relativity, with historical implications, analyzed in non-technical terms. Excellent accounts of contributions of Newton, Riemann, Weyl, Planck, Eddington, Maxwell, Lorentz, etc., are treated in terms of space, time, equations of electromagnetics, finiteness of universe, methodology of science. "Has become a standard work," Nature. 21 diagrams. 482pp. 5⅜ x 8. T2 Paperbound **$2.00**

BRIDGES AND THEIR BUILDERS, D. Steinman, S. R. Watson. Engineers, historians, everyone ever fascinated by great spans will find this an endless source of information and interest. Dr. Steinman, recent recipient of Louis Levy Medal, is one of the great bridge architects, engineers of all time. His analysis of great bridges of history is both authoritative and easily followed. Greek, Roman, medieval, oriental bridges; modern works such as Brooklyn Bridge, Golden Gate Bridge, etc. described in terms of history, constructional principles, artistry, function. Most comprehensive, accurate semi-popular history of bridges in print in English. New, greatly revised, enlarged edition. 23 photographs, 26 line drawings. xvii + 401pp. 5⅜ x 8. T431 Paperbound **$1.95**

CONCERNING THE NATURE OF THINGS, Sir William Bragg. Christmas lectures at Royal Society by Nobel laureate, dealing with atoms, gases, liquids, and various types of crystals. No scientific background is needed to understand this remarkably clear introduction to basic processes and aspects of modern science. "More interesting than any bestseller," London Morning Post. 32pp. of photos. 57 figures. xii + 232pp. 5⅜ x 8. **T31 Paperbound $1.35**

THE RISE OF THE NEW PHYSICS, A. d'Abro. Half million word exposition, formerly titled "The Decline of Mechanism," for readers not versed in higher mathematics. Only thorough explanation in everyday language of core of modern mathematical physical theory, treating both classical, modern views. Scientifically impeccable coverage of thought from Newtonian system through theories of Dirac, Heisenberg, Fermi's statistics. Combines history, exposition; broad but unified, detailed view, with constant comparison of classical, modern views. "A must for anyone doing serious study in the physical sciences," J. of the Franklin Inst. "Extraordinary faculty . . . to explain ideas and theories . . . in language of everyday life," Isis. Part I of set: philosophy of science, from practice of Newton, Maxwell, Poincaré, Einstein, etc. Modes of thought, experiment, causality, etc. Part II: 100 pp. on grammar, vocabulary of mathematics, discussions of functions, groups, series, Fourier series, etc. Remainder treats concrete, detailed coverage of both classical, quantum physics: analytic mechanics, Hamilton's principle, electromagnetic waves, thermodynamics, Brownian movement, special relativity, Bohr's atom, de Broglie's wave mechanics, Heisenberg's uncertainty, scores of other important topics. Covers discoveries, theories of d'Alembert, Born, Cantor, Debye, Euler, Foucault, Galois, Gauss, Hadamard, Kelvin, Kepler Laplace, Maxwell, Pauli, Rayleigh Volterra, Weyl, more than 180 others. 97 illustrations. ix + 982pp. 5⅜ x 8. **T3 Vol. 1 Paperbound $2.00** **T4 Vol. II Paperbound $2.00**

SPINNING TOPS AND GYROSCOPIC MOTION, John Perry. Well-known classic of science still unsurpassed for lucid, accurate, delightful exposition. How quasi-rigidity is induced in flexible, fluid bodies by rapid motions; why gyrostat falls, top rises; nature, effect of internal fluidity on rotating bodies; etc. Appendixes describe practical use of gyroscopes in ships, compasses, monorail transportation. 62 figures. 128pp. 5⅜ x 8. **T416 Paperbound $1.00**

FOUNDATIONS OF PHYSICS, R. B. Lindsay, H. Margenau. Excellent bridge between semi-popular and technical writings. Discussion of methods of physical description, construction of theory; valuable to physicist with elementary calculus. Gives meaning to data, tools of modern physics. Contents: symbolism, mathematical equations; space and time; foundations of mechanics; probability; physics, continua; electron theory; relativity; quantum mechanics; causality; etc. "Thorough and yet not overdetailed. Unreservedly recommended," Nature. Unabridged corrected edition. 35 illustrations. xi + 537pp. 5⅜ x 8. **S377 Paperbound $2.45**

FADS AND FALLACIES IN THE NAME OF SCIENCE, Martin Gardner. Formerly entitled "In the Name of Science," the standard account of various cults, quack systems, delusions which have masqueraded as science: hollow earth fanatics, orgone sex energy, dianetics, Atlantis, Forteanism, flying saucers, medical fallacies like zone therapy, etc. New chapter on Bridey Murphy, psionics, other recent manifestations. A fair reasoned appraisal of eccentric theory which provides excellent innoculation. "Should be read by everyone, scientist or non-scientist alike," R. T. Birge, Prof. Emeritus of Physics, Univ. of Calif; Former Pres., Amer. Physical Soc. x + 365pp. 5⅜ x 8. **T394 Paperbound $1.50**

ON MATHEMATICS AND MATHEMATICIANS, R. E. Moritz. A 10 year labor of love by discerning, discriminating Prof. Moritz, this collection conveys the full sense of mathematics and personalities of great mathematicians. Anecdotes, aphorisms, reminiscences, philosophies, definitions, speculations, biographical insights, etc. by great mathematicians, writers: Descartes, Mill, Locke, Kant, Coleridge, Whitehead, etc. Glimpses into lives of great mathematicians, from Archimedes to Euler, Gauss, Weierstrass. To mathematicians, a superb browsing-book. To laymen, exciting revelation of fullness of mathematics. Extensive cross index. 410pp. 5⅜ x 8. **T489 Paperbound $1.95**

GUIDE TO THE LITERATURE OF MATHEMATICS AND PHYSICS, N. G. Parke III. Over 5000 entries under approximately 120 major subject headings, of selected most important books, monographs, periodicals, articles in English, plus important works in German, French, Italian, Spanish, Russian (many recently available works). Covers every branch of physics, math, related engineering. Includes author, title, edition, publisher, place, date, number of volumes, number of pages. 40 page introduction on basic problems of research, study provides useful information on organization, use of libraries, psychology of learning, etc. Will save you hours of time. 2nd revised edition. Indices of authors, subjects. 464pp. 5⅜ x 8. **S447 Paperbound $2.49**

THE STRANGE STORY OF THE QUANTUM, An Account for the General Reader of the Growth of Ideas Underlying Our Present Atomic Knowledge, B. Hoffmann. Presents lucidly, expertly, with barest amount of mathematics, problems and theories which led to modern quantum physics. Begins with late 1800's when discrepancies were noticed; with illuminating analogies, examples, goes through concepts of Planck, Einstein, Pauli, Schroedinger, Dirac, Sommerfield, Feynman, etc. New postscript through 1958. "Of the books attempting an account of the history and contents of modern atomic physics which have come to my attention, this is the best," H. Margenau, Yale U., in Amer. J. of Physics. 2nd edition. 32 tables, illustrations. 275pp. 5⅜ x 8. **T518 Paperbound $1.45**

2

HISTORY OF SCIENCE
AND PHILOSOPHY OF SCIENCE

THE VALUE OF SCIENCE, Henri Poincaré. Many of most mature ideas of "last scientific universalist" for both beginning, advanced workers. Nature of scientific truth, whether order is innate in universe or imposed by man, logical thought vs. intuition (relating to Weierstrass, Lie, Riemann, etc), time and space (relativity, psychological time, simultaneity), Herz's concept of force, values within disciplines of Maxwell, Carnot, Mayer, Newton, Lorentz, etc. iii + 147pp. 5⅜ x 8.   S469 Paperbound **$1.35**

PHILOSOPHY AND THE PHYSICISTS, L. S. Stebbing. Philosophical aspects of modern science examined in terms of lively critical attack on ideas of Jeans, Eddington. Tasks of science, causality, determinism, probability, relation of world physics to that of everyday experience, philosophical significance of Planck-Bohr concept of discontinuous energy levels, inferences to be drawn from Uncertainty Principle, implications of "becoming" involved in 2nd law of thermodynamics, other problems posed by discarding of Laplacean determinism. 285pp. 5⅜ x 8.   T480 Paperbound **$1.65**

THE PRINCIPLES OF SCIENCE, A TREATISE ON LOGIC AND THE SCIENTIFIC METHOD, W. S. Jevons. Milestone in development of symbolic logic remains stimulating contribution to investigation of inferential validity in sciences. Treats inductive, deductive logic, theory of number, probability, limits of scientific method; significantly advances Boole's logic, contains detailed introduction to nature and methods of probability in physics, astronomy, everyday affairs, etc. In introduction, Ernest Nagel of Columbia U. says,"[Jevons] continues to be of interest as an attempt to articulate the logic of scientific inquiry." liii + 786pp. 5⅜ x 8.   S446 Paperbound **$2.98**

A HISTORY OF ASTRONOMY FROM THALES TO KEPLER, J. L. E. Dreyer. Only work in English to give complete history of cosmological views from prehistoric times to Kepler. Partial contents: Near Eastern astronomical systems, Early Greeks, Homocentric spheres of Euxodus, Epicycles, Ptolemaic system, Medieval cosmology, Copernicus, Kepler, much more. "Especially useful to teachers and students of the history of science . . . unsurpassed in its field," Isis. Formerly "A History of Planetary Systems from Thales to Kepler." Revised foreword by W. H. Stahl. xvii + 430pp. 5⅜ x 8.   S79 Paperbound **$1.98**

A CONCISE HISTORY OF MATHEMATICS, D. Struik. Lucid study of development of ideas, techniques, from Ancient Near East, Greece, Islamic science, Middle Ages, Renaissance, modern times. Important mathematicians described in detail. Treatment not anecdotal, but analytical development of ideas. Non-technical—no math training needed. "Rich in content, thoughtful in interpretations," U.S. Quarterly Booklist. 60 illustrations including Greek, Egyptian manuscripts, portraits of 31 mathematicians. 2nd edition. xix + 299pp. 5⅜ x 8.   S255 Paperbound **$1.75**

THE PHILOSOPHICAL WRITINGS OF PEIRCE, edited by Justus Buchler. A carefully balanced expositon of Peirce's complete system, written by Peirce himself. It covers such matters as scientific method, pure chance vs. law, symbolic logic, theory of signs, pragmatism, experiment, and other topics. "Excellent selection . . . gives more than adequate evidence of the range and greatness," Personalist. Formerly entitled "The Philosophy of Peirce." xvi + 368pp.   T217 Paperbound **$1.95**

SCIENCE AND METHOD, Henri Poincaré. Procedure of scientific discovery, methodology, experiment, idea-germination—processes by which discoveries come into being. Most significant and interesting aspects of development, application of ideas. Chapters cover selection of facts, chance, mathematical reasoning, mathematics and logic; Whitehead, Russell, Cantor, the new mechanics, etc. 288pp. 5⅜ x 8.   S222 Paperbound **$1.35**

SCIENCE AND HYPOTHESIS, Henri Poincaré. Creative psychology in science. How such concepts as number, magnitude, space, force, classical mechanics developed, how modern scientist uses them in his thought. Hypothesis in physics, theories of modern physics. Introduction by Sir James Larmor. "Few mathematicians have had the breadth of vision of Poincaré, and none is his superior in the gift of clear exposition," E. T. Bell. 272pp. 5⅜ x 8.   S221 Paperbound **$1.35**

ESSAYS IN EXPERIMENTAL LOGIC, John Dewey. Stimulating series of essays by one of most influential minds in American philosophy presents some of his most mature thoughts on wide range of subjects. Partial contents: Relationship between inquiry and experience; dependence of knowledge upon thought; character logic; judgments of practice, data, and meanings; stimuli of thought, etc. viii + 444pp. 5⅜ x 8.   T73 Paperbound **$1.95**

WHAT IS SCIENCE, Norman Campbell. Excellent introduction explains scientific method, role of mathematics, types of scientific laws. Contents: 2 aspects of science, science and nature, laws of chance, discovery of laws, explanation of laws, measurement and numerical laws, applications of science. 192pp. 5⅜ x 8.   S43 Paperbound **$1.25**

FROM EUCLID TO EDDINGTON: A STUDY OF THE CONCEPTIONS OF THE EXTERNAL WORLD, Sir Edmund Whittaker. Foremost British scientist traces development of theories of natural philosophy from western rediscovery of Euclid to Eddington, Einstein, Dirac, etc. 5 major divisions: Space, Time and Movement; Concepts of Classical Physics; Concepts of Quantum Mechanics; Eddington Universe. Contrasts inadequacy of classical physics to understand physical world with present day attempts of relativity, non-Euclidean geometry, space curvature, etc. 212pp. 5⅜ x 8. T491 Paperbound **$1.35**

THE ANALYSIS OF MATTER, Bertrand Russell. How do our senses accord with the new physics? This volume covers such topics as logical analysis of physics, prerelativity physics, causality, scientific inference, physics and perception, special and general relativity, Weyl's theory, tensors, invariants and their physical interpretation, periodicity and qualitative series. "The most thorough treatment of the subject that has yet been published," The Nation. Introduction by L. E. Denonn. 422pp. 5⅜ x 8. T231 Paperbound **$1.95**

LANGUAGE, TRUTH, AND LOGIC, A. Ayer. A clear introduction to the Vienna and Cambridge schools of Logical Positivism. Specific tests to evaluate validity of ideas, etc. Contents: function of philosophy, elimination of metaphysics, nature of analysis, a priori, truth and probability, etc. 10th printing. "I should like to have written it myself," Bertrand Russell. 160pp. 5⅜ x 8. T10 Paperbound **$1.25**

THE PSYCHOLOGY OF INVENTION IN THE MATHEMATICAL FIELD, J. Hadamard. Where do ideas come from? What role does the unconscious play? Are ideas best developed by mathematical reasoning, word reasoning, visualization? What are the methods used by Einstein, Poincaré, Galton, Riemann? How can these techniques be applied by others? One of the world's leading mathematicians discusses these and other questions. xiii + 145pp. 5⅜ x 8. T107 Paperbound **$1.25**

GUIDE TO PHILOSOPHY, C. E. M. Joad. By one of the ablest expositors of all time, this is not simply a history or a typological survey, but an examination of central problems in terms of answers afforded by the greatest thinkers: Plato, Aristotle, Scholastics, Leibniz, Kant, Whitehead, Russell, and many others. Especially valuable to persons in the physical sciences; over 100 pages devoted to Jeans, Eddington, and others, the philosophy of modern physics, scientific materialism, pragmatism, etc. Classified bibliography. 592pp. 5⅜ x 8. T50 Paperbound **$2.00**

SUBSTANCE AND FUNCTION, and **EINSTEIN'S THEORY OF RELATIVITY, Ernst Cassirer.** Two books bound as one. Cassirer establishes a philosophy of the exact sciences that takes into consideration new developments in mathematics, shows historical connections. Partial contents: Aristotelian logic, Mill's analysis, Helmholtz and Kronecker, Russell and cardinal numbers, Euclidean vs. non-Euclidean geometry, Einstein's relativity. Bibliography. Index. xxi + 464pp. 5⅜ x 8. T50 Paperbound **$2.00**

FOUNDATIONS OF GEOMETRY, Bertrand Russell. Nobel laureate analyzes basic problems in the overlap area between mathematics and philosophy: the nature of geometrical knowledge, the nature of geometry, and the applications of geometry to space. Covers history of non-Euclidean geometry, philosophic interpretations of geometry, especially Kant, projective and metrical geometry. Most interesting as the solution offered in 1897 by a great mind to a problem still current. New introduction by Prof. Morris Kline, N.Y. University. "Admirably clear, precise, and elegantly reasoned analysis," International Math. News. xii + 201pp. 5⅜ x 8. S233 Paperbound **$1.60**

THE NATURE OF PHYSICAL THEORY, P. W. Bridgman. How modern physics looks to a highly unorthodox physicist—a Nobel laureate. Pointing out many absurdities of science, demonstrating inadequacies of various physical theories, weighs and analyzes contributions of Einstein, Bohr, Heisenberg, many others. A non-technical consideration of correlation of science and reality. xi + 138pp. 5⅜ x 8. S33 Paperbound **$1.25**

EXPERIMENT AND THEORY IN PHYSICS, Max Born. A Nobel laureate examines the nature and value of the counterclaims of experiment and theory in physics. Synthetic versus analytical scientific advances are analyzed in works of Einstein, Bohr, Heisenberg, Planck, Eddington, Milne, others, by a fellow scientist. 44pp. 5⅜ x 8. S308 Paperbound **60¢**

A SHORT HISTORY OF ANATOMY AND PHYSIOLOGY FROM THE GREEKS TO HARVEY, Charles Singer. Corrected edition of "The Evolution of Anatomy." Classic traces anatomy, physiology from prescientific times through Greek, Roman periods, dark ages, Renaissance, to beginning of modern concepts. Centers on individuals, movements, that definitely advanced anatomical knowledge. Plato, Diocles, Erasistratus, Galen, da Vinci, etc. Special section on Vesalius. 20 plates. 270 extremely interesting illustrations of ancient, Medieval, Renaissance, Oriental origin. xii + 209pp. 5⅜ x 8. T389 Paperbound **$1.75**

SPACE-TIME-MATTER, Hermann Weyl. "The standard treatise on the general theory of relativity," (Nature), by world renowned scientist. Deep, clear discussion of logical coherence of general theory, introducing all needed tools: Maxwell, analytical geometry, non-Euclidean geometry, tensor calculus, etc. Basis is classical space-time, before absorption of relativity. Contents: Euclidean space, mathematical form, metrical continuum, general theory, etc. 15 diagrams. xviii + 330pp. 5⅜ x 8. S267 Paperbound **$1.75**

4

DOVER SCIENCE BOOKS

MATTER AND MOTION, James Clerk Maxwell. Excellent exposition begins with simple particles, proceeds gradually to physical systems beyond complete analysis; motion, force, properties of centre of mass of material system; work, energy, gravitation, etc. Written with all Maxwell's original insights and clarity. Notes by E. Larmor. 17 diagrams. 178pp. 5⅜ x 8.
S188 Paperbound **$1.25**

PRINCIPLES OF MECHANICS, Heinrich Hertz. Last work by the great 19th century physicist is not only a classic, but of great interest in the logic of science. Creating a new system of mechanics based upon space, time, and mass, it returns to axiomatic analysis, understanding of the formal or structural aspects of science, taking into account logic, observation, a priori elements. Of great historical importance to Poincaré, Carnap, Einstein, Milne. A 20 page introduction by R. S. Cohen, Wesleyan University, analyzes the implications of Hertz's thought and the logic of science. 13 page introduction by Helmholtz. xlii + 274pp. 5⅜ x 8.
S316 Clothbound **$3.50**
S317 Paperbound **$1.75**

FROM MAGIC TO SCIENCE, Charles Singer. A great historian examines aspects of science from Roman Empire through Renaissance. Includes perhaps best discussion of early herbals, penetrating physiological interpretation of "The Visions of Hildegarde of Bingen." Also examines Arabian, Galenic influences; Pythagoras' sphere, Paracelsus; reawakening of science under Leonardo da Vinci, Vesalius; Lorica of Gildas the Briton; etc. Frequent quotations with translations from contemporary manuscripts. Unabridged, corrected edition. 158 unusual illustrations from Classical, Medieval sources. xxvii + 365pp. 5⅜ x 8.
T390 Paperbound **$2.00**

A HISTORY OF THE CALCULUS, AND ITS CONCEPTUAL DEVELOPMENT, Carl B. Boyer. Provides laymen, mathematicians a detailed history of the development of the calculus, from beginnings in antiquity to final elaboration as mathematical abstraction. Gives a sense of mathematics not as technique, but as habit of mind, in progression of ideas of Zeno, Plato, Pythagoras, Eudoxus, Arabic and Scholastic mathematicians, Newton, Leibniz, Taylor, Descartes, Euler, Lagrange, Cantor, Weierstrass, and others. This first comprehensive, critical history of the calculus was originally entitled "The Concepts of the Calculus." Foreword by R. Courant. 22 figures. 25 page bibliography. v + 364pp. 5⅜ x 8.
S509 Paperbound **$2.00**

A DIDEROT PICTORIAL ENCYCLOPEDIA OF TRADES AND INDUSTRY, Manufacturing and the Technical Arts in Plates Selected from "L'Encyclopédie ou Dictionnaire Raisonné des Sciences, des Arts, et des Métiers" of Denis Diderot. Edited with text by C. Gillispie. First modern selection of plates from high-point of 18th century French engraving. Storehouse of technological information to historian of arts and science. Over 2,000 illustrations on 485 full page plates, most of them original size, show trades, industries of fascinating era in such great detail that modern reconstructions might be made of them. Plates teem with men, women, children performing thousands of operations; show sequence, general operations, closeups, details of machinery. Illustrates such important, interesting trades, industries as sowing, harvesting, beekeeping, tobacco processing, fishing, arts of war, mining, smelting, casting iron, extracting mercury, making gunpowder, cannons, bells, shoeing horses, tanning, papermaking, printing, dying, over 45 more categories. Professor Gillispie of Princeton supplies full commentary on all plates, identifies operations, tools, processes, etc. Material is presented in lively, lucid fashion. Of great interest to all studying history of science, technology. Heavy library cloth. 920pp. 9 x 12.
T421 2 volume set **$18.50**

DE MAGNETE, William Gilbert. Classic work on magnetism, founded new science. Gilbert was first to use word "electricity," to recognize mass as distinct from weight, to discover effect of heat on magnetic bodies; invented an electroscope, differentiated between static electricity and magnetism, conceived of earth as magnet. This lively work, by first great experimental scientist, is not only a valuable historical landmark, but a delightfully easy to follow record of a searching, ingenious mind. Translated by P. F. Mottelay. 25 page biographical memoir. 90 figures. lix + 368pp. 5⅜ x 8.
S470 Paperbound **$2.00**

HISTORY OF MATHEMATICS, D. E. Smith. Most comprehensive, non-technical history of math in English. Discusses lives and works of over a thousand major, minor figures, with footnotes giving technical information outside book's scheme, and indicating disputed matters. Vol. I: A chronological examination, from primitive concepts through Egypt, Babylonia, Greece, the Orient, Rome, the Middle Ages, The Renaissance, and to 1900. Vol. II: The development of ideas in specific fields and problems, up through elementary calculus. "Marks an epoch . . . will modify the entire teaching of the history of science," George Sarton. 2 volumes, total of 510 illustrations, 1355pp. 5⅜ x 8. Set boxed in attractive container.
T429, 430 Paperbound, the set **$5.00**

THE PHILOSOPHY OF SPACE AND TIME, H. Reichenbach. An important landmark in development of empiricist conception of geometry, covering foundations of geometry, time theory, consequences of Einstein's relativity, including: relations between theory and observations; coordinate definitions; relations between topological and metrical properties of space; psychological problem of visual intuition of non-Euclidean structures; many more topics important to modern science and philosophy. Majority of ideas require only knowledge of intermediate math. "Still the best book in the field," Rudolf Carnap. Introduction by R. Carnap. 49 figures. xviii + 296pp. 5⅜ x 8.
S443 Paperbound **$2.00**

5

CATALOGUE OF

FOUNDATIONS OF SCIENCE: THE PHILOSOPHY OF THEORY AND EXPERIMENT, N. Campbell. A critique of the most fundamental concepts of science, particularly physics. Examines why certain propositions are accepted without question, demarcates science from philosophy, etc. Part I analyzes presuppositions of scientific thought: existence of material world, nature of laws, probability, etc; part 2 covers nature of experiment and applications of mathematics: conditions for measurement, relations between numerical laws and theories, error, etc. An appendix covers problems arising from relativity, force, motion, space, time. A classic in its field. "A real grasp of what science is," Higher Educational Journal.
xiii + 565pp. 5⅝ x 8⅜. S372 Paperbound $2.95

THE STUDY OF THE HISTORY OF MATHEMATICS and THE STUDY OF THE HISTORY OF SCIENCE, G. Sarton. Excellent introductions, orientation, for beginning or mature worker. Describes duty of mathematical historian, incessant efforts and genius of previous generations. Explains how today's discipline differs from previous methods. 200 item bibliography with critical evaluations, best available biographies of modern mathematicians, best treatises on historical methods is especially valuable. 10 illustrations. 2 volumes bound as one.
113pp. + 75pp. 5⅜ x 8. T240 Paperbound $1.25

MATHEMATICAL PUZZLES

MATHEMATICAL PUZZLES OF SAM LOYD, selected and edited by Martin Gardner. 117 choice puzzles by greatest American puzzle creator and innovator, from his famous "Cyclopedia of Puzzles." All unique style, historical flavor of originals. Based on arithmetic, algebra, probability, game theory, route tracing, topology, sliding block, operations research, geometrical dissection. Includes famous "14-15" puzzle which was national craze, "Horse of a Different Color" which sold millions of copies. 120 line drawings, diagrams. Solutions.
xx + 167pp. 5⅜ x 8. T498 Paperbound $1.00

SYMBOLIC LOGIC and THE GAME OF LOGIC, Lewis Carroll. "Symbolic Logic" is not concerned with modern symbolic logic, but is instead a collection of over 380 problems posed with charm and imagination, using the syllogism, and a fascinating diagrammatic method of drawing conclusions. In "The Game of Logic" Carroll's whimsical imagination devises a logical game played with 2 diagrams and counters (included) to manipulate hundreds of tricky syllogisms. The final section, "Hit or Miss" is a lagniappe of 101 additional puzzles in the delightful Carroll manner. Until this reprint edition, both of these books were rarities costing up to $15 each. Symbolic Logic: Index. xxxi + 199pp. The Game of Logic: 96pp.
2 vols. bound as one. 5⅜ x 8. T492 Paperbound $1.50

PILLOW PROBLEMS and A TANGLED TALE, Lewis Carroll. One of the rarest of all Carroll's works, "Pillow Problems" contains 72 original math puzzles, all typically ingenious. Particularly fascinating are Carroll's answers which remain exactly as he thought them out, reflecting his actual mental process. The problems in "A Tangled Tale" are in story form, originally appearing as a monthly magazine serial. Carroll not only gives the solutions, but uses answers sent in by readers to discuss wrong approaches and misleading paths, and grades them for insight. Both of these books were rarities until this edition, "Pillow Problems" costing up to $25, and "A Tangled Tale" $15. Pillow Problems: Preface and Introduction by Lewis Carroll. xx + 109pp. A Tangled Tale: 6 illustrations. 152pp. Two vols.
bound as one. 5⅜ x 8. T493 Paperbound $1.50

NEW WORD PUZZLES, G. L. Kaufman. 100 brand new challenging puzzles on words, combinations, never before published. Most are new types invented by author, for beginners and experts both. Squares of letters follow chess moves to build words; symmetrical designs made of synonyms; rhymed crostics; double word squares; syllable puzzles where you fill in missing syllables instead of missing letter; many other types, all new. Solutions. "Excellent," Recreation. 100 puzzles. 196 figures. vi + 122pp. 5⅜ x 8.
T344 Paperbound $1.00

MATHEMATICAL EXCURSIONS, H. A. Merrill. Fun, recreation, insights into elementary problem solving. Math expert guides you on by-paths not generally travelled in elementary math courses—divide by inspection, Russian peasant multiplication; memory systems for pi; odd, even magic squares; dyadic systems; square roots by geometry; Tchebichev's machine; dozens more. Solutions to more difficult ones. "Brain stirring stuff . . . a classic," Genie.
50 illustrations. 145pp. 5⅜ x 8. T350 Paperbound $1.00

THE BOOK OF MODERN PUZZLES, G. L. Kaufman. Over 150 puzzles, absolutely all new material based on same appeal as crosswords, deduction puzzles, but with different principles, techniques. 2-minute teasers, word labyrinths, design, pattern, logic, observation puzzles, puzzles testing ability to apply general knowledge to peculiar situations, many others. Solutions. 116 illustrations. 192pp. 5⅜ x 8. T143 Paperbound $1.00

MATHEMAGIC, MAGIC PUZZLES, AND GAMES WITH NUMBERS, R. V. Heath. Over 60 puzzles, stunts, on properties of numbers. Easy techniques for multiplying large numbers mentally, identifying unknown numbers, finding date of any day in any year. Includes The Lost Digit, 3 Acrobats, Psychic Bridge, magic squares, triangles, cubes, others not easily found elsewhere. Edited by J. S. Meyer. 76 illustrations. 128pp. 5⅜ x 8. T110 Paperbound $1.00

6

DOVER SCIENCE BOOKS

PUZZLE QUIZ AND STUNT FUN, J. Meyer. 238 high-priority puzzles, stunts, tricks—math puzzles like The Clever Carpenter, Atom Bomb, Please Help Alice; mysteries, deductions like The Bridge of Sighs, Secret Code; observation puzzlers like The American Flag, Playing Cards, Telephone Dial; over 200 others with magic squares, tongue twisters, puns, anagrams. Solutions. Revised, enlarged edition of "Fun-To-Do." Over 100 illustrations. 238 puzzles, stunts, tricks. 256pp. 5⅜ x 8.   T337 Paperbound **$1.00**

101 PUZZLES IN THOUGHT AND LOGIC, C. R. Wylie, Jr. For readers who enjoy challenge, stimulation of logical puzzles without specialized math or scientific knowledge. Problems entirely new, range from relatively easy to brainteasers for hours of subtle entertainment. Detective puzzles, find the lying fisherman, how a blind man identifies color by logic, many more. Easy-to-understand introduction to logic of puzzle solving and general scientific method. 128pp. 5⅜ x 8.   T367 Paperbound **$1.00**

CRYPTANALYSIS, H. F. Gaines. Standard elementary, intermediate text for serious students. Not just old material, but much not generally known, except to experts. Concealment, Transposition, Substitution ciphers; Vigenere, Kasiski, Playfair, multafid, dozens of other techniques. Formerly "Elementary Cryptanalysis." Appendix with sequence charts, letter frequencies in English, 5 other languages, English word frequencies. Bibliography. 167 codes. New to this edition: solutions to codes. vi + 230pp. 5⅜ x 8⅜.
                                                            T97 Paperbound **$1.95**

CRYPTOGRAPHY, L. D. Smith. Excellent elementary introduction to enciphering, deciphering secret writing. Explains transposition, substitution ciphers; codes; solutions; geometrical patterns, route transcription, columnar transposition, other methods. Mixed cipher systems; single, polyalphabetical substitutions; mechanical devices; Vigenere; etc. Enciphering Japanese; explanation of Baconian biliteral cipher; frequency tables. Over 150 problems. Bibliography. Index. 164pp. 5⅜ x 8.   T247 Paperbound **$1.00**

MATHEMATICS, MAGIC AND MYSTERY, M. Gardner. Card tricks, metal mathematics, stage mind-reading, other "magic" explained as applications of probability, sets, number theory, etc. Creative examination of laws, applications. Scores of new tricks, insights. 115 sections on cards, dice, coins; vanishing tricks, many others. No sleight of hand—math guarantees success. "Could hardly get more entertainment . . . easy to follow," Mathematics Teacher. 115 illustrations. xii + 174pp. 5⅜ x 8.   T335 Paperbound **$1.00**

AMUSEMENTS IN MATHEMATICS, H. E. Dudeney. Foremost British originator of math puzzles, always witty, intriguing, paradoxical in this classic. One of largest collections. More than 430 puzzles, problems, paradoxes. Mazes, games, problems on number manipulations, unicursal, other route problems, puzzles on measuring, weighing, packing, age, kinship, chessboards, joiners', crossing river, plane figure dissection, many others. Solutions. More than 450 illustrations. viii + 258pp. 5⅜ x 8.   T473 Paperbound **$1.25**

THE CANTERBURY PUZZLES H. E. Dudeney. Chaucer's pilgrims set one another problems in story form. Also Adventures of the Puzzle Club, the Strange Escape of the King's Jester, the Monks of Riddlewell, the Squire's Christmas Puzzle Party, others. All puzzles are original, based on dissecting plane figures, arithmetic, algebra, elementary calculus, other branches of mathematics, and purely logical ingenuity. "The limit of ingenuity and intricacy," The Observer. Over 110 puzzles, full solutions. 150 illustrations. viii + 225 pp. 5⅜ x 8.   T474 Paperbound **$1.25**

MATHEMATICAL PUZZLES FOR BEGINNERS AND ENTHUSIASTS, G. Mott-Smith. 188 puzzles to test mental agility. Inference, interpretation, algebra, dissection of plane figures, geometry, properties of numbers, decimation, permutations, probability, all are in these delightful problems. Includes the Odic Force, How to Draw an Ellipse, Spider's Cousin, more than 180 others. Detailed solutions. Appendix with square roots, triangular numbers, primes, etc. 135 illustrations. 2nd revised edition. 248pp. 5⅜ x 8.   T198 Paperbound **$1.00**

MATHEMATICAL RECREATIONS, M. Kraitchik. Some 250 puzzles, problems, demonstrations of recreation mathematics on relatively advanced level. Unusual historical problems from Greek, Medieval, Arabic, Hindu sources; modern problems on "mathematics without numbers," geometry, topology, arithmetic, etc. Pastimes derived from figurative, Mersenne, Fermat numbers: fairy chess; latruncles: reversi; etc. Full solutions. Excellent insights into special fields of math. "Strongly recommended to all who are interested in the lighter side of mathematics," Mathematical Gaz. 181 illustrations. 330pp. 5⅜ x 8.
                                                            T163 Paperbound **$1.75**

FICTION

FLATLAND, E. A. Abbott. A perennially popular science-fiction classic about life in a 2-dimensional world, and the impingement of higher dimensions. Political, satiric, humorous, moral overtones. This land where women are straight lines and the lowest and most dangerous classes are isosceles triangles with 3° vertices conveys brilliantly a feeling for many concepts of modern science. 7th edition. New introduction by Banesh Hoffmann. 128pp. 5⅜ x 8.   T1 Paperbound **$1.00**

SEVEN SCIENCE FICTION NOVELS OF H. G. WELLS. Complete texts, unabridged, of seven of Wells' greatest novels: The War of the Worlds, The Invisible Man, The Island of Dr. Moreau, The Food of the Gods, First Men in the Moon, In the Days of the Comet, The Time Machine. Still considered by many experts to be the best science-fiction ever written, they will offer amusements and instruction to the scientific minded reader. "The great master," Sky and Telescope. 1051pp. 5⅜ x 8.   T264 Clothbound **$3.95**

28 SCIENCE FICTION STORIES OF H. G. WELLS. Unabridged! This enormous omnibus contains 2 full length novels—Men Like Gods, Star Begotten—plus 26 short stories of space, time, invention, biology, etc. The Crystal Egg, The Country of the Blind, Empire of the Ants, The Man Who Could Work Miracles, Aepyornis Island, A Story of the Days to Come, and 20 others "A master . . . not surpassed by . . . writers of today," The English Journal. 915pp. 5⅜ x 8.   T265 Clothbound **$3.95**

FIVE ADVENTURE NOVELS OF H. RIDER HAGGARD. All the mystery and adventure of darkest Africa captured accurately by a man who lived among Zulus for years, who knew African ethnology, folkways as did few of his contemporaries. They have been regarded as examples of the very best high adventure by such critics as Orwell, Andrew Lang, Kipling. Contents: She, King Solomon's Mines, Allan Quatermain, Allan's Wife, Maiwa's Revenge. "Could spin a yarn so full of suspense and color that you couldn't put the story down," Sat. Review. 821pp. 5⅜ x 8.   T108 Clothbound **$3.95**

CHESS AND CHECKERS

LEARN CHESS FROM THE MASTERS, Fred Reinfeld. Easiest, most instructive way to improve your game—play 10 games against such masters as Marshall, Znosko-Borovsky, Bronstein, Najdorf, etc., with each move graded by easy system. Includes ratings for alternate moves possible. Games selected for interest, clarity, easily isolated principles. Covers Ruy Lopez, Dutch Defense, Vienna Game openings; subtle, intricate middle game variations; all-important end game. Full annotations. Formerly "Chess by Yourself." 91 diagrams. viii + 144pp. 5⅜ x 8.   T362 Paperbound **$1.00**

REINFELD ON THE END GAME IN CHESS, Fred Reinfeld. Analyzes 62 end games by Alekhine, Flohr, Tarrasch, Morphy, Capablanca, Rubinstein, Lasker, Reshevsky, other masters. Only 1st rate book with extensive coverage of error—tell exactly what is wrong with each move you might have made. Centers around transitions from middle game to end play. King and pawn, minor pieces, queen endings; blockage, weak, passed pawns, etc. "Excellent . . . a boon," Chess Life. Formerly "Practical End Play." 62 figures. vi + 177pp. 5⅜ x 8.
T417 Paperbound **$1.25**

HYPERMODERN CHESS as developed in the games of its greatest exponent, ARON NIMZO-VICH, edited by Fred Reinfeld. An intensely original player, analyst, Nimzovich's approaches startled, often angered the chess world. This volume, designed for the average player, shows how his iconoclastic methods won him victories over Alekhine, Lasker, Marshall, Rubinstein, Spielmann, others, and infused new life into the game. Use his methods to startle opponents, invigorate play. "Annotations and introductions to each game . . . are excellent," Times (London). 180 diagrams. viii + 220pp. 5⅜ x 8.   T448 Paperbound **$1.35**

THE ADVENTURE OF CHESS, Edward Lasker. Lively reader, by one of America's finest chess masters, including: history of chess, from ancient Indian 4-handed game of Chaturanga to great players of today; such delights and oddities as Maelzel's chess-playing automaton that beat Napoleon 3 times; etc. One of most valuable features is author's personal recollections of men he has played against—Nimzovich, Emanuel Lasker, Capablanca, Alekhine, etc. Discussion of chess-playing machines (newly revised). 5 page chess primer. 11 illustrations. 53 diagrams. 296pp. 5⅜ x 8.   S510 Paperbound **$1.45**

THE ART OF CHESS, James Mason. Unabridged reprinting of latest revised edition of most famous general study ever written. Mason, early 20th century master, teaches beginning, intermediate player over 90 openings; middle game, end game, to see more moves ahead, to plan purposefully, attack, sacrifice, defend, exchange, govern general strategy. "Classic . . . one of the clearest and best developed studies," Publishers Weekly. Also included, a complete supplement by F. Reinfeld, "How Do You Play Chess?", invaluable to beginners for its lively question-and-answer method. 448 diagrams. 1947 Reinfeld-Bernstein text. Bibliography. xvi + 340pp. 5⅜ x 8.   T463 Paperbound **$1.85**

MORPHY'S GAMES OF CHESS, edited by P. W. Sergeant. Put boldness into your game by flowing brilliant, forceful moves of the greatest chess player of all time. 300 of Morphy's best games, carefully annotated to reveal principles. 54 classics against masters like Anderssen, Harrwitz, Bird, Paulsen, and others. 52 games at odds; 54 blindfold games; plus over 100 others. Follow his interpretation of Dutch Defense, Evans Gambit, Giuoco Piano, Ruy Lopez, many more. Unabridged reissue of latest revised edition. New introduction by F. Reinfeld. Annotations, introduction by Sergeant. 235 diagrams. x + 352pp. 5⅜ x 8.
T386 Paperbound **$1.75**

DOVER SCIENCE BOOKS

WIN AT CHECKERS, M. Hopper. (Formerly "Checkers.") Former World's Unrestricted Checker Champion discusses principles of game, expert's shots, traps, problems for beginner, standard openings, locating best move, end game, opening "blitzkrieg" moves to draw when behind, etc. Over 100 detailed questions, answers anticipate problems. Appendix. 75 problems with solutions, diagrams. 79 figures. xi + 107pp. 5⅜ x 8. T363 Paperbound **$1.00**

HOW TO FORCE CHECKMATE, Fred Reinfeld. If you have trouble finishing off your opponent, here is a collection of lightning strokes and combinations from actual tournament play. Starts with 1-move checkmates, works up to 3-move mates. Develops ability to lock ahead, gain new insights into combinations, complex or deceptive positions; ways to estimate weaknesses, strengths of you and your opponent. "A good deal of amusement and instruction," Times, (London). 300 diagrams. Solutions to all positions. Formerly "Challenge to Chess Players." 111pp. 5⅜ x 8. T417 Paperbound **$1.25**

A TREASURY OF CHESS LORE, edited by Fred Reinfeld. Delightful collection of anecdotes, short stories, aphorisms by, about masters; poems, accounts of games, tournaments, photographs; hundreds of humorous, pithy, satirical, wise, historical episodes, comments, word portraits. Fascinating "must" for chess players; revealing and perhaps seductive to those who wonder what their friends see in game. 49 photographs (14 full page plates). 12 diagrams. xi + 306pp. 5⅜ x 8. T458 Paperbound **$1.75**

WIN AT CHESS, Fred Reinfeld. 300 practical chess situations, to sharpen your eye, test skill against masters. Start with simple examples, progress at own pace to complexities. This selected series of crucial moments in chess will stimulate imagination, develop stronger, more versatile game. Simple grading system enables you to judge progress. "Extensive use of diagrams is a great attraction," Chess. 300 diagrams. Notes, solutions to every situation. Formerly "Chess Quiz." vi + 120pp. 5⅜ x 8. T433 Paperbound **$1.00**

MATHEMATICS:
ELEMENTARY TO INTERMEDIATE

HOW TO CALCULATE QUICKLY, H. Sticker. Tried and true method to help mathematics of everyday life. Awakens "number sense"—ability to see relationships between numbers as whole quantities. A serious course of over 9000 problems and their solutions through techniques not taught in schools: left-to-right multiplications, new fast division, etc. 10 minutes a day will double or triple calculation speed. Excellent for scientist at home in higher math, but dissatisfied with speed and accuracy in lower math. 256pp. 5 x 7¼.
Paperbound **$1.00**

FAMOUS PROBLEMS OF ELEMENTARY GEOMETRY, Felix Klein. Expanded version of 1894 Easter lectures at Göttingen. 3 problems of classical geometry: squaring the circle, trisecting angle, doubling cube, considered with full modern implications: transcendental numbers, pi, etc. "A modern classic . . . no knowledge of higher mathematics is required," Scientia. Notes by R. Archibald. 16 figures. xi + 92pp. 5⅜ x 8. T298 Paperbound **$1.00**

HIGHER MATHEMATICS FOR STUDENTS OF CHEMISTRY AND PHYSICS, J. W. Mellor. Practical, not abstract, building problems out of familiar laboratory material. Covers differential calculus, coordinate, analytical geometry, functions, integral calculus, infinite series, numerical equations, differential equations, Fourier's theorem probability, theory of errors, calculus of variations, determinants. "If the reader is not familiar with this book, it will repay him to examine it," Chem. and Engineering News. 800 problems. 189 figures. xxi + 641pp. 5⅜ x 8. S193 Paperbound **$2.25**

TRIGONOMETRY REFRESHER FOR TECHNICAL MEN, A. A. Klaf. 913 detailed questions, answers cover most important aspects of plane, spherical trigonometry—particularly useful in clearing up difficulties in special areas. Part I: plane trig, angles, quadrants, functions, graphical representation, interpolation, equations, logs, solution of triangle, use of slide rule, etc. Next 188 pages discuss applications to navigation, surveying, elasticity, architecture, other special fields. Part 3: spherical trig, applications to terrestrial, astronomical problems. Methods of time-saving, simplification of principal angles, make book most useful. 913 questions answered. 1738 problems, answers to odd numbers. 494 figures. 24 pages of formulas, functions. x + 629pp. 5⅜ x 8. T371 Paperbound **$2.00**

CALCULUS REFRESHER FOR TECHNICAL MEN, A. A. Klaf. 756 questions examine most important aspects of integral, differential calculus. Part I: simple differential calculus, constants, variables, functions, increments, logs, curves, etc. Part 2: fundamental ideas of integrations, inspection, substitution, areas, volumes, mean value, double, triple integration, etc. Practical aspects stressed. 50 pages illustrate applications to specific problems of civil, nautical engineering, electricity, stress, strain, elasticity, similar fields. 756 questions answered. 566 problems, mostly answered. 36pp. of useful constants, formulas. v + 431pp. 5⅜ x 8. T370 Paperbound **$2.00**

MONOGRAPHS ON TOPICS OF MODERN MATHEMATICS, edited by J. W. A. Young. Advanced mathematics for persons who have forgotten, or not gone beyond, high school algebra. 9 monographs on foundation of geometry, modern pure geometry, non-Euclidean geometry, fundamental propositions of algebra, algebraic equations, functions, calculus, theory of numbers, etc. Each monograph gives proofs of important results, and descriptions of leading methods, to provide wide coverage. "Of high merit," Scientific American. New introduction by Prof. M. Kline, N.Y. Univ. 100 diagrams. xvi + 416pp. 6⅛ x 9¼.
S289 Paperbound **$2.00**

MATHEMATICS IN ACTION, O. G. Sutton. Excellent middle level application of mathematics to study of universe, demonstrates how math is applied to ballistics, theory of computing machines, waves, wave-like phenomena, theory of fluid flow, meteorological problems, statistics, flight, similar phenomena. No knowledge of advanced math required. Differential equations, Fourier series, group concepts, Eigenfunctions, Planck's constant, airfoil theory, and similar topics explained so clearly in everyday language that almost anyone can derive benefit from reading this even if much of high-school math is forgotten. 2nd edition. 88 figures. viii + 236pp. 5⅜ x 8. T450 Clothbound **$3.50**

ELEMENTARY MATHEMATICS FROM AN ADVANCED STANDPOINT, Felix Klein. Classic text, an outgrowth of Klein's famous integration and survey course at Göttingen. Using one field to interpret, adjust another, it covers basic topics in each area, with extensive analysis. Especially valuable in areas of modern mathematics. "A great mathematician, inspiring teacher, . . . deep insight," Bul., Amer. Math Soc.

Vol. I. ARITHMETIC, ALGEBRA, ANALYSIS. Introduces concept of function immediately, enlivens discussion with graphical, geometric methods. Partial contents: natural numbers, special properties, complex numbers. Real equations with real unknowns, complex quantities. Logarithmic, exponential functions, infinitesimal calculus. Transcendence of e and pi, theory of assemblages. Index. 125 figures. ix + 274pp. 5⅜ x 8. S151 Paperbound **$1.75**

Vol. II. GEOMETRY. Comprehensive view, accompanies space perception inherent in geometry with analytic formulas which facilitate precise formulation. Partial contents: Simplest geometric manifold; line segments, Grassman determinant principles, classication of configurations of space. Geometric transformations: affine, projective, higher point transformations, theory of the imaginary. Systematic discussion of geometry and its foundations. 141 illustrations. ix + 214pp. 5⅜ x 8. S151 Paperbound **$1.75**

A TREATISE ON PLANE AND ADVANCED TRIGONOMETRY, E. W. Hobson. Extraordinarily wide coverage, going beyond usual college level, one of few works covering advanced trig in full detail. By a great expositor with unerring anticipation of potentially difficult points. Includes circular functions; expansion of functions of multiple angle; trig tables; relations between sides, angles of triangles; complex numbers; etc. Many problems fully solved. "The best work on the subject," Nature. Formerly entitled "A Treatise on Plane Trigonometry." 689 examples. 66 figures. xvi + 383pp. 5⅜ x 8. S353 Paperbound **$1.95**

NON-EUCLIDEAN GEOMETRY, Roberto Bonola. The standard coverage of non-Euclidean geometry. Examines from both a historical and mathematical point of view geometries which have arisen from a study of Euclid's 5th postulate on parallel lines. Also included are complete texts, translated, of Bolyai's "Theory of Absolute Space," Lobachevsky's "Theory of Parallels." 180 diagrams. 431pp. 5⅜ x 8. S27 Paperbound **$1.95**

GEOMETRY OF FOUR DIMENSIONS, H. P. Manning. Unique in English as a clear, concise introduction. Treatment is synthetic, mostly Euclidean, though in hyperplanes and hyperspheres at infinity, non-Euclidean geometry is used. Historical introduction. Foundations of 4-dimensional geometry. Perpendicularity, simple angles. Angles of planes, higher order. Symmetry, order, motion; hyperpyramids, hypercones, hyperspheres; figures with parallel elements; volume, hypervolume in space; regular polyhedroids. Glossary. 78 figures. ix + 348pp. 5⅜ x 8. S182 Paperbound **$1.95**

MATHEMATICS: INTERMEDIATE TO ADVANCED

GEOMETRY (EUCLIDEAN AND NON-EUCLIDEAN)

THE GEOMETRY OF RENÉ DESCARTES. With this book, Descartes founded analytical geometry. Original French text, with Descartes's own diagrams, and excellent Smith-Latham translation. Contains: Problems the Construction of Which Requires only Straight Lines and Circles; On the Nature of Curved Lines; On the Construction of Solid or Supersolid Problems. Diagrams. 258pp. 5⅜ x 8. S68 Paperbound **$1.50**

DOVER SCIENCE BOOKS

THE WORKS OF ARCHIMEDES, edited by T. L. Heath. All the known works of the great Greek mathematician, including the recently discovered Method of Archimedes. Contains: On Sphere and Cylinder, Measurement of a Circle, Spirals, Conoids, Spheroids, etc. Definitive edition of greatest mathematical intellect of ancient world. 186 page study by Heath discusses Archimedes and history of Greek mathematics. 563pp. 5⅜ x 8.   S9 Paperbound **$2.00**

COLLECTED WORKS OF BERNARD RIEMANN. Important sourcebook, first to contain complete text of 1892 "Werke" and the 1902 supplement, unabridged. 31 monographs, 3 complete lecture courses, 15 miscellaneous papers which have been of enormous importance in relativity, topology, theory of complex variables, other areas of mathematics. Edited by R. Dedekind, H. Weber, M. Noether, W. Wirtinger. German text; English introduction by Hans Lewy. 690pp. 5⅜ x 8.   S226 Paperbound **$2.85**

THE THIRTEEN BOOKS OF EUCLID'S ELEMENTS, edited by Sir Thomas Heath. Definitive edition of one of very greatest classics of Western world. Complete translation of Heiberg text, plus spurious Book XIV. 150 page introduction on Greek, Medieval mathematics, Euclid, texts, commentators, etc. Elaborate critical apparatus parallels text, analyzing each definition, postulate, proposition, covering textual matters, refutations, supports, extrapolations, etc. This is the full Euclid. Unabridged reproduction of Cambridge U. 2nd edition. 3 volumes. 995 figures. 1426pp. 5⅜ x 8.   S88, 89, 90, 3 volume set, paperbound **$6.00**

AN INTRODUCTION TO GEOMETRY OF N DIMENSIONS, D. M. Y. Sommerville. Presupposes no previous knowledge of field. Only book in English devoted exclusively to higher dimensional geometry. Discusses fundamental ideas of incidence, parallelism, perpendicularity, angles between linear space, enumerative geometry, analytical geometry from projective and metric views, polytopes, elementary ideas in analysis situs, content of hyperspacial figures. 60 diagrams. 196pp. 5⅜ x 8.   S494 Paperbound **$1.50**

ELEMENTS OF NON-EUCLIDEAN GEOMETRY, D. M. Y. Sommerville. Unique in proceeding step-by-step. Requires only good knowledge of high-school geometry and algebra, to grasp elementary hyperbolic, elliptic, analytic non-Euclidean Geometries; space curvature and its implications; radical axes; homopethic centres and systems of circles; parataxy and parallelism; Gauss' proof of defect area theorem; much more, with exceptional clarity. 126 problems at chapter ends. 133 figures. xvi + 274pp. 5⅜ x 8.   S460 Paperbound **$1.50**

THE FOUNDATIONS OF EUCLIDEAN GEOMETRY, H. G. Forder. First connected, rigorous account in light of modern analysis, establishing propositions without recourse to empiricism, without multiplying hypotheses. Based on tools of 19th and 20th century mathematicians, who made it possible to remedy gaps and complexities, recognize problems not earlier discerned. Begins with important relationship of number systems in geometrical figures. Considers classes, relations, linear order, natural numbers, axioms for magnitudes, groups, quasi-fields, fields, non-Archimedian systems, the axiom system (at length), particular axioms (two chapters on the Parallel Axioms), constructions, congruence, similarity, etc. Lists: axioms employed, constructions, symbols in frequent use. 295pp. 5⅜ x 8.
     S481 Paperbound **$2.00**

CALCULUS, FUNCTION THEORY (REAL AND COMPLEX), FOURIER THEORY

FIVE VOLUME "THEORY OF FUNCTIONS" SET BY KONRAD KNOPP. Provides complete, readily followed account of theory of functions. Proofs given concisely, yet without sacrifice of completeness or rigor. These volumes used as texts by such universities as M.I.T., Chicago, N.Y. City College, many others. "Excellent introduction . . . remarkably readable, concise, clear, rigorous," J. of the American Statistical Association.

ELEMENTS OF THE THEORY OF FUNCTIONS, Konrad Knopp. Provides background for further volumes in this set, or texts on similar level. Partial contents: Foundations, system of complex numbers and Gaussian plane of numbers, Riemann sphere of numbers, mapping by linear functions, normal forms, the logarithm, cyclometric functions, binomial series. "Not only for the young student, but also for the student who knows all about what is in it," Mathematical Journal. 140pp. 5⅜ x 8.   S154 Paperbound **$1.35**

THEORY OF FUNCTIONS, PART I, Konrad Knopp. With volume II, provides coverage of basic concepts and theorems. Partial contents: numbers and points, functions of a complex variable, integral of a continuous function, Cauchy's intergral theorem, Cauchy's integral formulae, series with variable terms, expansion and analytic function in a power series, analytic continuation and complete definition of analytic functions, Laurent expansion, types of singularities. vii + 146pp. 5⅜ x 8.   S156 Paperbound **$1.35**

THEORY OF FUNCTIONS, PART II, Konrad Knopp. Application and further development of general theory, special topics. Single valued functions, entire, Weierstrass. Meromorphic functions: Mittag-Leffler. Periodic functions. Multiple valued functions. Riemann surfaces. Algebraic functions. Analytical configurations, Riemann surface. x + 150pp. 5⅜ x 8.
     S157 Paperbound **$1.35**

11

PROBLEM BOOK IN THE THEORY OF FUNCTIONS, VOLUME I, Konrad Knopp. Problems in elementary theory, for use with Knopp's "Theory of Functions," or any other text. Arranged according to increasing difficulty. Fundamental concepts, sequences of numbers and infinite series, complex variable, integral theorems, development in series, conformal mapping. Answers. viii + 126pp. 5⅜ x 8.   S 158 **Paperbound $1.35**

PROBLEM BOOK IN THE THEORY OF FUNCTIONS, VOLUME II, Konrad Knopp. Advanced theory of functions, to be used with Knopp's "Theory of Functions," or comparable text. Singularities, entire and meromorphic functions, periodic, analytic, continuation, multiple-valued functions, Riemann surfaces, conformal mapping. Includes section of elementary problems. "The difficult task of selecting . . . problems just within the reach of the beginner is here masterfully accomplished," AM. MATH. SOC. Answers. 138pp. 5⅜ x 8.
                                                                S159 Paperbound **$1.35**

ADVANCED CALCULUS, E. B. Wilson. Still recognized as one of most comprehensive, useful texts. Immense amount of well-represented, fundamental material, including chapters on vector functions, ordinary differential equations, special functions, calculus of variations, etc., which are excellent introductions to these areas. Requires only one year of calculus. Over 1300 exercises cover both pure math and applications to engineering and physical problems. Ideal reference, refresher. 54 page introductory review. ix + 566pp. 5⅜ x 8.
                                                                S504 Paperbound **$2.45**

LECTURES ON THE THEORY OF ELLIPTIC FUNCTIONS, H. Hancock. Reissue of only book in English with so extensive a coverage, especially of Abel, Jacobi, Legendre, Weierstrass, Hermite, Liouville, and Riemann. Unusual fullness of treatment, plus applications as well as theory in discussing universe of elliptic integrals, originating in works of Abel and Jacobi. Use is made of Riemann to provide most general theory. 40-page table of formulas. 76 figures. xxiii + 498pp. 5⅜ x 8.   S483 Paperbound **$2.55**

THEORY OF FUNCTIONALS AND OF INTEGRAL AND INTEGRO-DIFFERENTIAL EQUATIONS, Vito Volterra. Unabridged republication of only English translation, General theory of functions depending on continuous set of values of another function. Based on author's concept of transition from finite number of variables to a continually infinite number. Includes much material on calculus of variations. Begins with fundamentals, examines generalization of analytic functions, functional derivative equations, applications, other directions of theory, etc. New introduction by G. C. Evans. Biography, criticism of Volterra's work by E. Whittaker. xxxx + 226pp. 5⅜ x 8.   S502 Paperbound **$1.75**

AN INTRODUCTION TO FOURIER METHODS AND THE LAPLACE TRANSFORMATION, Philip Franklin. Concentrates on essentials, gives broad view, suitable for most applications. Requires only knowledge of calculus. Covers complex qualities with methods of computing elementary functions for complex values of argument and finding approximations by charts; Fourier series; harmonic anaylsis; much more. Methods are related to physical problems of heat flow, vibrations, electrical transmission, electromagnetic radiation, etc. 828 problems, answers. Formerly entitled "Fourier Methods." x + 289pp. 5⅜ x 8.
                                                                S452 Paperbound **$1.75**

THE ANALYTICAL THEORY OF HEAT, Joseph Fourier. This book, which revolutionized mathematical physics, has been used by generations of mathematicians and physicists interested in heat or application of Fourier integral. Covers cause and reflection of rays of heat, radiant heating, heating of closed spaces, use of trigonometric series in theory of heat, Fourier integral, etc. Translated by Alexander Freeman. 20 figures. xxii + 466pp. 5⅜ x 8.
                                                                S93 Paperbound **$2.00**

ELLIPTIC INTEGRALS, H. Hancock. Invaluable in work involving differential equations with cubics, quatrics under root sign, where elementary calculus methods are inadequate. Practical solutions to problems in mathematics, engineering, physics; differential equations requiring integration of Lamé's, Briot's, or Bouquet's equations; determination of arc of ellipse, hyperbola, lemiscate; solutions of problems in elastics; motion of a projectile under resistance varying as the cube of the velocity; pendulums; more. Exposition in accordance with Legendre-Jacobi theory. Rigorous discussion of Legendre transformations. 20 figures. 5 place table. 104pp. 5⅜ x 8.   S484 Paperbound **$1.25**

THE TAYLOR SERIES, AN INTRODUCTION TO THE THEORY OF FUNCTIONS OF A COMPLEX VARIABLE, P. Dienes. Uses Taylor series to approach theory of functions, using ordinary calculus only, except in last 2 chapters. Starts with introduction to real variable and complex algebra, derives properties of infinite series, complex differentiation, integration, etc. Covers biuniform mapping, overconvergence and gap theorems, Taylor series on its circle of convergence, etc. Unabridged corrected reissue of first edition. 186 examples, many fully worked out. 67 figures. xii + 555pp. 5⅜ x 8.   S391 Paperbound **$2.75**

LINEAR INTEGRAL EQUATIONS, W. V. Lovitt. Systematic survey of general theory, with some application to differential equations, calculus of variations, problems of math, physics. Includes: integral equation of 2nd kind by successive substitutions; Fredholm's equation as ratio of 2 integral series in lambda, applications of the Fredholm theory, Hilbert-Schmidt theory of symmetric kernels, application, etc. Neumann, Dirichlet, vibratory problems. ix + 253pp. 5⅜ x 8.   S175 Clothbound **$3.50**
                                                                S176 Paperbound **$1.60**

DOVER SCIENCE BOOKS

DICTIONARY OF CONFORMAL REPRESENTATIONS, H. Kober. Developed by British Admiralty to solve Laplace's equation in 2 dimensions. Scores of geometrical forms and transformations for electrical engineers, Joukowski aerofoil for aerodynamics, Schwartz-Christoffel transformations for hydro-dynamics, transcendental functions. Contents classified according to analytical functions describing transformations with corresponding regions. Glossary. Topological index. 447 diagrams. 6⅛ x 9¼.   .S160 Paperbound **$2.00**

ELEMENTS OF THE THEORY OF REAL FUNCTIONS, J. E. Littlewood. Based on lectures at Trinity College, Cambridge, this book has proved extremely successful in introducing graduate students to modern theory of functions. Offers full and concise coverage of classes and cardinal numbers, well ordered series, other types of series, and elements of the theory of sets of points. 3rd revised edition. vii + 71pp. 5⅜ x 8.   S171 Clothbound **$2.85**
                                                                  S172 Paperbound **$1.25**

INFINITE SEQUENCES AND SERIES, Konrad Knopp. 1st publication in any language. Excellent introduction to 2 topics of modern mathematics, designed to give student background to penetrate further alone. Sequences and sets, real and complex numbers, etc. Functions of a real and complex variable. Sequences and series. Infinite series. Convergent power series. Expansion of elementary functions. Numerical evaluation of series. v + 186pp. 5⅜ x 8.
                                                                  S152 Clothbound **$3.50**
                                                                  S153 Paperbound **$1.75**

THE THEORY AND FUNCTIONS OF A REAL VARIABLE AND THE THEORY OF FOURIER'S SERIES, E. W .Hobson. One of the best introductions to set theory and various aspects of functions and Fourier's series. Requires only a good background in calculus. Exhaustive .coverage of: metric and descriptive properties of sets of points; transfinite numbers and order types; functions of a real variable; the Riemann and Lebesgue integrals; sequences and series of numbers; power-series; functions representable by series sequences of continuous functions; trigonometrical series; representation of functions by Fourier's series; and much more. "The best possible guide," Nature. Vol. I: 88 detailed examples, 10 figures. Index. xv + 736pp. Vol. II: 117 detailed examples, 13 figures. x + 780pp. 6⅛ x 9¼.
                                                   Vol. I: S387 Paperbound **$3.00**
                                                  Vol. II: S388 Paperbound **$3.00**

ALMOST PERIODIC FUNCTIONS, A. S. Besicovitch. Unique and important summary by a well known mathematician covers in detail the two stages of development in Bohr's theory of almost periodic functions: (1) as a generalization of pure periodicity, with results and proofs; (2) the work done by Stepanof, Wiener, Weyl, and Bohr in generalizing the theory. xi + 180pp. 5⅜ x 8.   S18 Paperbound **$1.75**

INTRODUCTION TO THE THEORY OF FOURIER'S SERIES AND INTEGRALS, H. S. Carslaw. 3rd revised edition, an outgrowth of author's courses at Cambridge. Historical introduction, rational, irrational numbers, infinite sequences and series, functions of a single variable, definite integral, Fourier series, and similar topics. Appendices discuss practical harmonic analysis, periodogram analysis, Lebesgue's theory. 84 examples. xiii + 368pp. 5⅜ x 8.
                                                                   S48 Paperbound **$2.00**

SYMBOLIC LOGIC

THE ELEMENTS OF MATHEMATICAL LOGIC, Paul Rosenbloom. First publication in any language. For mathematically mature readers with no training in symbolic. logic. Development of lectures given at Lund Univ., Sweden, 1948. Partial contents: Logic of classes, fundamental theorems, Boolean algebra, logic of propositions, of propositional functions, expressive languages, combinatory logics, development of math within an object language, paradoxes, theorems of Post, Goedel, Church, and similar topics. iv + 214pp. 5⅜ x 8.
                                                                  S227 Paperbound **$1.45**

INTRODUCTION TO SYMBOLIC LOGIC AND ITS APPLICATION, R. Carnap. Clear, comprehensive, rigorous, by perhaps greatest living master. Symbolic languages analyzed, one constructed. Applications to math (axiom systems for set theory, real, natural numbers), topology (Dedekind, Cantor continuity explanations), physics (general analysis of determination, causality, space-time topology), biology (axiom system for basic concepts). "A masterpiece," Zentralblatt für Mathematik und Ihre Grenzgebiete. Over 300 exercises. 5 figures. xvi + 241pp. 5⅜ x 8.   S453 Paperbound **$1.85**

AN INTRODUCTION TO SYMBOLIC LOGIC, Susanne K. Langer. Probably clearest book for the philosopher, scientist, layman—no special knowledge of math required. Starts with simplest symbols, goes on to give remarkable grasp of Boole-Schroeder, Russell-Whitehead systems, clearly, quickly. Partial Contents: Forms, Generalization, Classes, Deductive System of Classes, Algebra of Logic, Assumptions of Principia Mathematica, Logistics, Proofs of Theorems, etc. "Clearest . . . simplest introduction . . . the intelligent non-mathematician should have no difficulty," MATHEMATICS GAZETTE. Revised, expanded 2nd edition. Truth-value tables. 368pp. 5⅜ 8.   S164 Paperbound **$1.75**

TRIGONOMETRICAL SERIES, Antoni Zygmund. On modern advanced level. Contains carefully organized analyses of trigonometric, orthogonal, Fourier systems of functions, with clear adequate descriptions of summability of Fourier series, proximation theory, conjugate series, convergence, divergence of Fourier series. Especially valuable for Russian, Eastern European coverage. 329pp. 5⅜ x 8. S290 Paperbound **$1.50**

THE LAWS OF THOUGHT, George Boole. This book founded symbolic logic some 100 years ago. It is the 1st significant attempt to apply logic to all aspects of human endeavour. Partial contents: derivation of laws, signs and laws, interpretations, eliminations, conditions of a perfect method, analysis, Aristotelian logic, probability, and similar topics. xvii + 424pp. 5⅜ x 8. S28 Paperbound **$2.00**

SYMBOLIC LOGIC, C. I. Lewis, C. H. Langford. 2nd revised edition of probably most cited book in symbolic logic. Wide coverage of entire field; one of fullest treatments of paradoxes; plus much material not available elsewhere. Basic to volume is distinction between logic of extensions and intensions. Considerable emphasis on converse substitution, while matrix system presents supposition of variety of non-Aristotelian logics. Especially valuable sections on strict limitations, existence theorems. Partial contents: Boole-Schroeder algebra; truth value systems, the matrix method; implication and deductibility; general theory of propositions; etc. "Most valuable," Times, London. 506pp. 5⅜ x 8. S170 Paperbound **$2.00**

GROUP THEORY AND LINEAR ALGEBRA, SETS, ETC.

LECTURES ON THE ICOSAHEDRON AND THE SOLUTION OF EQUATIONS OF THE FIFTH DEGREE, Felix Klein. Solution of quintics in terms of rotations of regular icosahedron around its axes of symmetry. A classic, indispensable source for those interested in higher algebra, geometry, crystallography. Considerable explanatory material included. 230 footnotes, mostly bibliography. "Classical monograph . . . detailed, readable book," Math. Gazette. 2nd edition. xvi + 289pp. 5⅜ x 8. S314 Paperbound **$1.85**

INTRODUCTION TO THE THEORY OF GROUPS OF FINITE ORDER, R. Carmichael. Examines fundamental theorems and their applications. Beginning with sets, systems, permutations, etc., progresses in easy stages through important types of groups: Abelian, prime power, permutation, etc. Except 1 chapter where matrices are desirable, no higher math is needed. 783 exercises, problems. xvi + 447pp. 5⅜ x 8. S299 Clothbound **$3.95** / S300 Paperbound **$2.00**

THEORY OF GROUPS OF FINITE ORDER, W. Burnside. First published some 40 years ago, still one of clearest introductions. Partial contents: permutations, groups independent of representation, composition series of a group, isomorphism of a group with itself, Abelian groups, prime power groups, permutation groups, invariants of groups of linear substitution, graphical representation, etc. "Clear and detailed discussion . . . numerous problems which are instructive," Design News. xxiv + 512pp. 5⅜ x 8. S38 Paperbound **$2.45**

COMPUTATIONAL METHODS OF LINEAR ALGEBRA, V. N. Faddeeva, translated by C. D. Benster. 1st English translation of unique, valuable work, only one in English presenting systematic exposition of most important methods of linear algebra—classical, contemporary. Details of deriving numerical solutions of problems in mathematical physics. Theory and practice. Includes survey of necessary background, most important methods of solution, for exact, iterative groups. One of most valuable features is 23 tables, triple checked for accuracy, unavailable elsewhere. Translator's note. x + 252pp. 5⅜ x 8. S424 Paperbound **$1.95**

THE CONTINUUM AND OTHER TYPES OF SERIAL ORDER, E. V. Huntington. This famous book gives a systematic elementary account of the modern theory of the continuum as a type of serial order. Based on the Cantor-Dedekind ordinal theory, which requires no technical knowledge of higher mathematics, it offers an easily followed analysis of ordered classes, discrete and dense series, continuous series, Cantor's transfinite numbers. "Admirable introduction to the rigorous theory of the continuum . . . reading easy," Science Progress. 2nd edition. viii + 82pp. 5⅜ x 8. S129 Clothbound **$2.75** / S130 Paperbound **$1.00**

THEORY OF SETS, E. Kamke. Clearest, amplest introduction in English, well suited for independent study. Subdivisions of main theory, such as theory of sets of points, are discussed, but emphasis is on general theory. Partial contents: rudiments of set theory, arbitrary sets, their cardinal numbers, ordered sets, their order types, well-ordered sets, their cardinal numbers. vii + 144pp. 5⅜ x 8. S141 Paperbound **$1.35**

CONTRIBUTIONS TO THE FOUNDING OF THE THEORY OF TRANSFINITE NUMBERS, Georg Cantor. These papers founded a new branch of mathematics. The famous articles of 1895-7 are translated, with an 82-page introduction by P. E. B. Jourdain dealing with Cantor, the background of his discoveries, their results, future possibiilties. ix + 211pp. 5⅜ x 8. S45 Paperbound **$1.25**

data to support his deductions and they had no direct influence upon the progress of astronomy.

The real beginning of double star astronomy dates from the activities of Christian Mayer and of Sir William Herschel, in the last quarter of the eighteenth century. If a definite date is desired we may well follow Lewis in adopting the year 1779, for that year is marked by the appearance of Mayer's small book entitled *De novis in Coelo Sidereo Phaenominis in miris Stellarum fixarum Comitibus*, wherein he speculates upon the possibility of small suns revolving around larger ones, and by the beginning of Herschel's systematic search for double stars.

The difference between Mayer's speculations and earlier ones is that his rest in some degree at least upon observations. These were made with an 8-ft. Bird mural quadrant at Mannheim, in 1777 and 1778. At any rate, in his book just referred to, he publishes a long list of faint companions observed in the neighborhood of brighter stars.* As one result of his observations he sent to Bode, at Berlin, the first collection or catalogue of double stars ever published. The list contained earlier discoveries as well as his own and is printed in the *Astronomisches Jahrbuch* for the year 1784 (issued in 1781) under the caption "Verzeichnis aller bisher entdeckten Doppelsterne." The following tabulation gives the first five entries:

Grösse	Gerade Aufst. G. M.	Abwei- chung G. M.	Unterschied		Abstand Sec.	Stellung des Klei- nern
			in der Aufst. Sec.	in der Abw. Sec.		
Andromeda beyde 9ter	8 38	29 45 N	45	24	46	S. W.
Andromeda beyde 9ter	13 13	20 18 N	15	29	32	S. O.
ʒ Fische 6. und 7ter	15 33	6 25 N	22	9	24	N. O.
beyμ Fische beyde 7ter	19 24	5 0 N	0	4	4	S.
γ Widder beyde 5ter	25 22	18 13 N	3	12	12	S. W.

In all, there are 80 entries, many of which, like *Castor* and γ *Virginis*, are among the best known double stars. Others

* This list, rearranged according to constellations, was reprinted by Schjellerup in the journal *Copernicus*, **3**, 57, 1884.

are too wide to be found even in Herschel's catalogues and a
few cannot be identified with certainty.   Southern pairs, like
α *Centauri*, are of course not included, and, curiously enough,
θ *Orionis* is not listed.   The relative positions given for the
stars in each pair are little better than estimates, for precise
measures were not practicable until the invention of the "revolving micrometer."

In his comments on Mayer's catalogue, Bode points out that
careful observations of such pairs might become of special

Sir William Herschel.

value in the course of time for the discovery of proper motions,
since it would be possible to recognize the fact of motion in
one or the other star as soon as the distance between them had
changed by a very few seconds of arc.   Mayer himself seems
to have had proper motions in view in making his observations
and catalogue rather than any idea of orbital motions.

Sir William Herschel "began to look at the planets and the
stars" in May, 1773; on Mar. 1, 1774, "he commenced his
astronomical journal by noting that he had viewed Saturn's
ring with a power of forty, appearing 'like two slender arms'
and also 'the lucid spot in Orion's sword belt.'"   The earliest
double star measure recorded in his first catalogue is that of
θ *Orionis*, on Nov. 11, 1776, and he made a few others in the

two years following. It was not until 1779, however, that he set to work in earnest to search for these objects, for it was then that he conceived the idea of utilizing them to test a method of measuring stellar parallax suggested long before by Galileo. The principle involved is very simple. If two stars are in the same general direction from us and one is comparatively near us while the other is extremely distant, the annual revolution of the Earth about the Sun will produce a periodic variation in the relative positions of the two. As a first approximation, we may regard the more distant star as absolutely fixed and derive the parallax of the nearer one from the measured displacements.

It seemed clear to Herschel that the objects best fitted for such an investigation were close double stars with components of unequal brightness. He pointed out in his paper *On the Parallaxes of the Fixed Stars*, read before the Royal Society in 1781, that the displacement could be more easily and certainly detected in a close double star than in a pair of stars more widely separated and also that in the former case the observations would be free from many errors necessarily affecting the measures in the latter.

As soon as I was fully satisfied [he continues] that in the investigation of parallax the method of double stars would have many advantages above any other, it became necessary to look out for proper stars. This introduced a new series of observations. I resolved to examine every star in the heavens with the utmost attention and a very high power, that I might collect such materials for this research as would enable me to fix my observations upon those that would best answer my ends.

In this reasoning, Herschel assumes that there is no physical connection between the components of such close double stars, —a fact upon which every writer on the history of double-star astronomy has commented. This was not an oversight on his part, for at the close of his first catalogue of double stars he remarks:

I preferred that expression [*i.e.*, double stars] to any other, such as *Comes*, Companion, or Satellite; because, in my opinion, it is much too soon to form any theories about small stars revolving round large ones, and I therefore thought it advisable carefully to avoid any expression that might convey that idea.

Herschel's telescopes were more powerful than any earlier ones and with them he soon discovered a far larger number of double stars than he had anticipated. With characteristic thoroughness he nevertheless decided to carry out his plan of examining "every star in the heavens," and carefully recorded full details of all his observations. These included a general description of each pair and also estimates, or measures with the "revolving micrometer," or "lamp micrometer," both invented by himself, of the apparent distance between the two components and of the direction of the smaller star from the larger. The direction, or position angle, of the smaller star, by his definition, was the angle at the larger star between the line joining the two stars and a line parallel to the celestial equator. The angle was always made less than 90°, the letters, *nf, sf, sp,* and *np* being added to designate the quadrant. His first catalogue, presented to the Royal Society on Jan. 10, 1782, contains 269 double stars, "227 of which, to my present knowledge, have not been noticed by any person." A second catalogue, containing 434 additional objects, was presented to the same society in 1784. The stars in these catalogues were divided into six classes according to angular separation.

In the first [he writes] I have placed all those which require indeed a very superior telescope, the utmost clearness of air, and every other favorable circumstance to be seen at all, or well enough to judge of them. . . . In the second class I have put all those that are proper for estimations by the eye or very delicate measures of the micrometer. . . . In the third class I have placed all those . . . that are more than five but less than 15″ asunder; . . . The fourth, fifth, and sixth classes contain double stars that are from 15″ to 30″, from 30″ to 1′ and from 1′ to 2′ or more asunder.

Class I, in the two catalogues, includes 97 pairs, and contains such systems as τ *Ophiuchi,* δ *Herculis,* ε *Boötis,* ξ *Ursae Majoris,* 4 *Aquarii,* and ζ *Cancri.* In general, Herschel did not attempt micrometer measures of the distances of these pairs because the finest threads available for use in his micrometers subtended an angle of more than 1″. The following extracts will show this method of estimating the distance in such cases and of recording the position angle, and also the care with which he described the appearance of each object. The dates of discovery, or of the first observation, here printed above the descriptions, are set in the margin at the left in the original.

H. 1. September 9, 1779

ε Boötis, Flamst. 36. Ad dextrum femur in perizomate. Double.
Very unequal. *L.* reddish; *S.* blue, or rather a faint lilac. A very beautiful object. The vacancy or black division between them, with 227 is
¾ diameter of *S.*; with 460, 1¼ diameter of *L.*; with 932, near 2 diameters of *L.*; with 1,159, still farther; with 2,010 (extremely distinct),
⅔ diameters of *L.* These quantities are a mean of two years' observation. Position 31° 34′ n preceding.

H. 2. May 2, 1780

ξ Ursae Majoris. Fl. 53. In dextro posteriore pede. Double. A
little unequal. Both w [white] and very bright. The interval with 222
is ⅔ diameter of *L.*; with 227, 1 diameter of *L*; with 278, near 1½
diameter of *L.* Position 53° 47′ s following.

Careful examination of the later history of the stars of Herschel's Class I shows that the majority had at discovery an
angular separation of from 2″ to 3″.5; a half dozen pairs as
wide as 5″ are included (one with the manuscript remark, "Too
far asunder for one of the first class"); and a number as close
as or closer than 1″. Seven of these stars do not appear in the
great catalogue of Struve, but five of these have been recovered by
later observers, leaving only two that cannot be identified.

In passing judgment upon the accuracy, or the lack of it, in
Herschel's measures of double stars, it is necessary to hold in
mind the conditions under which he had to work. His reflectors (all of his own construction) were indeed far more powerful
telescopes than any earlier ones, especially the "twenty-feet
reflector," with mirror of 18¾-in. aperture, and the great
"forty-feet telescope," with its 4-ft. mirror. But these telescopes
were unprovided with clockwork; in fact, their mountings were
of the alt-azimuth type. It was therefore necessary to move the
telescope continuously in both coordinates to keep a star in the
field of view and the correcting motions had to be particularly
delicate when high-power eyepieces, such as are necessary in the
observation of close double stars, were employed. Add the
crude forms of micrometers at his disposal, and it will appear
that only an observer of extraordinary skill would be able to
make measures of any value whatever.

No further catalogues of double stars were published by
Herschel until June 8, 1821, about a year before his death,

when he presented to the newly founded Royal Astronomical Society a final list of 145 new pairs, not arranged in classes, and, for the most part, without measures.

After completing his second catalogue, in 1784, Herschel seems to have given relatively little attention to double stars until about the close of the century and, though he doubtless tested it fully, there is no mention of his parallax method in his published writings after the first paper on the subject. A thorough review of his double star discoveries which he instituted about the year 1797, with careful measures, repeated in some cases on many nights in different years, revealed a remarkable change in the relative positions of the components in a number of double stars during the interval of nearly 20 years since their discovery, but this change was of such a character that it could not be produced by parallax.

We have seen that, in 1782, Herschel considered the time not ripe for theorizing as to the possible revolution of small stars about larger ones. Probably no astronomer of his own or of any other age was endowed in a higher degree than Herschel with what has been termed the scientific imagination; certainly no one ever more boldly speculated upon the deepest problems of sidereal astronomy; but his speculations were the very opposite of guesswork; invariably they were the results of critical analyses of the data given by observation and were tested by further observations when possible. Michell, in 1783, applied his earlier argument from the theory of probabilities to the double stars in Herschel's first catalogue and concluded that practically all of them were physical systems; but it was not until July, 1802, that Herschel himself gave any intimation of holding similar views. On that date he presented to the Royal Society a paper entitled *Catalogue of 500 new Nebulae, nebulous Stars, planetary Nebulae, and Clusters of Stars; with Remarks on the Construction of the Heavens*, in which he enumerates "the parts that enter into the construction of the heavens" under 12 heads, the second being, "II. Of Binary sidereal Systems, or double Stars." In this section he gives the distinction between optical and binary systems quoted in my Introduction and argues as to the possibility of systems of the latter type under the law of gravitation.

On June 9, 1803, followed the great paper in which he gave the actual demonstration, on the basis of his measures, that certain double stars are true binary systems. This paper, the fundamental document in the history of double stars as physical systems, is entitled, *Account of the Changes that have happened, during the last Twenty-five Years, in the relative Situation of Double-stars; with an Investigation of the Cause to which they are owing.* After pointing out that the actual existence of binary systems is not proved by the demonstration that such systems *may* exist, Herschel continues, "I shall therefore now proceed to give an account of a series of observations on double stars, comprehending a period of about twenty-five years which, if I am not mistaken, will go to prove, that many of them, are not merely double in appearance, but must be allowed to be real binary combinations of two stars, intimately held together by the bonds of mutual attraction."

Taking *Castor* as his first example, he shows that the change in the position of the components is real and not due to any error of observation. Then, by a masterly analysis of every possible combination of motions of the Sun and the components in this, and in five other systems, he proves that orbital motion is the simplest and most probable explanation in any one case, and the *only reasonable one* when all six are considered. His argument is convincing, his conclusion incontrovertible, and his paper, a year later, containing a list of 50 additional double stars, many of which had shown motion of a similar character, simply emphasizes it.

This practically concluded Sir William Herschel's contributions to double star astronomy, for his list of 145 new pairs, published in 1821, was based almost entirely upon observations made before 1802. In fact, little was done in this field by any one from 1804 until about 1816. Sir John Herschel, in that year, decided to review and extend his father's work and had made some progress when Sir James South, who had independently formed similar plans, suggested that they cooperate. The suggestion was adopted and the result was a catalogue of 380 stars, based upon observations made in the years 1821 to 1823 with South's 5-ft. and 7-ft. refractors, of 3¾-in. and 5-in. aperture, respectively. These telescopes were mounted equatorially but were not provided with driving clocks. They were, however, equipped with micrometers in which the parallel threads were fine spider lines. The value of the catalogue was greatly increased by the inclusion of all of Sir William

Herschel's measures, many of which had not before been published.

Both of these astronomers devoted much attention to double stars in following years, working separately, however, South with his refractors, Herschel with a 20-ft. reflector (18-in. mirror) and later with the 5-in. refractor which he had purchased from South. They not only remeasured practically all of Sir William Herschel's double stars, some of them on many nights in different years, but they, and in particular Sir John Herschel, added a large number of new pairs. Indeed, so numerous were J. Herschel's discoveries and so faint were many of the stars that he deemed some apology necessary. He says,

. . . so long as no presumption *a priori* can be adduced why the most minute star in the heavens should not give us that very information respecting parallax, proper motion, and an infinity of other interesting points, which we are in search of, and yet may never obtain from its brighter rivals, the minuteness of an object is no reason for neglecting its examination. . . . But if small double stars are to be watched, it is first necessary that they should become known; nor need we fear that the list will become overwhelming. It will be curtailed at one end, by the rejection of uninteresting and uninstructive objects, at least as fast as it is increased on the other by new candidates.

The prediction made in the closing sentence was not immediately verified; on the contrary, as late as 1905 Burnham included in his *General Catalogue of All Double Stars within* 121° *of the North Pole* every pair published as a double star, even those which had been rejected by their discoverers when they revised their lists.

The long series of measures and of discoveries of double stars by Herschel and South were of great value in themselves and perhaps of even greater value in the stimulus they gave to the observation of these objects by astronomers generally, and well merited the gold medals awarded to their authors by the Royal Astronomical Society. The measures, however, are now assigned small weight on account of the relatively large errors of observation due to the conditions under which they were of necessity made; and of the thousands of new pairs very few indeed have as yet proved of interest as binaries. The great majority are too wide to give the slightest evidence of orbital motion in the course of a century.

The true successor to Sir William Herschel, the man who made the next real advance in double star astronomy, an advance so great that it may indeed be said to introduce a new period in its history, was F. G. W. Struve. Wilhelm Struve became the director of the observatory at Dorpat, Russia, in 1813, and soon afterward began measuring the differences in right ascension and in declination between the components of double

F. G. W. Struve.

stars with his transit instrument, the only instrument available. A little later he acquired a small equatorial, inferior to South's, with which he continued his work, and, in 1822, he published his *Catalogus* 795 *stellarum duplicium*. This volume is interesting but calls for no special comment because Struve's great work did not really begin until two years later, in November, 1824, when he received the celebrated Fraunhofer refractor.

That telescope as an instrument for precise measurements was far superior to any previously constructed. The tube was 13 ft. long, the objective had an aperture of nine Paris inches,* the mounting was equatorial and of very convenient form, and, best of all, was equipped with an excellent driving clock.

---

* This is Struve's own statement. Values ranging from 9½ to 9.9 in. (probably English inches) are given by different authorities.

So far as I am aware, this was the first telescope employed in actual research to be provided with clockwork though Passement, in 1757, had "presented a telescope to the King [of France], so accurately driven by clockwork that it would follow a star all night long." A finder of 2½-in. aperture and 30-in. focus, a full battery of eyepieces, and accurate and convenient micrometers completed the equipment, over which Struve was pardonably enthusiastic. After careful tests he concluded that "we may perhaps rank this enormous instrument with the most celebrated of all reflectors, *viz.*, Herschel's."

Within four days after its arrival Struve had succeeded in erecting it in a temporary shelter and at once began the first part of his well planned program of work. His object was the study of double stars as physical systems and so carefully had he considered all the requirements for such an investigation and so thorough, systematic, and skillful was the execution of his plans that his work has served as a model to all of his successors. His program had three divisions: the search for double stars; the accurate determination of their positions in the sky with the meridian circle as a basis for future investigations of their proper motions; and the measurement with the micrometer attached to the great telescope of the relative positions of the components of each pair to provide the basis for the study of motions within the system.

The results are embodied in three great volumes, familiarly known to astronomers as the *Catalogus Novus*, the *Positiones Mediae*, and the *Mensurae Micrometricae*. The first contains the list of the double stars found in Struve's survey of the sky from the North Pole to −15° declination. For the purposes of this survey he divided the sky into zones from 7½° to 10° wide in declination and swept across each zone from north to south, examining with the main telescope all stars that were bright enough, in his estimation, to be visible in the finder at a distance of 20° from the full Moon. He considered that these would include all stars of the eighth magnitude and the brighter ones of those between magnitudes 8 and 9. Struve states that the telescope was so easy to manipulate and so excellent in its optical properties that he was able to examine 400 stars an hour; and he did, in fact, complete his survey, estimated to embrace the examination of 120,000 stars, in 129 nights of actual work in the period from November, 1824, to February, 1827.

Since each star had to be chosen in the finder, then brought into the field of view of the large telescope, examined, and, if double, entered in the observing record, with a general description, and an approximate position determined by circle readings, it is obvious that at the rate of 400 stars an hour, only a very few seconds could be devoted to the actual examination of each star. If not seen double, or suspiciously elongated at the first glance, it must, as a rule, have been passed over. Struve indeed definitely states that at the first instant of observation it was generally possible to decide whether a star was single or double. This is in harmony with my own experience in similar work, but I have never been content to turn away from a star apparently single until satisfied that further examination on that occasion was useless. As a matter of fact, later researches have shown that Struve overlooked many pairs within his limits of magnitude and angular separation, and hence easily within the power of his telescope; but even so the *Catalogus Novus*, with its short supplement, contains 3,112 entries. In two instances a star is accidentally repeated with a different number so that 3,110 separate systems are actually listed. Many of these had been seen by earlier observers and a few that had entirely escaped Struve's own search were included on the authority of Bessel or some other observer.

Struve did not stop to make micrometer measures of his discoveries while engaged in his survey, and the *Catalogus Novus* therefore gives simply a rough classification of the pairs according to their estimated angular separation, with estimates of magnitude and approximate positions in the sky based on the equatorial circle readings. He rejected Herschel's classes V and VI, taking 32″ as his superior limit of distance and dividing the stars within this limit into four classes: (1) those under 4″; (2) those between 4″ and 8″; (3) those between 8″ and 16″; and (4) those between 16″ and 32″. Stars in the first class were further distinguished as of three grades by the use of the adjectives *vicinae*, *pervicinae*, and *vicinissimae*. The following lines (page 14) will illustrate the form of the catalogue, the numbers in the last column indicating the stars that had been published in his prior catalogue of 795 pairs.

The *Catalogus Novus*, published in 1827, furnished the working program on which Struve's two other great volumes were based, though the *Positiones Mediae* includes meridian circle

Nume- rus	Nomen Stellae	A. R.	Decl.		Descriptio	Num. C. P.
1		0h 0ʹ.0	+36°	15ʹ	II (8.9) (9)	
2	Cephei 316	−0.0	+78	45	I (6.7) (6.7), *vicinae*	
3	Andromedae 31	−0.4	+45	25	II (7.8) (10) = H.II 83	1
4		−0.9	+ 7	29	II (9), Besseli mihi non inventa	
5	34 Piscium	−1.1	+10	10	III (6) (10), etiam Besseli	

measures made as early as 1822, and the *Mensurae Micrometricae* some micrometer measures made in the years 1824 to 1828. Micrometer work was not actively pushed until 1828 and four-fifths of the 10,448 measures in the *Mensurae* were made in the six years 1828 to 1833. The final measures for the volume were secured in 1835 and it was published in 1837. The meridian observations were not completed until 1843, and the *Positiones Mediae* appeared nine years later, in 1852.

The latter volume does not specially concern us here, for it is essentially a star catalogue, giving the accurate positions of the Σ (the symbol always used to designate Struve's double stars) stars for the epoch 1830.0. The *Mensurae Micrometricae*, on the other hand, merits a more detailed description, for the measures within it hold in double star astronomy a position comparable to that of Bradley's meridian measures in our studies of stellar proper motions. They are fundamental. The book is monumental in form as well as in contents, its pages measuring 17½ by 11 in. It is, as Lewis remarks, not to be taken lightly, and its gravity is not lessened by the fact that the notes and the Introduction of 180 pages are written in Latin. Every serious student of double stars, however, should read this Introduction carefully.

Looking first at the actual measures, we find the stars arranged in eight classes, Class I of the *Catalogus Novus* being divided into three, to correspond to the grades previously defined by adjectives, and classes III and IV, into two each. The upper limits of the eight classes, accordingly, are 1, 2, 4, 8, 12, 16, 24, and 32 seconds of arc, respectively. The stars in each class are further distinguished according to magnitude, being graded as *lucidae* if both components of the pair are brighter than 8.5 magnitude, and *reliquae* if either component is fainter than this.

Sir John Herschel had early proposed that the actual date of every double star measure be published and that it be given in years and the decimal of a year. About the year 1828 he further suggested that position angles be referred to the north pole instead of to the equator as origin and be counted through 360°. This avoids the liability to mistakes inherent in Sir William Herschel's method. Both suggestions were adopted by Struve and have been followed by all later observers. Generally the date is recorded to three decimals, thus defining the day, but Struve gives only two. The position angle increases from North (0°) through East, or following (90°), South (180°), and West or preceding (270°).

The heading of the first section, and the first entry under it will illustrate the arrangement of the measures in the *Mensurae Micrometricae:*

DUPLICES LUCIDAE ORDINIS PRIMI
Quarum distantiae inter 0″.00 et 1″.00

Epocha	Amplif.	Distant.	Angulus	Magnitudines
2	Cephei 316.	$\alpha = 0^h0.0.$	$\delta = 78°\ 45'$	
Major—6.3 flava;			*minor = 6.6 certe flavior*	
1828.22	600	0″.72	342.°5	6.5, 7
1828.27	600	0.84	343.4	6.5, 7
1832.20	600	0.94	339.3	6, 6
1832.24	480	0.70	337.5	6, 6.5
1833.34	800	0.85	344.8	6.5, 6.5*m*
Medium 1830.85		0.810	341.50	

The Introduction contains descriptions of the plan of work, the instrument, and the methods of observing, and thorough discussions of the observations. The systems of magnitudes and of color notation, the division of the stars into classes by distance and magnitude, the proper and orbital motions detected, are among the topics treated. One who does not care to read the Latin original will find an excellent short summary in English in Lewis's volume on the Struve Double Stars published in 1906 as Vol. LVI of the *Memoirs of the Royal Astronomical Society of London.* Three or four of Struve's general conclusions are still of interest and importance. He concludes, for example,

that the probable errors of his measures of distance are somewhat greater than those of his measures of position angle and
that both increase with the angular separation of the components,
with their faintness, and with the difference in their magnitudes.
Modern observers note the same facts in the probable errors of
their measures.   In their precision, moreover, and in freedom
from systematic errors, Struve's measures compare very favorably
with the best modern ones.

His observations of star colors show that when the two components of a pair are of about the same magnitude they are
generally of the same color, and that the probability of color
contrast increases with increasing difference in the brightness
of the components, the fainter star being the bluer.   Very few
exceptions to these results have been noted by later observers.

Finally, in connection with his discussion of the division of
double stars into classes by distance, Struve argues, on the
theory of probabilities, that practically all the pairs in his first
three classes (distance under 4″.00) and the great majority in
his first five classes (distance less than 12″) are true binary
systems.   With increasing angular separation he finds that the
probability that optical systems will be included increases,
especially among the pairs in which both components are as
faint as, or fainter than, 8.5 magnitude.   This again is in harmony with the results from more recent investigations.

The Russian government, in 1839, called upon Struve to build
and direct the new Imperial Observatory at Pulkowa.   Here
the principal instruments were an excellent Repsold meridian
circle and an equatorial telescope with an object glass of 15-in.
aperture.   This was then the largest refractor in the world,
as the 9-in. Dorpat telescope had been in 1824.

One of the first pieces of work undertaken with it was a
resurvey of the northern half of the sky to include all stars as
bright as the seventh magnitude.   In all, about 17,000 stars
were examined, and the work was completed in 109 nights of
actual observing between the dates Aug. 26, 1841, and Dec. 7,
1842.   The immediate object was the formation of a list of
all the brighter stars, with approximate positions, to serve
as a working program for precise observations with the meridian
circle.   It was thought, however, that the more powerful
telescope might reveal double stars which had escaped detection
with the 9-in. either because of their small angular separation

or because of the faintness of one component. This expectation was fully realized. The survey, which after the first month was conducted by Wilhelm Struve's son, Otto, resulted in the discovery of 514 new pairs, a large percentage of which were close pairs. These, with Otto Struve's later discoveries which raised the total to 547, are known as the OΣ or Pulkowa double stars. The list of 514 was published in 1843 without measures, and when, in 1850, a corrected catalogue, with measures, was issued, 106 of the original 514 were omitted because not really double, or wider than the adopted distance limits, or for other reasons. But, as Hussey says, "it is difficult effectively to remove a star which has once appeared in the lists." Nearly all of the OΣ stars rejected because of wide separation have been measured by later observers and are retained in Hussey's Catalogue of the OΣ Stars and in Burnham's General Catalogue.

The early period of double star discovery ended with the appearance of the Pulkowa Catalogue. New double stars were indeed found by various observers as incidents in their regular observing which was mainly devoted to the double stars in the great catalogues which have been described and especially to those in the Σ and the OΣ lists. The general feeling, however, was that the Herschels and the Struves had practically completed the work of discovery.

Many astronomers, in the half century from 1820 to 1870, devoted great energy to the accurate measurement of double stars; and the problem of deriving the elements of the orbit of a system from the data of observation also received much attention. This problem was solved as early as 1827, and new methods of solution have been proposed at intervals from that date to the present time. Some of these will be considered in Chap. IV.

One of the most notable of the earlier of these observers was the Rev. W. R. Dawes, who took up this work as early as 1830, using a 3.8-in. refractor. Later, from 1839 to 1844, he had the use of a 7-in. refractor at Mr. Bishop's observatory, and still later, at his own observatory, he installed first a 6-in. Merz, than a 7½-in. Alvan Clark, and finally an 8½-in. Clark refractor. Mr. Dawes possessed remarkable keenness of vision, a quality which earned for him the sobriquet, the eagle-eyed, and, as Sir George Airy says, was also "distinguished . . . by a habitual, and (I may say) contemplative precision in the use of his instruments." His observations, which are to be found in the volumes of the *Monthly Notices* and the *Memoirs of the Royal Astronomical Society*, "have commanded a degree of respect which has not often been obtained by the productions of larger instruments."

Another English observer whose work had great influence upon the progress of double star astronomy was Admiral W. H. Smythe, who also began his observing in 1830. His observations were not in the same class with those of Dawes, but his *Bedford Catalogue* and his *Cycle of Celestial Objects* became justly popular for their descriptions of the double and multiple stars, nebulae, and clusters of which they treat, and are still "anything but dull reading."

Far more important and comprehensive than that of any other astronomer of the earlier period after W. Struve was the double star work of Baron Ercole Dembowski who made his first measures at his private observatory near Naples in 1851. His telescope had an excellent object glass, but its aperture was only 5 in. and the mounting had neither driving clock nor position circles. His micrometer, although it could be rotated, was not provided with a circle from which the position angle could be read off. His procedure was to use two parallel fixed wires separated by a known distance. As the pair was brought to the first wire, he would set for position angle and measure with the micrometer thread the position of the primary star on that wire. Then, letting the star pass to the second wire by the diurnal motion, he would measure its position on that wire also. The difference of the two readings and the known distance between the two wires gave him the two sides of a right triangle from which the position angle could be computed. With this instrument Dembowski made some 2,000 sets of measures of high quality in the course of eight years, though how he managed to accomplish it is well-nigh a mystery to observers accustomed to the refinements of modern micrometers and telescope mountings.

In 1859, he secured a 7-in. Merz refractor with circles, micrometer, and a good driving clock, and, in 1862, he resumed his double star observing with fresh enthusiasm. His general plan was to remeasure all of the double stars in the Dorpat and Pulkowa catalogues, repeating the measures in successive years for those stars in which changes were brought to light. His skill and industry enabled him, by the close of the year

1878, to accumulate nearly 21,000 sets of measures, including measures of all of the Σ stars, except 64 which for one reason or another were too difficult for his telescope. About 3,000 of the measures pertain to the OΣ stars and about 1,700 to stars discovered by Burnham and other observers. Each star was measured on several different nights and for the more interesting stars long series of measures extending over 12 or 15 or even more years were secured. The comprehensive character of his program, the systematic way in which he carried it into execution, and the remarkable accuracy of his measures combine to make Dembowski's work one of the great contributions to double star astronomy. He died before his measures could be published in collected form, but they were later (1883–1884) edited and published by Otto Struve and Schiaparelli in two splendid quarto volumes which are as indispensable to the student of double stars as the *Mensurae Micrometricae* itself.

Mädler at Dorpat, Secchi at Rome, Bessel at Königsberg, Knott at Cuckfield, Engelmann at Leipzig, Wilson and Gledhill at Bermerside, and many other able astronomers published important series of double star measures in the period under consideration. It is impossible to name them all here. Lewis, in his volume on the Struve Stars, and Burnham, in his *General Catalogue* of *Double Stars*, give full lists of the observers, the latter with complete references to the published measures.

CHAPTER II

HISTORICAL SKETCH: THE MODERN PERIOD

The feeling that the Herschels, South, and the Struves had practically exhausted the field of double star discovery, at least for astronomers in the northern hemisphere, continued for thirty years after the appearance of the Pulkowa Catalogue in 1843. Nor were any new lines of investigation in double star astronomy developed during this period. Then, in 1873, a modest paper appeared in the *Monthly Notices of the Royal Astronomical Society*, entitled "Catalogue of Eighty-one Double Stars, Discovered with a Six-inch Alvan Clark Refractor. By S. W. Burnham, Chicago, U. S. A."
The date of the appearance of this paper may be taken as the beginning of the modern period of double star astronomy, for to Burnham belongs the great credit of being the first to demonstrate and utilize the full power of modern refracting telescopes in visual observations; and the 40 years of his active career as an observer cover nearly all of the modern developments in binary star astronomy, including the discovery and observation of spectroscopic binaries, the demonstration that the eclipsing variable stars are binary systems, and the application of photographic methods to the measurement of visual double stars.

Within a year after the appearance of his first catalogue Burnham had published two additional ones, raising the number of his discoveries to 182. At that time he was not a professional astronomer but an expert stenographer employed as official reporter in the United States Courts at Chicago. He had secured, in 1861, a 3-in. telescope with alt-azimuth mounting, and, some years later, a 3¾-in. refractor with equatorial mounting. "This was just good enough," he tells us, "to be of some use, and poor enough . . . to make something better more desirable than ever." In 1870, accordingly, he purchased the 6-in. refractor from Alvan Clark and erected it in a small observatory at his home in Chicago. With this instrumental equipment and an astronomical library consisting principally of a copy of the first edition of Webb's *Celestial Objects for Common Telescopes*, Burnham began his career as a student of double stars. His first new pair (β 40) was found on April 27, 1870.

The 6-in. telescope, which his work so soon made famous, was not at first provided with a micrometer and his earliest list of discoveries was printed without measures. Later, position angles were measured, but the distances continued to be

S. W. Burnham.

estimated. This lack of measures by him was covered to a considerable extent by the measures of Dembowski and Asaph Hall.

Burnham's later career was unique. He held positions in four observatories, the Dearborn, the Washburn, the Lick, and the Yerkes, and discovered double stars also with the 26-in. refractor at the United States Naval Observatory, the 16-in. refractor of the Warner Observatory, and the 9.4-in. refractor at the Dartmouth College Observatory. In all, he discovered about 1,340 new double stars and made many thousands of measures which are of inestimable value because of their great accuracy and because of the care with which he prepared his observing programs. And yet, except for the two short periods spent respectively at Madison and at Mount Hamilton, he continued his work as Clerk of the United States District Court of Chicago until 1910! He retired from the Yerkes Observatory in 1912 and died in 1921.

Burnham's plan in searching for new double stars was very different from that followed by his great predecessors. He did not attempt a systematic survey of the sky but examined the stars in a more random way. In his earlier work, while identifying the objects described in Webb's book, he made a practice of examining the other stars near them. Later, whenever he measured a double star, he continued this practice, examining in this manner probably the great majority of the naked eye and brighter telescopic stars visible from our latitudes. Many of the double stars he discovered with the 6-in. refractor are difficult objects to measure with an aperture of 36 inches. They include objects of two classes almost unrepresented in the earlier catalogues: pairs in which the components are separated by distances as small as $0''.2$, and pairs in which one component is extremely faint, and close to a bright primary. In his first two lists he set his limit at $10''$, but later generally rejected pairs wider than $5''$. The result is that the percentage of very close pairs, and therefore of pairs in comparatively rapid orbital motion, is far higher in his catalogue than in any of the earlier ones.

Burnham's work introduced the modern era of double star discovery, the end of which has not yet come. No less distinguished an authority than the late Rev. T. W. Webb, in congratulating Burnham upon his work in 1873, warned him that he could not continue it for any great length of time for want of material. Writing in 1900, Burnham's comment was: "Since that time more than one thousand new double stars have been added to my own catalogues, and the prospect of future discoveries is as promising and encouraging as when the first star was found with the six-inch telescope."

Working with the $18\frac{1}{2}$-in. refractor of the Dearborn Observatory, G. W. Hough discovered 648 double stars in the quarter century from 1881 to 1906. In 1896 and 1897, T. J. J. See, assisted by W. A. Cogshall and S. L. Boothroyd, examined the stars in the zone from $-20°$ to $-45°$ declination, and in half of the zone (from 4^h to 16^h R. A.) from $-45°$ to $-65°$ declination with the 24-in. refractor of the Lowell Observatory, and discovered 500 new double stars. See states that not less than

10,000 stars were examined, "many of them, doubtless, on several occasions." This is probably an overestimate for it leads to a remarkably small percentage of discoveries.

In England, in 1901, the Rev. T. E. H. Espin began publishing lists of new double stars discovered with his 17¼-in. reflector.[1] The first list contained pairs casually discovered in the course of other work; later, Mr. Espin undertook the systematic observation of all the stars in the Bonn Durchmusterung north of +30°, recording, and, as far as possible measuring, all pairs under 10″ not already known as double. Since 1917, W. Milburn has been his assistant in this work, which is not yet completed. In 1932, Espin's published discoveries numbered 2,444 and Milburn's, 673.

Shorter lists of discoveries have been published by E. S. Holden, F. Küstner, H. A. Howe, O. Stone, Alvan and A. G. Clark, E. E. Barnard, and others, and many doubles were first noted by the various observers participating in the preparation of the great Astronomische Gesellschaft Catalogue.

In France, in 1909, Robert Jonckheere began double star work at the Observatory of the University of Lille at Hem and in the course of five years discovered 1,319 new pairs. Forced by the war to give up his work in France, he went to the Royal Observatory at Greenwich, England, and for some years continued his observations with the 28-in. refractor. The majority of his double stars, though close, are quite faint, a large percentage of them falling outside of the 9.5 magnitude limit of the Bonn Durchmusterung. In 1917 he published a catalogue of all double stars under 5″ discovered visually in the years 1905 to 1916 in the sky area within 105° of the North Pole.

Many pairs, generally wider than 5″ and often quite faint, have been found in the various sections of the *Astrographic Catalogue* and listed by Scheiner, Stein, Barton, and others.

My own work in this field of astronomy began when I came to the Lick Observatory in June, 1895. At first my time was devoted to the measurement with the 12-in. refractor of list of stars selected by Prof. Barnard, and the work was done under his direction. Later, longer lists were measured both with this telescope and with the 36-in. refractor; and in selecting the stars for measurement I had the benefit of advice—so generously given by him to many double star observers of my generation—

---

[1] A 24-in. reflector was added later. Mr. Espin died on Dec. 1, 1934.

from Prof. Burnham, then at the Yerkes Observatory. My attention was early drawn to questions relating to double star statistics, and before long the conviction was reached that a prerequisite to any satisfactory statistical study of double star distribution was a resurvey of the sky with a large modern telescope that should be carried to a definite limiting magnitude. I decided to undertake such a survey, and, adopting the magnitude 9.0 of the Bonn Durchmusterung as a limit, began the preparation of charts of convenient size and scale showing every star in the BD as bright as 9.0 magnitude, with notes to mark those already known to be double. The actual work of comparing these charts with the sky was begun early in April, 1899.

Professor W. J. Hussey, who came to the Lick Observatory in January, 1896, also soon took up the observation of double stars. His first list consisted of miscellaneous stars, but, in 1898, he began the remeasurement of all of the double stars discovered by Otto Struve, including the "rejected" pairs. This work was carried out with such energy and skill that in 1901, in Volume V of the *Lick Observatory Publications*, a catalogue of the $O\Sigma$ stars was published which contained not only Hussey's measures of every pair but also a complete collection of all other published measures of these stars, with references to the original publications, and discussions of the motion shown by the various systems. In the course of this work, Hussey had found an occasional new double star and had decided that at its conclusion he would make more thorough search for new pairs. In July, 1899, we accordingly combined forces for the survey of the entire sky from the North Pole to $-22°$ declination on the plan which I had already begun to put into execution; Hussey, however, charted also the 9.1 BD stars. Each observer undertook to examine about half the sky area, in zones 4° wide in declination. When Hussey left the Lick Observatory in 1905 to become director of the Observatory of the University of Michigan, I took over his zones in addition to those assigned to me in our division of the work and early in 1915 completed the entire survey to $-22°$ declination, as originally planned, between 13^h and 1^h in right ascension, but only to $-14°$ declination in the remaining 12^h. These come to the meridian in our winter months when conditions are rarely satisfactory for work at low altitudes. Subsequently, by agreement with the observers at the Union Observatory, South Africa, whose work will be described on a later page, I extended the survey in these 12 hours to −18° declination.

The survey has resulted in the discovery of more than 4,400 new pairs, 1,329 by Hussey, the others by me, practically all of which fall within the distance limit of 5″. Some statistical conclusions based upon this material will be presented in a later chapter.

It may seem that undue emphasis has been placed upon the *discovery* of double stars in this historical sketch. That a particular star is or is not double is indeed of relatively little consequence; the important thing is to secure accurate measures through a period of time sufficiently long to provide the data for a definite determination of the orbit of the system. But the discovery must precede the measures, as Sir John Herschel said long ago; moreover, such surveys as that of Struve, the one recently completed at the Lick Observatory and those in progress in the southern hemisphere, afford the only basis for statistical investigations relating to the number and spatial distribution of the double stars. Further, the comparison of the distance limits adopted by the successive discoverers of double stars and an analysis of the actual distances of the pairs in their catalogues afford the most convenient measure of the progress made in the 140 years since Herschel began his work, both in the power of the telescopes available and in the knowledge of the requirements for advance in this field of astronomy.

The data in the first four lines of the following table are taken from Burnham's General Catalogue of his own discoveries, and in the last two lines I have added the corresponding figures for the Lick Observatory double star survey.

PERCENTAGE OF CLOSE PAIRS IN CERTAIN CATALOGUES OF DOUBLE STARS

	Class I, number of stars	Class II, number of stars	Sum	Percentage of close pairs
William Herschel, catalogue of 812 stars.	12	24	36	4.5
Wilhelm Struve, catalogue of 2,640 stars	91	314	405	15.0
Otto Struve, catalogue of 547 stars.....	154	63	217	40.0
Burnham, catalogue of 1,260 stars.....	385	305	690	55.0
Hussey, catalogue of 1,327 stars.......	674	310	984	74.2
Aitken, catalogue of 3,105 stars........	1,595	710	2,305	74.3

The increasing percentage of close pairs is, of course, due in part to the earlier discovery of the wider pairs, but the absolute numbers of the closer pairs testify to the increase of telescopic power in the period since 1780. If Class I had been divided into two subclasses including pairs under $0''.50$ and pairs between $0''.51$ and $1''.00$, respectively, the figures would have been even more eloquent, for 60 per cent of the Class I pairs in the last two catalogues enumerated have measured distances of $0''.50$ or less.

While the modern period is thus characterized by the number of visual binaries, and, in particular, those of very small angular distance discovered within it, it is still more notable for the development of an entirely new field in binary star astronomy. In August, 1889, Prof. E. C. Pickering announced that certain lines in the objective-prism spectrograms of ζ *Ursae Majoris* (*Mizar*) were double on some plates, single on others, the cycle being completed in about 104 days.* An explanation of the phenomenon was found in the hypothesis that the star consisted of two components, approximately equal in brightness, in rapid revolution about their center of mass.

If the orbit plane of such a system is inclined at a considerable angle to the plane of projection, the velocities in the line of sight of the two components will vary periodically, as is evident from Fig. 1; and, on the Doppler-Fizeau principle,† there will be a slight displacement of the lines of the spectrum of each component from their mean positions toward the violet end when that component is approaching the Earth, relatively to the motion of the center of mass of the system, and toward the red end when it is receding, relatively. It is clear from the figure that when one component is approaching the Earth, relatively, the other will be receding, and that the lines of the two spectra at such times will be displaced in opposite directions, thus appearing double on the spectrograms. Twice, also, in each revolution the orbital motion of the two components will evidently be directly across the line of sight and the radial velocity of each at these times is the same, and is equal to that of the system as a whole. The lines of the two spectra, if similar, will then coincide and appear single on the plates. There is no question but that this explana-

---

* The true period, deduced from many plates taken with slit spectrographs, is about one-fifth of this value, a little more than 20.5 days.

† Explained in Chap. V.

tion is the correct one, and *Mizar* therefore has the honor of being the first star discovered to be a *spectroscopic binary system.*

A moment's consideration is enough to show that if one of the two components in such a system is relatively faint or "dark," only one set of spectral lines, that produced by the brighter star, will appear upon the plate, but that these lines will be shifted periodically from their mean positions just as are the lines in the double spectrum of *Mizar.* If the plane of the system lies so nearly in the line of sight that each star partly or completely eclipses the other once in every revolution, the

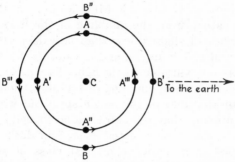

FIG. 1.—*A, A', A'', A'''* = primary star at points of maximum, minimum, and mean radial velocity. *B, B', B'', B'''* = position of the companion star at the corresponding instants. *C* is the center of gravity of the system. There is no star or other body at this point.

presence of the darker star may be revealed by a periodic dimming of the light of the brighter one; if the orbit plane, as will more commonly happen, is inclined at such an angle to the line of sight that there is no occultation or eclipse of the stars for observers on the Earth, the variable radial velocity of the brighter star will be the sole evidence of the existence of its companion.

Algol (β Persei) is a variable star whose light remains nearly constant about four-fifths of the time; but once in every two and one-half days it rapidly loses brightness and then in a few hours' time returns to its normal brilliancy. As early as 1782, Goodericke, the discoverer of the phenomenon, advanced the the :y that the periodic loss of light resulted from the partial ecli se of the bright star by a (relatively) dark companion. In No ber, 1889, Prof. H. C. Vogel, who had been photographing the sp ectr m of the star at Potsdam, announced that this theory was correct, for his spectrograms showed that before light mini-

mum the spectral lines were shifted toward the red from their
mean position by an amount corresponding to a velocity of recession from the Earth of about 27 miles a second. While the star
was recovering its brightness, on the other hand, the shift of the
lines toward the violet indicated a somewhat greater velocity of
approach, and the period of revolution determined by means of
the curve plotted from the observed radial velocities was identical
with the period of light variation. *Algol* thus became the second
known spectroscopic binary star and the first of the special class
later called *eclipsing binaries*.

Within a few months two other spectroscopic binary stars
were discovered; β *Aurigae* by Miss Maury at the Harvard
College Observatory from the doubling of the lines in its spectrum at intervals of slightly less than two days (the complete
revolution period is 3.96 days), and α *Virginis*, by Vogel. The
latter star was not variable in its light, like *Algol*, nor did its
spectrum show a periodic doubling of the lines,* like *Mizar* and
β *Aurigae*, but the lines of the single spectrum were displaced
periodically, proving that the star's radial velocity varied, and
the cycle of variation was repeated every four days. α *Virginis*
is thus the first representative of that class of spectroscopic
binary systems in which one component is relatively dark, as
in the case of *Algol*, but in which the orbit plane does not
coincide with the line of sight. It is to this class that the great
majority of spectroscopic binary stars now known belong.
The reader must not infer that the companion stars in systems
of this class emit no light; the expression *relatively* dark may
simply mean that the companion is two or three magnitudes
fainter than its primary. If the latter were not present, the
companion in many systems would be recognized as a bright
star; even the companion of *Algol* radiates enough light to permit
the secondary eclipse, when the primary star is the occulting
body, to be detected by our delicate modern photometers.

The story of the modern spectrograph and its revelations of
the chemical composition of the stars and nebulae and of the
physical conditions that prevail in them is a marvelous one,
but this is not the place to tell it. We must limit ourselves to
the simple statement that in the years since 1889 the spectrograph has also given us a vast amount of information with

* The secondary spectrum of α *Virginis* has been photographed in more
recent years.

regard to the radial velocities of the stars and, as a byproduct, with regard to spectroscopic binary systems. In this development the Lick Observatory has taken a leading part, for by the application of sound engineering principles in the design of the Mills spectrograph, and by patient and skilful experimental work extended over several years, Dr. Campbell was enabled, in the late 1890's, to secure an accuracy of measurement of radial velocity far surpassing any previously attained. The New Mills spectrograph, mounted in 1903, led to even better results, and it is now possible, in the more favorable cases, to detect a variation in the radial velocity even if the range is only 1.5 km/sec.* Other observers and institutions have also been most active and successful, and the number of known spectroscopic binaries has increased with great rapidity. The *First Catalogue of Spectroscopic Binaries*, compiled by Campbell and Curtis to include the systems observed to Jan. 1, 1905, had 140 entries; by Jan. 1, 1910, when Campbell prepared his *Second Catalogue of Spectroscopic Binary Stars*, the number had grown to 306; the Third Catalogue, compiled by Dr. J. H. Moore in 1924 had 1,054 entries, and in December, 1931, the card catalogue which is kept up to date at the Lick Observatory listed 1,340 stars with known variable radial velocity and 122 more in which variation was indicated or suspected. In the vast majority of cases the variation in radial velocity was detected at observatories in the United States and Canada or at the Chile Station of the Lick Observatory.

The institutions that have engaged most actively in the measurement of stellar radial velocities and the consequent discovery of spectroscopic binary stars, are the Lick (with its branch station at Santiago, Chile, until 1929), the Yerkes, the Mount Wilson, the Dominion Astrophysical (Victoria), and the Dominion (Ottawa) Observatories. Other observatories in the United States, those at Pulkowa, Potsdam, and Bonn, in Europe, and the Cape Observatory, in South Africa, have also made notable contributions in this field.

The discoveries of the spectroscopic binary stars are ordinarily credited to observatories rather than individuals because it is often a matter for fine discrimination to decide with whom the

---

* This is six times the probable error of measurement of the best plates. No one, however, would announce a radial velocity of so small a range on the basis of only two or three plates.

credit for a particular discovery should rest. In general, at least three spectrograms are required to prove that a star is a spectroscopic binary star. These may all be taken and measured by a single observer, or the three plates may be exposed by as many different observers in the course of carrying out a program of work planned by a fourth; the plates may be measured by one or more of the four or by others; variation in the radial velocity may be suspected from the second plate and confirmed by the third or only by a fourth or still later plate.

Not all stars showing variable radial velocity are spectroscopic binary stars. When, as in the case of *Mizar*, or of β *Aurigae*, two sets of lines appear upon the spectrogram, it is certain that we have to do with a double star system. When only one set of lines appears, but this set exhibits a periodic variation, as in the case of α *Virginis*, it is almost certain that the light producing the spectrum comes from the brighter component of such a system. But in some cases—the *Cepheid* variable stars, for example—the apparent variation in radial velocity may be the consequence of rhythmic or pulsating motion in the atmosphere of a single star, rather than of the orbital motion of a component in a binary system. Such stars, and also those in which the observed variation in radial velocity is quite irregular, will be considered later.

The problem of finding the elements of the orbit of a spectroscopic binary from the data given by the measures of radial velocity was solved as early as 1891 by Rambaut, and in 1894, Lehmann-Filhés published the method which has been the chief one used ever since. A number of other methods have been proposed in more recent years, some analytical, others graphical, and doubtless others still will be developed. This phase of the subject is treated in Chap. VI.

At the present time orbits for more than 320 systems have been computed, a number greatly exceeding that of the visual binary systems with known orbits. The reason is not far to seek. The visual binaries are systems of vast dimensions and their revolution periods range from a minimum (so far as known at present) of 4.6 years to a maximum that is certainly greater than 1,000 years. *Castor*, for example, was one of the first double stars to be observed, and it was the one in which the fact of orbital motion was first demonstrated; but although the observations extend from the year 1719 to date, the length of the revolution period is still quite uncertain. The spectroscopic binary stars, on the other hand, are, in general, systems of relatively small dimensions, the revolution periods ranging from five or six hours, as a minimum, to a few years. The masses of the systems being assumed to be of the same order, the smaller the dimensions, the greater the orbital velocity, and the greater the probability of the detection of the system by means of the spectrograph, for the amount of the displacement of the lines in the spectrum is a function of the radial velocity of the star.

Now, if the revolution of a system is accomplished in, say, two or three days, or even in two or three weeks, or months, it is possible for an observer to secure ample data for the computation of its definite orbit in a single season. Indeed, if the spectrograph is devoted to this purpose exclusively and the percentage of clear nights is large, a single telescope may in one season secure the data for the orbits of twenty or more systems.

As in the work of their discovery, so in the computation of the orbits of the spectroscopic binary stars the American observatories are taking the lead. Inspection of the table of orbits given in the appendix to this volume will show that more than 90 per cent of the orbits have been computed by astronomers at the Dominion Astrophysical Observatory, at Victoria, and the Dominion Observatory at Ottawa, in Canada, and by those at the Lick, Allegheny, Yerkes, Mount Wilson, and Detroit Observatories in the United States.

While the spectroscopic binary stars have been receiving ever increasing attention in recent years, the visual binary stars are by no means being neglected. The work of measuring and remeasuring the double stars discovered has been carried on enthusiastically by scores of able observers with small telescopes and with large ones. It is impossible to comment upon all of these or to give details of the hundreds of series of measures they have published but I cannot refrain from referring here to two of the most prominent observers of the generation that has just passed away—G. V. Schiaparelli and Asaph Hall. Schiaparelli's measures are published in two quarto volumes, the first containing the measures made at Milan with the 8-in. refractor, in the years 1875 to 1885; the second, the series made with the 18-in. refractor at the same observatory in the interval from 1886 to 1900. Hall's work, carried out with the 26-in. refractor of the United States Naval Observatory at Washington,

is also printed in two quarto volumes, the first containing the
measures made in the years 1875 to 1880; the second, those made
from 1880 to 1891. The working lists of both observers were
drawn principally from the Dorpat and Pulkowa catalogues,
but include many of Burnham's discoveries and some made by
Hough and by others. The high accuracy of their measures
and the fact that they—and Schiaparelli in particular—repeated
the measures of the more interesting stars year after year makes
the work of these observers of the greatest importance.

At present, double stars are regularly measured at two or
three of the larger observatories of this country, at several
important observatories in England and on the continent of
Europe,* and by many enthusiastic amateurs in this country
and abroad. So voluminous is the literature of the subject
that one who wishes to trace the full record of one of the double stars discovered by Herschel or by Struve in the original
sources must have access to a large astronomical library. This
condition was recognized many years ago, and as early as
1874 Sir John Herschel's *A Catalogue of* 10,300 *Multiple and
Double Stars, Arranged in Order of R. A.* was published as a
Memoir of the Royal Astronomical Society. This catalogue
attempted merely to give a consecutive list of the known double
stars, without measures and did not go far toward meeting
the needs of observers or computers. The first really service-
able compendium was that published by Flammarion in 1878,
entitled *Catalogue des Étoiles Doubles et Multiples en Mouve-
ment relatif certain.* The volume aimed to include all pairs
known from the actual measures to be in motion; 819 systems
are listed, each with a fairly complete collection of the published
measures, about 14,000 in all, and notes on the nature of the
motion. For thirty years this book formed a most excellent
guide to observers.

The following year, 1879, *A Handbook of Double Stars*, prepared by Crossley, Gledhill, and Wilson, was published in
London—a work that had a wide circulation and that proved
of the greatest service to students of double-star astronomy.
It is divided into three parts, the first two giving a general
account of double-star discoveries and methods of observing and
of orbit computation. The third section contains a "Catalogue

* This statement refers to the northern hemisphere; an account of the
work in the southern hemisphere is given on later pages.

of 1,200 double stars and extensive lists of measures." An appendix gives a list of the principal papers on double stars.

In 1900, Burnham published a General Catalogue of his own discoveries containing a complete collection of all known measures of these stars with notes discussing the motion when such was apparent, and references to the original sources from which the measures were taken. This proved to be the first of a series of such volumes. Hussey's catalogue of the Otto Struve stars, to which reference has already been made, was published in 1901, and five years later, in 1906, Lewis's great volume on the Struve stars appeared. This is, in effect, a revision of the *Mensurae Micrometricae* and gives all of the Σ stars in the order of their original numbers, disregarding the inconvenient division into classes. Such of the Σ "rejected" stars as have been measured by later observers are also included, and all or nearly all of the published measures of each pair. The notes give an analysis and discussion of the motions that have been observed, and form one of the most valuable features of the work, for the author had devoted many years to a comprehensive study of double star astronomy in all its phases. In 1907, Eric Doolittle published a catalogue of the Hough stars, all of which he had himself reobserved, and in 1915, Fox included in Vol. I of *The Annals of the Dearborn Observatory* catalogues of the discoveries of Holden and of Küstner with a new series of measures of these stars. More recently Van Biesbroeck (*Publications of the Yerkes Observatory*, Vol. V, Part I, 1927) has published measures of all of Hussey's pairs, 1,298 in all, that were within reach of observation from the Yerkes Observatory. Thus all of the longer catalogues of new double stars discovered at observatories in the northern hemisphere, except my own and some other of the very recent ones and those of Sir John Herschel, have now been revised and brought up to date, for Sir William Herschel's discoveries, except the very wide pairs, are practically all included in the *Mensurae Micrometricae*.

Every one of the volumes named is most convenient for reference and contains information not easily to be found elsewhere; but they were all surpassed by Burnham's comprehensive and indispensable work, *A General Catalogue of Double Stars within* 121° *of the North Pole*, which was published by The Carnegie Institution of Washington in 1906. This monumental work consists of two parts, printed in separate quarto volumes. Part I contains a catalogue of 13,665 double stars, including essentially every pair, close or wide, within the sky area named, that had been listed as a double star before 1906. The positions, for 1880, are given, with the discovery date and measure or estimate. Part II contains measures, notes and complete references to all published papers relating to each pair. This catalogue proved to be a most valuable guide to double star observers and it was in no small measure responsible for the great activity in double star discovery and observation in the following years.

In 1917, M. Robert Jonckheere published, in the *Memoirs of the Royal Astronomical Society* (Vol. 61) a *Catalogue and Measures of Double Stars discovered visually from* 1905 *to* 1916 *within* 105° *of the North Pole and under* 5″ *Separation.* This is, in effect, an extension of Burnham's General Catalogue, though the author excluded pairs wider than 5″ instead of recording every pair announced by its discoverer as double and adopted −15° instead of −31° for the southern sky limit. The volume is particularly valuable because it gives in collected form Jonckheere's own discoveries with measures at a second epoch as well as at the time of discovery. The other long lists in the volume are Espin's discoveries and those made at the Lick Observatory; in all, there are 3,950 entries.

On his retirement from the Yerkes Observatory, Burnham turned over to Prof. Eric Doolittle, Director of the Flower Observatory, the material he had accumulated for a revision or extension of his catalogue. Doolittle set up a card catalogue planned to contain a complete record of measures and orbits published after 1906. This catalogue and a collection of books and pamphlets on double stars came to me after Doolittle's untimely death in 1920, for, in 1919, in response to his urgent request, I had promised to carry on the work if he did not live to complete it.

The result was the publication, early in 1932, of a *New General Catalogue of Double Stars within* 120° *of the North Pole.** Designed, in a general way, to supplement Burnham's great work, it gives for each pair listed in it the earliest available measure

---

* *New General Catalogue of Double Stars within* 120° *of the North Pole*, by Robert Grant Aitken, in succession to the late Eric Doolittle, Carnegie Institution of Washington, *Publication* 417, 2 Vols., 1932.

and all later measures, except those quoted or referred to by Burnham, together with appropriate notes.

Not all pairs listed in the earlier work, however, are included in this new catalogue. It was thought that the wider and fainter pairs could to advantage be omitted, and limits were therefore set, based upon the apparent magnitude and the angular separation of the components. These limits are defined by the equation

$$\log \rho = 2.8 - 0.2m,$$

in which ρ is the angular separation and m the apparent magnitude. The constant, 2.8, sets the limit at $10''$ for a pair whose apparent magnitude is 9.0. Although approximately three out of every ten pairs listed by Burnham are excluded by these limits, so numerous have been the later discoveries that the new catalogue has 17,181 entries as compared with Burnham's 13,665. The catalogue includes all measures known to me that were made prior to 1927.0. A card catalogue of measures published later is kept up to date at the Lick Observatory.

It has been convenient in this narrative to confine attention to this point to the double star work done at observatories in the northern hemisphere, for, until quite recent years it was there that this branch of astronomy received most attention. Now, however, conditions are changed and the most active and fruitful work in the discovery and measurement of double stars is that carried on at the observatories in South Africa.

We have seen that two of the earliest double stars discovered—α *Centauri* and α *Crucis*—were stars not visible from European latitudes; but the first extensive list of double stars collected at a southern observatory was James Dunlop's catalogue of 253 pairs observed at Parametta, N.S.W., in the years 1825 to 1827 with a 9-ft. reflecting telescope. These stars, however, are as a rule very wide pairs and are of comparatively little interest. A few double stars are contained in Brisbane's Parametta catalogue, published in 1835, and more in the later meridian catalogues of the Royal Observatory at the Cape of Good Hope, the Argentine National Observatory at Cordoba, and of other southern observatories.

The most important early paper on southern double stars is beyond question the chapter upon them in Sir John Herschel's

Results of Astronomical Observations made during the Years
1834, 1835, 1836, 1837, 1838 *at the Cape of Good Hope* which
was published in 1847. Innes says, "The sections on double
stars in this work are to the southern heavens what Struve's
Mensurae Micrometricae are to the northern heavens." A
catalogue is given of the discoveries made at Feldhausen, C. G. H.,
with the 20-ft. reflector which contains the pairs h 3347 to
h 5449, together with measures of such previously known
pairs as were encountered in the "sweeps." Many of the new
pairs are wide and faint, resembling the h stars discovered
at Slough, in England; but many others are comparatively
close, many are very bright, and a number are among the finest
double stars in the southern sky. Another division of this
chapter gives the micrometer measures, made with the five-inch
refractor, of many of these new pairs and of some of the known
ones. Innes says that "the angles of the pairs are all through
of high excellence"; but Herschel himself points out the sources
of weakness in his measures of distances.

Herschel's station at Feldhausen was not a permanent observatory, and when he returned to England work there was
discontinued; nor was double star work seriously pursued at
any other southern station until about 40 years later. In
1882, a list of 350 new pairs was published by H. C. Russell,
director of the Sydney Observatory, N.S.W., the measures
being made by Russell and by L. Hargrave. In 1884, an additional list of 130 pairs, mostly wide, was published, and in
the following years several lists of measures by these observers
and their colleague, J. A. Pollock, a few of the measured pairs
being new. In 1893, R. P. Sellors published a short list (14 pairs,
all under 2″) discovered by him at the same observatory, and
in the following years he contributed many measures of known
pairs and discoveries of a few additional new ones.

A new chapter in the history of double star astronomy in the
southern hemisphere was opened in 1896, when Dr. R. T. A. Innes
joined the staff of the Royal Observatory at the Cape of Good
Hope. Innes had already published as "probably new" two
short lists of 26 and 16 stars, respectively, discovered at Sydney,
N.S.W., in 1895 and 1896, with a 6¼-in. refractor and a small
reflector. At the Cape Observatory, in addition to work in
other lines, he continued his double star observing with the
7-in., and later with the 18-in. (McClean) refractor. With these

instruments he brought the total of his discoveries to 432 and made fine series of measures of these and of other southern double stars. In 1903 he became Government Astronomer at the Union Observatory, Johannesburg, South Africa. Here he worked with a 9-in. refractor until April, 1925, when the 26½-in. Grubb refractor, ordered some years before the war began, was finally installed.

In August, 1925, Dr. W. H. van den Bos, who had been doing excellent double star work at Leiden, came to the Union Observatory. A plan, which Innes had long cherished, for a systematic survey of the southern sky along the general lines of the one of the northern sky carried out at the Lick Observatory, was immediately put into execution. The major part of this survey has been carried out by van den Bos, though Dr. W. S. Finsen and other assistants in the observatory (as well as Innes himself until he retired in 1927) have participated. The survey is still in progress but is nearing completion. Including the earlier work at the Union Observatory by Innes and others, fully 4,000 double stars had been discovered before the close of the year 1931. Innes' own discoveries total 1,613, Finsen's 300, while those of van den Bos exceed 2,000. These are all close pairs, comparable in every respect with those discovered at the Lick Observatory.

In 1911, Hussey accepted the directorship of the observatory of the La Plata University, Argentina, in addition to his duties at Ann Arbor, Michigan. During his periods of residence at La Plata he used the 17-in. refractor in searching for and measuring southern double stars. His discoveries there brought his total number of new pairs up to 1,650, and measures of these later pairs were promptly published.

Mr. Bernhard H. Dawson assisted Prof. Hussey at La Plata until 1917, when Hussey resigned the directorship, and has since continued to give part of his time to double star work. Hussey now found it possible to plan for further double star work in the southern hemisphere with a more powerful telescope, the funds for the construction of which had been provided by his friend and college classmate, Mr. R. P. Lamont. A 27-in. lens was ordered from the John A. Brashear Company, and Hussey personally supervised the designs for the mounting. Delays were encountered, however, and the war came on, with the result that the telescope was not ready for use until the summer of 1926.

Professor Hussey, in 1924, had personally selected a site at Bloemfontein, South Africa, for his southern station, and was on his way there to supervise the erection of the telescope and to carry on double star work when he died of heart disease, in London, on Oct. 23, 1926. The telescope, however, was erected in accordance with his plans, Prof. R. A. Rossiter being placed in charge, with Morris K. Jessup and Henry F. Donner as assistants.

Arrangements were made with the Union Observatory for cooperative work in prosecuting the survey of the southern heavens, with gratifying results. By October, 1931, 4,712 new double stars were discovered and measured on one or more nights; 1,961 by Rossiter, 1,424 by Jessup, and 1,327 by Donner. These measures, for the most part, are as yet unpublished.*

At the Union Observatory, all stars as bright as 9.0 magnitude in the Cape Photographic Durchmusterung are examined, as well as those of fainter photographic magnitude which are estimated to be as bright as 9.0 visual magnitude. The distance limit for pairs listed as double stars is set by the curve $\log \rho = 2.5 - 0.2m$, which gives $5\overset{''}{.}0$ for a pair of 9.0 magnitude.

At the Lamont Hussey Observatory, the survey is being carried to all stars as bright as 9.5 in CPD, and the distance limit is that given by the curve $\log \rho = 2.625 - 0.2m$, giving $6\overset{''}{.}75$ at 9.0 magnitude, and pairs even wider (to the limit set by $\log \rho = 2.8 - 0.2m$) are retained. The result is that while 3,206 pairs fall within the limits of the Union Observatory curve, the percentage of pairs fainter than 9.0 and comparatively wide is very high.

Any statistical discussion of the number and distribution of double stars based upon the material that will be available after these southern surveys are completed, must take account of the systematic difference between visual and photographic magnitudes and of those between the various systems of visual magnitudes. To be significant, such a discussion must include

---

* Rossiter's first list of measures of the pairs of his own discovery has since been published in the *Memoirs of the Royal Astronomical Society*, Vol. LXV, Part II, 1933. In his introductory note he states that his discoveries to date exceed 2,350 pairs. Measures only of those found prior to October, 1932, however, a total of 2,232 pairs, are included in his paper. The list is notable for the large number of very close faint pairs contained in it.

the double stars in both hemispheres and should be based upon accurate photometric magnitudes.

Innes, in 1899, published a *Reference Catalogue of Southern Double Stars*, designed to include "all known double stars having southern declination at the equinox of 1900." The author, however, set limits defining the pairs of stars to be regarded as "double stars," the limits ranging from 1" for pairs of the ninth magnitude to 30" for those of the first magnitude. In principle, this procedure is correct, but Innes' actual narrow limits are open to criticism. He abandoned these limits when, with the assistance of Dawson and van den Bos, he compiled his loose-leaf catalogue that was planned to contain every known double star within the limits of the Cape Photographic Durchmusterung (*i.e.*, south of −19° at the equinox of 1875.0) "that had been measured on more than one occasion as well as many measured only once." This loose-leaf catalogue was completed in 1927, but it was regarded as merely a temporary guide to southern observers, the declared intention being to issue a complete catalogue in more permanent form after the termination of the survey of the southern skies, initiated in 1925. Meanwhile, a card catalogue of all discoveries and published measures is kept up to date at the Union Observatory.

Our knowledge of the spectroscopic binary stars in the far southern skies rests almost entirely upon the work carried on at the D. O. Mills Station of the Lick Observatory, established at Santiago, Chile, in 1903, and maintained until April, 1929, when it was sold to the Catholic University of Chile. The instrumental equipment consisted of a 37¼-in. silver-on-glass reflector and spectrographs similar in design to those in use on Mount Hamilton. The working program was the measurement of the radial velocities of the stars and nebulae which are too far south to be photographed at the Lick Observatory itself. The discovery of binary stars was not the object in view, but a large percentage of the entire number of these systems known at the present time were found at this Station in the 26 years of its existence. When we add to this number the spectroscopic binary stars with southern declinations which have been detected by observers at stations in the northern hemisphere, we shall find that in this field there is little or no disparity between the two hemispheres of the sky.

References

In addition to general accounts of the binary stars in standard textbooks on astronomy, reference may be made to two recent publications:

HENROTEAU, F. C.: "Double and Multiple Stars," *Handbuch der Astrophysik*, Band VI, Chap. 4, pp. 299–474, Berlin, 1928.

BAIZE, P.: L'Astronomie des Étoiles Doubles, *Bull. Soc. Astron. de France* **44**, 268, 359, 395, 505; **45**, 21, Paris, 1930–1931.

[Dr. Hamilton M. Jeffers and Mrs. Frances Greeby at Lick Observatory have been keeping up visual binary orbit data. Their new general catalogue is now ready for publication. It lists about 65,000 double stars, and indicates each pair for which an orbit has been calculated. North of −20°, the compilation has been made at Lick Observatory. South of −20°, the catalogue of Dr. Willem H. van den Bos is incorporated. Mrs. Greeby plans to keep up the catalogue of observations, and additions and changes to the general catalogue.

Attention should also be called to the new catalogue (to be published) by Charles Worley of the Naval Observatory.—J.T.K.]

CHAPTER III

OBSERVING METHODS, VISUAL BINARY STARS

The operation of measuring a double star is a very simple one. The object is to define at a given instant the position of one star, called the *companion*, with respect to the other, known as the *primary*. When the two stars are of unequal magnitude the brighter is chosen as the primary; when they are of equal brightness, it is customary to accept the discoverer's designations.

From the first work by Sir William Herschel, the measures have been made in polar coordinates; and since about 1828, when Sir John Herschel recommended the practice, the *position angle* has been referred to the North Pole as zero point and has been counted through 360°.

That is, the position angle is the angle at the primary star between the line drawn from it to the North Pole and one drawn from it to the companion, the angle increasing from zero when the companion is directly north, through 90° when it is at the east, 180° when it is south, 270° when it is west, up to 360° when it is once more directly north. The *distance* is the angular separation between the two stars measured at right angles to the line joining their centers. The two coordinates are usually designated by the Greek letters θ and ρ, or by the English letters p and s.

THE MICROMETER

The filar or parallel-wire micrometer is the instrument now in almost universal use for visual measurements of double stars.*

* Mr. F. J. Hargreaves has recently perfected a comparison-image micrometer which he finds more accurate than the filar micrometer, particularly in the measurement of angular distances. Two artificial star images are projected into the field of view side by side with the images of the double star to be measured. The artificial star images may be made comparable to those of the real stars in both color and brightness and their position angle and angular separation may be brought into accurate agreement with those of the double star. A full description is given in the *Monthly Notices, R.A.S.* (**92,** 72, 1931), but the instrument has not yet come into general use.

A complete description of it is not necessary here; for this, the reader is referred to Gill's article on the Micrometer in the *Encyclopaedia Britannica* (9th ed.), in which other forms are also described. Essentially it consists of a tube or adapter firmly fitted into the eye end of the telescope and carrying on its outer end a graduated circle (the position circle) reading from 0° to 360° in a direction contrary to the figures on a clock dial. A circular plate fitting closely within the position circle and adjusted to turn freely within it carries an index, or a vernier,

PLATE II.—The micrometer for the 36-in. refractor, Lick Observatory.

or both, to give the circle reading. In the micrometers in use at the Lick Observatory, this plate is rotated about the optical axis of the telescope by an arm carrying a pinion which meshes into rack teeth cut on the outer circumference of the position circle. A clamp is provided to hold the plate and circle together at any desired reading, and a tangent screw to give a slow motion. Upon the vernier plate an oblong box is mounted within which the parallel wires or threads (they are usually spider lines) are placed. This box is movable longitudinally by a well-cut, but not very fine screw. One thread, the *fixed* thread, is attached to the inner side of the upper plate of the box, and the other, the *micrometer* or *movable* thread, is attached to a frame or fork which slides freely in the box longitudinally, but without any lateral play. The fork is moved by a very fine and accurately cut screw which enters the box at one end. At its outer extremity, this screw carries a milled head divided into 100 parts, the readings increasing as the screw draws the micrometer thread toward the head. Strong springs at the opposite end of the fork carrying this thread prevent slack or lost motion.

The two threads, the fixed and the micrometer, must be so nearly in the same plane—the focal plane of the objective—that they can be brought into sharp focus simultaneously in an eyepiece of any power that may be used, but at the same time must pass each other freely, without the slightest interference. Instead of a single fixed thread, some micrometers carry systems of two, three, or more fixed threads, and frequently also one or more fixed transverse threads. Some also substitute two parallel threads separated a few seconds of arc for the single movable thread. For double star work, the simple micrometer with only two threads is unquestionably to be preferred, and even for comet, asteroid, satellite, and other forms of micrometric work I regard it as superior to the more complicated forms and less liable to lead to mistakes of record. Not all observers, however, will agree with me on this last point.

The telescope is assumed to be mounted stably and to be in good adjustment. Assured as to these two points and as to the firm attachment of the micrometer to the telescope tube so that the zero reading of his position circle shall remain constant, the double star observer has still to determine the value of one revolution of his micrometer screw and the zero or north point reading of his position circle before beginning actual measurements. The reading for coincidence of the threads is eliminated by the method of double-distance measures, as will be shown presently, and the distances themselves are, in general, so small, and modern screws so accurate, that irregularities in the screw and corrections for temperature may be regarded as negligible. If desired, however, they may be determined in connection with measures for the revolution value.

THE ZERO POINT

The determination of the zero point will be considered first. The simplest practical method, and the one adopted by observers generally, is to put on the lowest power eyepiece that utilizes the entire beam of light, direct the telescope upon an equatorial star near the meridian, stop the driving clock, and turn the micrometer by the box screw and the position-circle pinion until the star "trails" along the thread across the entire field of view. The star should be bright enough to be seen easily behind the thread, but not too bright. With the 12-in. telescope I find a star of the seventh or eighth magnitude most satisfactory; with the 36-in. telescope, one of the ninth or tenth magnitude. A little practice will enable the observer to determine his "parallel" reading with an uncertainty not greater than one-fifth of one division of his circle. On the micrometer used with the 36-in. telescope, this amounts to $0°.05$. Several independent determinations should be made. If the micrometer is not removed from the telescope and is set firmly to the tube, it is probable that the parallel reading need be checked only once or twice a week. When, as at the Lick Observatory, the micrometer is liable to be removed almost any day and is certainly removed several times every week, the observer very promptly forms the habit of determining the parallel at the beginning of his work *every night;* my own practice is to check the value at the close of work also.

Ninety degrees added to the parallel gives the north point or zero reading.

REVOLUTION OF THE MICROMETER SCREW

The value of one revolution of the micrometer screw should be determined with the greatest care and the investigation should be repeated after a reasonable time interval to detect any wear of the screw. Two different methods of procedure are about equally favored by observers: the method of transits of circumpolar stars and the method of direct measures of the difference in declination of suitable pairs of stars.

In the first method the position circle is set for the *zero* reading (*i.e.*, 90° from the reading for parallel) and the telescope turned upon the star a short time before it culminates. (The driving clock, of course, is stopped.) Set the micrometer thread just in advance of the star as it enters the field of view (it is convenient to start with the milled head set at zero of a revolution) and note the time of the star's transit either on the chronograph or by the eye-and-ear method. Advance the thread one revolution or a suitable fraction of a revolution and take another transit, and repeat this procedure until the star has crossed the entire field of view. A low-power eyepiece should be used and the series of measures so planned that they will extend over from forty to eighty revolutions of the screw, about half of the transits being taken before the star crosses the meridian, the other half after. Great care must be taken not to disturb the instrument during the course of the observations for the slightest changes in its position will introduce errors into the measures. It is well to repeat the observations on a number of nights, setting the telescope alternately east and west of the pier. A sidereal timepiece should be used in recording the time of transits and if it has a large rate, it will be necessary to take this into account.

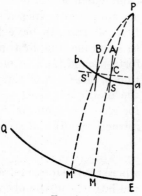

Fig. 2.

In Fig. 2, let P be the pole, EP the observer's meridian, ab the diurnal path of a star, AS the position of the micrometer thread when at the center of the field and parallel to an hour circle PM, and BS' any other position of the thread. Now let m_0 be the micrometer reading, t_0 the hour angle, and T_0 the sidereal time when the star is at S, and m, t, and T the corresponding quantities when the star is at S', and let R be the value of one revolution of the screw.

Through S' pass an arc of a great circle $S'C$ perpendicular to AS. Then, in the triangle $CS'P$, right-angled at C, we have

$$CS' = (m - m_0)R, \quad S'P = 90° - \delta, \quad CPS' = t - t_0 = T - T_0$$

and we can write

$$\sin [(m - m_0)R] = \sin (T - T_0) \cos \delta \qquad (1)$$

or, since $(m - m_0)R$ is always small,

$$(m - m_0)R = \sin (T - T_0) \frac{\cos \delta}{\sin 1''} \qquad (2)$$

Similarly, for another observation,

$$(m' - m_0)R = \sin (T' - T_0) \frac{\cos \delta}{\sin 1''} \qquad (3)$$

Combining these to eliminate the zero point,

$$(m' - m)R = \sin (T' - T_0) \frac{\cos \delta}{\sin 1''} - \sin (T - T_0) \frac{\cos \delta}{\sin 1''} \quad (4)$$

from which the value of R is obtained.   The micrometer readings are supposed to increase with the time.*

If 80 transits have been taken, it will be most convenient to combine the first and the forty-first, the second and the forty-second, and so on, and thus set up 40 equations of condition of the form of Eq. (4).   The solution of these equations by the method of least squares will give the most probable value for R.   The value of R given by Eq. (4) must be corrected for refraction.   It will suffice to use the approximate formula

$$dR = -R \tan 1'' \cot (\delta - \varphi)r \quad (5)$$

where r is the mean refraction, δ, the declination of the star, and φ, the latitude of the observer.   If a star is observed at lower culmination, δ must be replaced by $(180° - \delta)$.

If the value of R is to be determined by direct measures of the difference of declination between two stars, the stars should satisfy the following conditions: they should lie on, or very nearly on, the same hour circle; their proper motions as well as their absolute positions at a given epoch should be accurately known; they should be nearly of the same magnitude and, if possible, of nearly the same color; the difference of declination should amount to from fifty to one hundred revolutions of the micrometer screw; and, since this will ordinarily exceed the diameter of the field of view of the eyepiece, one or more intermediate stars (whose positions do not need to be so accurately known) should lie nearly on the line joining them and at convenient intervals to serve as steps.

There are not many pairs of stars which answer all of the requirements.   Probably the most available ones are to be found in the *Pleiades* and other open clusters which have been triangulated by heliometer observations.

The measures should be made only on the most favorable nights and at times when the stars are high enough in the sky to make the correction for refraction small.   The difference of declination should be measured from north star to south star and also in the opposite direction and the measures should

* From Campbell's *Practical Astronomy.*

be repeated on several nights. If extreme accuracy is desired in the refraction corrections the thermometer and barometer should be read at the beginning and also at the end of each set of measures, and if the effect of temperature is to be included in the determination of R, measures must be made at as wide a range of temperature as is practicable.

In making the reductions, the star places are first brought forward from the catalogue epoch to the date of the actual observations by correcting rigorously for precession, proper motion, and the reduction from mean to apparent place. The apparent place of each star must then be corrected for refraction. It will generally be sufficiently accurate to use Comstock's formula, in the following form:

$$\text{Refraction in } \delta = -\frac{983b}{460 + t} \tan z \cos q \qquad (6)$$

where z is the apparent zenith distance, and q the parallactic angle of the star, b the barometer reading in inches and t the temperature of the atmosphere in degrees Fahrenheit. In practice I have found it more convenient to correct each star for refraction in the manner described than to correct the difference in declination by the use of differential formula.

The following pairs of stars in the *Pleiades* have actually been used by Prof. Barnard in determining the value of one revolution of the micrometer screw of the 40-in. telescope of the Yerkes Observatory:

BD	Mag.		BD	Mag.	Δδ
+ 23°537	(7.5)	and	+ 23°542	(8.2)	696″.19
+ 23°516	(4.8)	and	+ 23°513	(9.0)	285.94
+ 23°557	(4.0)	and	+ 23°559	(8.4)	599.58
+ 23°561	(7.5)	and	+ 23°562	(7.8)	479.11
+ 23°558	(6.2)	and	+ 23°562	(7.8)	401.10
+ 23°563	(7.2)	and	+ 23°569	(7.5)	494.14
+ 23°557	(4.0)	and	+ 23°558	(6.2)	300.25
+ 23°507	(4.7)	and	+ 23°505	(6.5)	633.40

The differences in declination given in the final column are for the epoch 1903.0 and are the results of Dr. Elkin's measures with the Yale heliometer.

The last pair in the list consists of the bright stars *Electra* and *Celaeno*, and the table that follows gives the measures of them made by Barnard, in 1912, to determine the screw value for the

Measures of $\Delta\delta$ *Electra* and *Celaeno*

1912	Electra and *2	*2 and *1	*1 and Celaeno	Measured $\Delta\delta$	Hour angle	Refraction correction	Scale reading	Scale correction	True $\Delta\delta$
Sept. 21	18ʳ.208	25ʳ.626	21ʳ.750	65ʳ.584	$+2^h 30^m$	$+0^r.020$	2.26	$-0^r.004$	65ʳ.600
22	18.195	25.601	21.752	65.548	+2 20	+0.020	2.30	-0.007	65.561
29	18.219	25.596	21.731	65.546	+2 25	+0.020	2.28	-0.006	65.560
Oct. 1	18.232	25.600	21.746	65.578	+1 40	+0.020	2.24	-0.003	65.595
6	18.224	25.604	21.726	65.554	+1 10	+0.019	2.28	-0.006	65.567
22	18.216	25.606	21.736	65.558	+2 0	+0.020	2.21	0.000	65.578
29	18.194	25.606	21.725	65.525	+2 40	+0.022	2.20	0.000	65.545
	18.213	25.606	21.738	65.556		+0.020		-0.003	65.572

This gives for one revolution of the screw:

$$\frac{633''.44}{65^r.572} = 9''.6602$$

Professor Barnard's measures from nine pairs of stars in 1902 and in 1912 lead to the mean value 9″.6617 at temperature 50°F.

micrometer of the 40-in. Yerkes refractor. Step stars of magnitude 11.0 and 11.5, respectively, lying nearly in the line joining the two bright stars were used to reduce the intervals actually measured. Both the tube of the 40-in. telescope and the screw of the micrometer are of steel and therefore mutually correct each other in temperature changes, at least approximately; but the focal length of the object glass is ¾ in. shorter in winter than in summer whereas the tube shortens only ½ in. A slight correction is therefore necessary if all of the measures are to be reduced to the focus for a common temperature. The column Scale reading, in the table of measures, gives the readings for focus on the draw tube of the telescope and the following column, the corrections required to reduce the measures to the focal length corresponding to a temperature of 50°F. The remaining columns are self-explanatory.

If a suitable measuring engine, like those used in measuring positions of images on a photographic plate, is available, it may be used to measure the value of the revolution of the micrometer screw in terms of millimeters, provided the pitch of the screw is known accurately. Dividing the result by the focal length of the telescope, in millimeters, and multiplying by the value of the radius of a circle expressed in seconds (206,264.8) will reduce it to seconds of arc. Burnham's original measure of the screw value of the 36-in. micrometer of the Lick Observatory was 9″.907 ± 0″.006. This was based on measures of the difference in declination of two stars, seven different pairs being measured. Wright has recently measured the screw under one of our measuring engines, finding 9″.9045 ± 0″.0005, the value corresponding to a temperature of 62° F.

MEASURING A DOUBLE STAR

When the telescope has been directed upon the star and clamped, the star is brought up to the threads by means of the screw moving the entire micrometer box. The position angle is then measured, and in doing this my practice is to run the micrometer thread well to one side of the field of view, bring the double star up to the fixed thread by means of the screw moving the box and then rotate the micrometer by means of the pinion provided, keeping, meanwhile, the fixed thread upon the primary star, until the thread also passes centrally through the companion star. It is most convenient to manipulate the box screw with the left hand and the pinion with the right.

The tangent screw giving a slow motion in position angle is never used; in fact, it has been removed from the micrometer. When the seeing is good, the star images round, small, and steady, it is easy to hold both images on the thread until the eye is assured of their precise bisection. Under less favorable conditions a rapid to and fro motion of the box screw places the stars alternately on either side of the thread while the pinion is being rotated backward and forward until the eye is satisfied of the parallelism of the thread to the line joining the centers of the star images.

Ordinarily four independent settings for position angle are made, the circle being read, not by the vernier but by an index, directly to half degrees in the case of the 12-in. micrometer, to quarter degrees in the case of the 36-in., and by estimation to the one-fifth of a division, i.e., to $0°1$ and $0°05$, respectively. To insure the independence of the readings, the micrometer is rotated backward and forward through an arc of 60° to 80° after each setting. The eye is, of course, removed from the eyepiece, and the box is turned directly with the hands, without the use of the rotation pinions.

The circle is next set to a reading 90° greater (or less) than the mean of the readings for position angle and the distance is measured by bisecting one star with the fixed thread, the other with the micrometer thread. It is most convenient to turn the micrometer screw with the right hand, the box screw with the left. Then interchange the threads, placing the micrometer thread on the first star, the fixed thread on the other. The difference between the two readings of the micrometer screw-head gives the double distance, i.e., twice the angular separation, and eliminates the zero or coincidence reading. Three measures of the double distance are generally made. The milled head of the screw, which is divided to hundredths of a revolution, is read to the 1/1,000 revolution by estimation. Care is always taken to run the micrometer thread back several seconds of arc after each setting and to make the final turn of the screw at each bisection *forward* or against the springs. The bisection of the star by the fixed thread should be made anew at each setting with the micrometer screw, because, under even the best conditions, it cannot be assumed that the star images will remain motionless during the time of observation.

Any ordinary notebook will answer as a record book. At the Lick Observatory, we have found convenient a book 7 by $8\frac{1}{2}$ in. containing 150 pages of horizontally ruled, sized paper suitable for ink as well as pencil marks. The observing record is made with pencil, the reductions in ink. No printed forms are necessary or even convenient. A sample entry taken from my observing book shows the form of record adopted, and also the very simple reductions:

			36″ Sat. Jan. 27, 1917.
80 Tauri $= \Sigma$ 554			Parallel $= 10°25$
$128°75 \, nf \, 0.9 \pm$	49.401	9.581	4^h3
$129.70 \, \Delta m = 3$	9.400	9.578	1,000
129.30	9.403	9.580	2 to 2+
130.40	———	———	Well separated with
———	49.401	9.580	520-power
129.54		9.401	
100.25		———	
———		2)0.179	
$29°3 = \theta_0$		$0.089R = 0''88 = \rho_0$	

Two or three such entries are ordinarily made to the page. The column at the left records the four settings for position angle; the mean is taken and the reading of the circle for parallel plus 90° is subtracted to obtain the position angle. Whether this value is the correct one or whether 180° is to be added to it is decided by the note made of the quadrant while observing —*nf* in the present case. When recording the quadrant, which is done after the position angle settings have been entered, I record also an *estimate* of the distance and of the difference of magnitude of the components, or, when the companion is very faint, a direct estimate of its magnitude. At this time, too, I record, at the right, the date, the sidereal time to the tenth of an hour, the power of the eyepiece used, an estimate of the seeing on a scale on which 5 stands for perfect conditions and any observing notes, Measures of distance are then made and recorded. Here the reduction consists in taking half the difference of the two means and multiplying the result by the value of one revolution of the micrometer screw (in this instance $9''907$).

The results are transferred to a "ledger," or, preferably, to the cards of a card catalogue, the date being recorded as a decimal of the year. The ledger entry for the above observation is:

$$80 \text{ Tauri } = \Sigma 554.$$
$$1917.075 \quad 29°3 \quad 0\rlap{.}{''}88, \quad \Delta m = 3, \quad 4\rlap{.}{^h}3, \quad 1000, \quad 2 \text{ to } 2 +, \quad \text{bk. } 87,147$$

the last item being the number and page of the observing book.

Practically all observers agree in the method of measuring the angular distance, but many prefer a somewhat different procedure for determining the position angle. They bring the two threads fairly close together—to a separation twice or three times the diameter of the primary's apparent disk— and then, placing the two stars between the threads, turn the micrometer until the line joining the stars appears to be parallel to the threads. I have found that I can secure equally satis-factory measures by this method when the two stars are well separated and of nearly equal magnitude, but not when the angular distance is small or when the stars differ much in bright-ness. While it may be a matter of personal adaptation I am inclined to think that measures made in this manner are more likely to be affected by systematic errors than those made by the method first described.*

Whatever method is adopted, it is of the first importance that the head of the observer be so held that the line between his eyes is parallel or perpendicular to the line joining the two stars. I can make the bisections with more assurance when the line between the eyes is parallel to the one joining the two stars, and hold my head accordingly unless the line is inclined more than 45° to the horizon. Some observers prefer the perpendicular position. When the line joining the stars makes an angle of approximately 45° to the horizon, it is well to make settings in both positions of the eyes. In pairs with components of unequal magnitude, a systematic difference between the two sets of readings may be expected.

There are some other precautions that must be taken to secure satisfactory results. The star images as well as the threads must be brought sharply into focus; the images must be sym-

* It should be noted that one or two good observers determine the position angle by setting the threads as nearly as possible *perpendicular* to the line joining the two stars. This practice is not recommended.

metrically placed with respect to the optical axis; and the threads must be uniformly illuminated on either side. In modern micrometers the illumination is usually provided by a small incandescent lamp placed in such a position that a small mirror can throw the light through a narrow opening in one end of the micrometer box. This mirror can be rotated through 90° thus permitting a variation in the intensity of the light from full illumination to zero. Suitable reflectors placed within the micrometer box, at the opposite end, insure equality in the illumination on both sides of the threads. Glass slides or color filters can also be placed in front of the opening admitting the light in order to vary its intensity or its color as may be desired. The earlier double star observers frequently illuminated the field of view instead of the threads and an occasional observer still advocates this practice, but the great majority, I think, are agreed that this is a less satisfactory arrangement.

It is hardly necessary to say that the micrometer threads must be stretched to a tension sufficient to keep them perfectly straight, even when the atmosphere is very moist, and that they must be free from dust or other irregularities and accurately parallel. A cocoon of spider thread should be obtained from an instrument maker and kept on hand with the necessary adjusting tools and the micrometer threads replaced as often as they become unsatisfactory. A little practice will enable the observer to set a thread in position in a very short space of time; in fact, from Burnham's days to the present time, a new thread has frequently been set into the 36-in. micrometer during the night and observing resumed within an hour.

The most important precaution to be taken in double star observing is quite independent of instrumental adjustments. It is *to make measures only on nights when the observing conditions are good.* Measures made under poor observing conditions are at best of little value, and at worst are a positive nuisance to the student of double star motions. They annoy or mislead him in his preliminary investigations and are practically rejected in his later work. I make this statement with all possible emphasis.

It is of almost equal consequence to select stars suited to the power of the telescope employed. This, however, is to a considerable extent a matter involving the personal equation. A Dawes, a Dembowski, or a Burnham can measure with

comparatively small apertures stars that other observers find
difficult with much larger telescopes.

MAGNITUDE ESTIMATES

It is well known that the magnitudes assigned to the components of the same double star by different observers frequently show a range that is excessively large. Whatever excuse
there may have been for this in earlier days, there is certainly
little at the present time when the magnitudes of all of the
brighter stars are given in the photometric catalogues and
those of all stars to at least 9.5 magnitude in the various
Durchmusterungen. It is certainly advisable to take the combined magnitude of the two components (or the magnitude of
the brighter star, if the companion is very faint) from these
sources instead of making entirely independent estimates.
The *difference of magnitude* is then the only quantity the double
star observer need estimate. If this difference is not too
great it can be estimated with comparative accuracy; if one
component is very faint, a direct estimate of its brightness
may be based upon the limiting magnitude visible in the telescope used, *care being taken to allow for the effect of the bright
companion* which will always make the faint star appear fainter
than it really is.

To derive the brightness of each component when the combined magnitude and the difference of magnitude are known,
we have the relations, $A = C + x$, $B = A + d$, in which A and
B are the magnitudes of the brighter and fainter component,
respectively, C the combined magnitude, and d the estimated
difference of magnitude, while x is given by the equation

$$x = \frac{\log\left(1 + \frac{1}{2.512^d}\right)}{0.4}$$

We may tabulate x for different values of d as in the following table which is abbreviated from the one in Innes' *Reference
Catalogue:*

d	x	d	x
0.0	0.75	1.5	0.25
0.25	0.6	2.0	0.15
0.5	0.5	2.5	0.1
0.75	0.4	3.0	0.05
1.0	0.3	4.0	0.0

To illustrate the use of the table let d, the observed difference in brightness, be 0.7m (it is desirable to estimate the difference to the nearest tenth of a magnitude), and let the photometric magnitude, C, be 7.0. Then, from the table, $x = 0.4$, and the magnitudes of A and B are 7.4 and 8.1 (to the nearest even tenth). Conversely, we may find C from A and B.

THE OBSERVING PROGRAM

It has happened in the past that certain well-known double stars have been measured and remeasured beyond all reasonable need, while other systems of equal importance have been almost entirely neglected. The general catalogues described in the preceding chapter make it comparatively easy for observers to avoid such mistakes hereafter. In the light of the knowledge these catalogues give of past observations and of the motions in the various systems, the observer who wishes his work to be of the greatest possible value will select stars which are suited to his telescope and which are in need of measurement at a given epoch either because of scarcity of earlier measures or because the companion is at a critical point in its orbit.

It has often been said that a careful set of measures of any pair of stars made at any time is valuable. Granting this to be so, it is certain that its value is greatly enhanced if it is made to contribute to the advancement of a program having a definite end in view. If the aim is to increase the number of known orbits as rapidly as possible, attention should be centered upon the closer pairs, particularly those under 0″.5 and those which have already been observed over considerable arcs of their orbits. Though I have felt myself obliged to devote my observing time in recent years to the remeasurement of as many as possible of the pairs of my own discovery, I am none the less convinced that it is, in general, wise for an observer possessing the necessary telescopic equipment to devote his energy largely to the measurement of a limited number of rapidly moving systems, repeating the measures every year, or every two or five years, as may be required by the rapidity of the orbital motion, for a long series of years. Such a series can be investigated for systematic as well as accidental errors of measure far more effectively than an equal number of measures scattered over a much larger program, and will add more to our knowledge of the orbits of the binary systems. The wider pairs, and particularly those in the older catalogues, now need comparatively little attention, so far as orbital motion is concerned. Even moderately close pairs, with distance from 1″ to 5″, need, in general, to be measured but once in every 10 or 20 years. Useful programs, however, may be made from wider pairs for the detection of proper motions, or for the determination of the relative masses in binary systems by means of measures connecting one of the components with one or more distant independent stars. Photographic measures of these wider pairs are, in general, more accurate than visual ones.

It is hardly necessary to add that an hour in the dome on a good night is more valuable than half a dozen hours at the desk in daylight. Everything possible should therefore be done to prevent loss of observing time. In this connection I have found charts based on the Durchmusterung invaluable for quick identification of stars.

THE RESOLVING POWER OF A TELESCOPE

It has been shown that the diffraction pattern of the image of a point source of light, like a star, formed by a lens "is a disk surrounded by bright rings, which are separated by circles at which the intensity vanishes."*

Schuster gives the formula

$$\rho = m\frac{f\lambda}{D} \tag{7}$$

in which ρ is the radius of a circle of zero intensity (dark ring), D the diameter of the lens, f its local length, λ the wave length of the light from the point source, and m a coefficient that must be calculated for each ring. For the first dark ring it is 1.220, and the values for the successive rings increase by very nearly one unit. Nearly all of the light (0.839) is in the central disk, and the intensity of the bright diffraction rings falls off very rapidly. Now it is generally agreed that the minimum distance at which a double star can be distinctly seen as two separate stars is reached when the central disk of the image of the companion star falls upon the first dark ring of the image of the primary, and the radius of this ring, expressed in seconds of arc, is therefore frequently called the limit of the

---

* Schuster, *Theory of Optics*, p. 130, 1904.

telescope's resolving power. If we adopt for λ the wave length 5,500 A, the expression for ρ in angular measure becomes

$$\rho = \frac{5\rlap{.}''45}{D} \qquad (8)$$

from which the resolving power of a telescope of aperture D (in inches) may be obtained. For the 36-in. Lick refractor, the formula gives $0\rlap{.}''15$, for the 12-in., $0\rlap{.}''45$.

It will be observed that the resolving power as thus derived rests partly upon a theoretical and partly upon an empirical basis. When the central disk of each star image of a pair falls upon the first dark ring of the other image, the intensity curve of the combined image will show two maxima separated by a distinct minimum. When the disks fall closer together, this minimum disappears, the image becomes merely elongated, perhaps with slight notches to mark the position of the disappearing minimum. The pair is now no longer "resolved," according to the definition given, but to the experienced observer its character may still be unmistakable. For example, in the Lick Observatory double star survey, Hussey and I have found with the 36-in. at least five double stars with measured distances of $0\rlap{.}''11$ or less, the minimum for each observer being $0\rlap{.}''09$; and we have found many pairs with the 12-in. telescope whose distances, measured afterward with the 36-in., range from $0\rlap{.}''20$ to $0\rlap{.}''25$. In all these cases the magnitudes were, of course, nearly equal.

Lewis[*] published a very interesting table of the most difficult double stars measured and discovered by various observers using telescopes ranging in aperture from 4 to 36 in. He tabulated in separate columns the values for the bright and faint pairs of nearly equal magnitude, and for the bright and faint pairs of unequal magnitude, each value representing the mean of about five of the closest pairs for a given observer and telescope. A final column gave the theoretical resolving power derived, not from the equation given above, but from Dawes' well-known empirical formula—resolving power equal $4\rlap{.}''56$ divided by the aperture in inches (a)—which assumes the two stars to be of about the sixth magnitude. Lewis found that, in general, this formula gave values which were too small even for the bright

---

[*] The *Observatory*, **37**, 378, 1914.

equal pairs, and he suggested the following as representing more precisely the results of observation:

Equal bright pairs $\dfrac{4\overset{''}{.}8}{a}$, mean magnitudes 5.7 and   6.4

Equal faint pairs $\dfrac{8\overset{''}{.}5}{a}$, mean magnitudes 8.5 and   9.1

Unequal pairs $\dfrac{16\overset{''}{.}5}{a}$, mean magnitudes 6.2 and   9.5

Very unequal pairs $\dfrac{36\overset{''}{.}0}{a}$, mean magnitudes 4.7 and 10.4

Lewis was careful to state that his table did not necessarily represent the minimum limits that may be reached with a given telescope under the best conditions, and I have just shown that it does not represent the limits actually reached at the Lick Observatory. Taking from each of the three lists of new double stars β 1,026 to β 1,274, Hu 1 to Hu 1,327, and A 1 to A 3104 "about five" of the closest bright, and closest faint, equal pairs discovered by each of the three observers, Burnham, Hussey, and Aitken—29 pairs in all—I find the following formula for the 36-in. telescope:

Equal bright pairs $\dfrac{4\overset{''}{.}3}{a}$, mean magnitudes 6.9 and   7.1

Equal faint pairs $\dfrac{6\overset{''}{.}1}{a}$, mean magnitudes 8.8 and   9.0

The most interesting point about these formulas is that they show much less difference between the values for faint and bright pairs than Lewis' do.

While it is a matter of decided interest to compare the limits actually attained with a given telescope with the theoretical resolving power, an observer, in making out his working program for double star measurement, will do well to select pairs that run considerably above such limiting distances. My deliberate judgment is that, under *average good observing conditions*, the angular separation of the pairs measured should be nearly double the theoretical limit. Observers with the most powerful telescopes, however, are confronted with the fact that if they do not measure the very closest known pairs these must go unmeasured.*

* Some of them may, however, be measured with the interferometer. The method is described on p. 67.

EYEPIECES

The power of the eyepiece to be used is a matter of practical importance, but one for which it is not easy to lay down specific rules. The general principle is—*use the highest power the seeing will permit.* When the seeing is poor, the images "dancing" or blurred, increase in the magnifying power increases these defects in the images and frequently more than offsets in this way the gain from increase in the scale. On such nights, if they are suitable for any work, choose wider pairs and use lower powers. The practical observer soon realizes that it is not worth while to measure close pairs except with high powers. With the 36-in. telescope my own practice is to use an eyepiece magnifying about 520 diameters for pairs with angular separation of 2″ or more. If the distance is only 1″, I prefer a power of 1,000, and for pairs under 0″.5 I use powers from 1,000 to 3,000, according to the angular distance and the conditions. The closeness and brightness of the pair and the quality of the definition are the factors that determine the choice. Very close pairs are never attempted unless powers of 1,500 or higher can be used to advantage.

The simplest method of measuring the magnifying power of an eyepiece in conjunction with a given objective is to find the ratio of the diameter of the objective to that of its image formed by the eyepiece—the telescope being focused and directed to the bright daylight sky. Two fine lines ruled on a piece of oiled paper to open at a small angle form a convenient gage for measuring the diameter of the image. A very small error in this measure, however, produces a large error in the ratio and the measure should be repeated many times and the mean result adopted. The magnifying power of an eyepiece may, of course, also be measured by a dynameter if one is available.

DIAPHRAGMS

It is sometimes said that the quality of star images is improved by placing a diaphragm over the objective to cut down its aperture. I question this. It is certain that the experience of such observers as Schiaparelli and Burnham was directly opposed to it, and experiments made with the 12-in. and 36-in. telescopes offer no support for it. Indeed, it is difficult to understand how cutting off part of the beam of light falling upon an object glass of good figure can improve the character of the image, unless it is assumed that the amplitude of such atmospheric disturbances as affect the definition is small enough to enter the problem. The only possible gain might be in the reduction of the brightness of the image when one star of a pair is exceptionally bright, as in *Sirius;* but this reduction can be effected more conveniently by the use of colored shade glasses over the eyepiece. These are occasionally of advantage.*

A hexagonal diaphragm placed over the objective, however, may prove of great value in measuring stars, like *Sirius* or *Procyon,* which are attended by companions relatively very faint; but this is because such a diaphragm entirely changes the pattern of the diffraction image of the star, not because it cuts down the aperture of the telescope. The pattern is now a central disk from which six thin rays run; between these rays the field appears dark even close to the bright star, and a faint object there can be seen readily that would be invisible otherwise. Professor Barnard† used such a diaphragm to advantage with the 40-in. Yerkes refractor. Provision should be made for rotating the diaphragm through an angle of about 60° and it will be convenient in the case of a large instrument to be able to do this by means of gearing attached to a rod running down to the eye end.

ERRORS OF OBSERVATION

All measures of angles or of distances are affected by errors, both accidental and systematic, and when, as in double star work, the measured quantities are very minute, these errors must be most carefully considered. The accidental errors may be reduced by careful work and by repeating the measures a suitable number of times. Little is to be gained, in this respect or in any other, by making too large a number of settings upon an object on any one night; because such factors as the seeing, the hour angle, the observer's physiological condition, all remain nearly constant. As a rule, four settings for position angle and three measures of double distance are enough

---

* Van den Bos, in a recent letter, argues that under poor atmospheric conditions, an iris diaphragm, to reduce aperture, is helpful, particularly in the measurement of unequal or very bright pairs.

† *A.N.* **182,** 13, 1909.

to make on one night, but the measures should be repeated on one or more additional nights. This is not only to reduce the accidental error of measure but to guard against outright mistakes in reading the circles, recording, etc. As to the number of nights on which a system should be measured at a given epoch, opinions will differ. Some observers run to excess in this matter. Generally, it may be said that it is time wasted to measure a system on more than four nights at any epoch and ordinarily the mean of three nights' measures, or even of two, if the pair is easy to measure and the measures themselves are accordant, is as satisfactory as the mean from a larger number. In critical cases, however, a larger number is sometimes desirable.

The systematic errors of measurement are far more troublesome, for they vary not only with the individual but are different for the same observer at different times and for different objects. Aside from the personality of the observer, they depend upon the relative magnitudes of the two components of a double star, the angular distance, the angle which the line joining the stars makes with the horizontal, and, in unequal pairs, upon the position of the faint star with respect to the bright one. Various methods have been adopted to determine these errors or to eliminate them.

The most elaborate investigation in this line is probably the one made by Otto Struve, who measured "artificial double stars formed by small ivory cylinders placed in holes in a black disk." He deduced formulae by means of which he calculated corrections to be applied to all his measures; but it is very doubtful whether these corrections really improve the results. I agree with Lewis when he says, "I would prefer his original measures—in part because the stars were so particularly artificial." The actual conditions when observing the stars at night are of necessity widely different from those under which the test measures were made. Certainly, in the case of Otto Struve, the corrected angles and distances are frequently more at variance with the general run of all of the measures by good observers than the original values. The student of double star motions will generally find it advantageous to use the original uncorrected measures of every observer in his preliminary work and then to derive values for the systematic or personal errors of each by comparing his measures with the curve representing the means of all available measures.

The observer, on the other hand, may profitably adopt observing methods designed to eliminate, in part at least, systematic errors. Innes' plan of measuring each pair on each side of the meridian is an excellent one because, in general, the line joining the two stars changes its angle with respect to the horizon in passing the meridian. In the extreme case, if the smaller star is above the primary when the pair is east of the meridian, it will be below when west of the meridian. When Innes' two measures made in this way were not sufficiently accordant, he repeated them on two additional nights, one night in each position of the instrument.

In 1908, MM. Salet and Bosler* published the results of an investigation of the systematic errors in measures of position angle in which they made use of a small total reflecting prism mounted between the eyepiece and the observer's eye and capable of being rotated in such manner as to invert the field of view. Theoretically, half the sum of the measures made without and with the prism should represent the angle freed from errors depending upon the inclination of the images to the horizon. In fact, Salet and Bosler found that, whereas their measures without the prism and those made with it both showed a personal equation varying in amount with the star, the means of the two sets were remarkably free from personality. Here, for example, are their measures of γ *Leonis:*

Observer	Date	Without prism	With prism	Mean
Salet	1907.19	119°04	113°50	116°27
Bosler	1907.23	116.80	116.07	116.44
(S−B)		+2.24	−2.57	−0.17

Hermann Struve and J. Voûte later published measures made in this manner and each concluded that the results were far better than his measures made entirely without the use of the prism. In one of his papers† Voûte states that "it is principally in observing in the perpendicular (:) position that the observations show a pronounced systematic error," while "the parallel (..) observations are in general free from systematic errors."

* *Bull. Astronomique* **25**, 18, 1908.
† *Union Obs. Circ.* **27**, 1915.

Dawes* long ago pointed out that in "rather close double stars," the measures of distance "will almost inevitably be considerably *too large*," unless the observer has taken into account the change made in the apparent form of the star disk when a thread of the micrometer is placed over it. This change is in the nature of a swelling out of the disk on each side of the thread, producing an approximately elliptical disk. When two images are nearly in contact and the threads are placed over them, this swelling obliterates the interval between the disks and the threads are therefore set *too far apart*. The effect disappears when the disks are well separated.

In my investigations of double star orbits I have frequently noticed that distance measures of a given system made with small apertures are greater than those made with large telescopes even when made by the same observer, provided the system is a close one as viewed in the smaller instrument. I have found such a systematic difference in the distances in stars which I have measured with the 12-in. and with the 36-in. telescope, and Schlesinger† has also called attention to this difference, giving a table derived from my measures as printed in Vol. XII of the *Publications of the Lick Observatory*. This table is here reproduced with a column of differences added:

MEASURED SEPARATIONS

Number of stars	With the 12-in.	With the 36-in.	Difference
20	0″.52	0″.42	+0″.10
25	0.62	0.54	+0.08
20	0.71	0.64	+0.07
24	0.81	0.79	+0.02
24	1.07	1.03	+0.04
21	1.38	1.39	−0.01
26	2.13	2.10	+0.03
18	4.49	4.53	−0.04

The systematic difference is clearly shown in all the pairs having a separation less than twice the resolving power (0″.42) of the 12-in. telescope; in the wider pairs it is negligibly small.

Occasionally an observer's work shows systematic differences of precisely the opposite sign. Thus Schlesinger (*loc. cit.*)

* *Mem. R. A. S.*, **35**, 153, 1867.
† *Science*, N. S., **44**, 573, 1916.

in analyzing the measures by Fox in the *Annals of the Dearborn Observatory*, Vol. I, (1915) finds that the distances are measured smaller with the 12-in. than with the $18\frac{1}{2}$-in. or with the 40-in., "the differences being largest for small separations and becoming negligibly small for separations in the neighborhood of 5"." The personal equation revealed in such comparisons as these must obviously be taken into account in orbit computations.

PHOTOGRAPHIC MEASURES

The first double star to be discovered visually was also the first for which measurable photographic images were obtained. G. P. Bond photographed ζ *Ursae Majoris*, angular separation 14".2, on a collodion plate in 1857, giving an 8-sec. exposure. Pickering and Gould in America, M. Henry in France, and the Greenwich observers in England, among others, followed up this early success and secured results of value for a number of pairs, a few of them as close as 1". More recently, extensive programs have been carried out at several observatories and it has become evident that photographic measures, made under proper conditions, are of the same order of accuracy as visual ones for pairs with angular distances of from 1" to 2", if the components are not very unequal in magnitude, and that they exceed visual measures in accuracy for wider pairs. A photographic observation of a double star, moreover, has the great advantage, as Hertzsprung has pointed out, of being a "permanent document" which can be reexamined as often as may be desirable.

Hertzsprung, working at Potsdam in the years 1914 to 1919, made a thorough investigation of the possibilities of the photographic method as applied to the measurement of double stars, including a study of the sources of accidental and systematic errors, and of the procedure necessary to eliminate such errors or, failing this, to reduce to a minimum their effects upon the measures.

It appears that the chief sources of error are (1) the difference in magnitude of the components of a pair, (2) refraction, and more particularly, the change of refraction with the color of a star, and (3) the Eberhard effect, or the effect upon a photographic star image produced by the close proximity of another star image. There are, of course, also the accidental errors of measurement, and the errors arising from incorrect scale value and imperfect orientation, errors that are comparable to those in visual observations from corresponding sources.

1. The Magnitude Equation.—The images of the two components of a double star are so nearly in contact on the photographic plate that the methods of eliminating the error arising from difference in magnitude in use in parallax determinations and other precise photographic measurements are not applicable. A rotating sector, for example, would, for all but the relatively wide pairs, cut down the light from both components in substantially the same degree.

The method that has given the best results up to the present time is the one adopted by Hertzsprung and others of covering the objective of the telescope with a coarse grating made of rods of uniform thickness, uniformly spaced. Such a grating will give, in addition to the principal image of a star, spectra symmetrically placed on either side of it, and if it is made so coarse that the first-order spectra are just clearly separated from the principal image, they, too, will have sensibly stellar images. Further, by proper choice of rod thickness and free spacing the difference in magnitude between the principal image and its first-order spectra may be made to vary from one to four or more magnitudes. It is well to have a set of six or more such gratings so calculated that the magnitude difference may be varied by steps of approximately a magnitude. It will then be possible in practically all cases to bring the brightness of the first-order spectra of the primary within half a magnitude of that of the principal image of the companion. A difference of half a magnitude will have little or no effect upon the measures. The gratings, it is to be noted, will reduce the brightness of the principal images of both components by an amount depending upon the grating constant, and the exposure time will also vary with the grating used.

The practical difficulties in using this method with telescopes of large aperture arise from the expense involved in constructing good gratings of large size and from the inconvenience of interchanging them in the course of a night's observing.

2. Refraction and Star Color.—On account of atmospheric dispersion, the refraction varies with the effective wave length of a star's light. A systematic error of measurement may, therefore, result when the colors of the two components of a double star differ appreciably. To eliminate it, take the photographs in light of a restricted range in wave length, by using appropriate filters and, if necessary, special plates. The particular filters and plates required will vary with the telescope used. It is desirable also, to avoid taking photographs at great zenith distances.

3. The Photographic Star Image.—Eberhard, many years ago, showed that the work done by a developer in blackening any small area on a photographic plate depended upon how much more work it had to do in the immediate vicinity. The density of a star image, for a given exposure and development, therefore, depends not only upon the brightness of the star but in part also upon the presence of other star images in its immediate proximity. In the case of a double star the outer edge of the image of each component will be denser than its inner edge— the edge nearest the other component. The effective centers of the two images are therefore displaced in opposite directions and the apparent or measured distance is larger than the true distance between them. But Hertzsprung also found evidence of a displacement in the opposite sense in the case of some photographs of very close pairs taken under relatively poor conditions. Apparently, however, both effects appear only in pairs in which the images of the two components are nearly or quite in contact. *For pairs with clearly separated images,* the error from this source is so small that it may be neglected.

In addition to the precautions to be taken with respect to the sources of systematic error just described, it is, of course, necessary to put the plate accurately in focus, and to determine the parallel carefully. To provide means for determining the parallel a bright star in the immediate neighborhood may be allowed to trail on the plate, or images of the double star (with the plate displaced slightly in declination) may be taken both near the preceding and near the following edge of the plate, the clock being stopped between the two exposures. The exposure time will depend upon the star and the telescope. It is desirable to have distinct images but not denser than necessary for easy measurement.

Finally, the importance of photographing only on calm nights, and of having an accurate driving mechanism for the telescope is to be particularly emphasized.

The plates thus secured should be measured in rectangular coordinates and it will be advantageous to use an engine in which the plate, rather than the eyepiece, is moved by the micrometer screw. In this case the value of a revolution of the screw, in seconds of arc, is independent of the power of the eyepiece, and the plate may be measured both film side up and through the glass. It is hardly necessary to add that the scale value of the plates must be determined accurately and that the plates must be oriented with great care. Since the first-order spectra are symmetrically placed with respect to the center of the principal image, the mean of their positions may be adopted as the position of the primary.

It has already been noted that in recent years lists of new double stars detected on parallax plates and lists of others found in the examination of the astrographic star catalogue for different zones have been published by Scheiner, Stein, Barton, Olivier, and others. The pairs in the astrographic lists are all relatively wide and for the most part faint, and the measures of position angles and distances are not of a high order of accuracy. The lists from parallax plates also consist of faint pairs, but some of them have angular distance not greatly in excess of a second of arc. The measures of these pairs are probably quite as accurate as visual measures would be.

INTERFEROMETER MEASURES

The advantages of the photographic method are so great that it will undoubtedly come into ever more general use in the measurement of all double stars that can be resolved on the photographic plate. The closer pairs, and particularly those whose components differ greatly in magnitude, must be left to the visual observer working with the filar micrometer, with or without the reversing prisms, or instruments that are improvements upon it. Hargreaves, for example, has recently designed a comparison image micrometer* that promises to give more accurate results, for the angular distance, at least, than the filar micrometer.

The lower limit for accurate micrometric measurements of angular separation with existing telescopes is about $0''.13$, though under the best conditions fairly good estimates may be made for pairs as close as $0''.10$. The only instrument that promises good results for still closer pairs is the interferometer.

* See footnote, p. 41.

Michelson, more than 40 years ago, showed that such extremely small angles as the diameter of a small satellite or the distance between the components of a double star could be measured "by observing the interference fringes produced at the focus of a telescope when only two portions of the objective, located on the same diameter, are used." He demonstrated that "as the distance apart of the apertures is increased the visibility of the fringes reaches a minimum for a distance equal to $1.22\lambda/a$, or $0.5\lambda/a$, for a disk or double star, respectively, where λ is the effective wave length and a is the desired angle." He applied the method to the measurement of the diameters of the satellites of *Jupiter*, with the 12-in. refractor of the Lick Observatory in 1891. Four years later,[*] Schwarzschild applied the principle to the measurement of double stars, using a specially designed interferometer placed over the objective of the 10-in. refractor at Munich. He measured a number of pairs with angular distances ranging from $0''.9$ to $3''.7$. No one else seems to have made interferometer measures of double stars until Anderson,[†] early in 1920, using an interferometer of his own design, attached to the 100-in. reflector at Mount Wilson, measured the position angle and distance of *Capella*, with an accuracy far exceeding the accuracy of the best micrometer measures of a close double star. Merrill,[‡] using the same instrument, secured additional measures of *Capella* later in the same year and in 1921, and also measured κ *Ursae Majoris* = A1585, which he and Anderson had discovered as a double, *by the use of the interferometer*, before they knew of my earlier micrometric measures. My measures had shown a rapid decrease in angular distance, the value in 1919.29 being $0''.15$. Their measures, in 1921, gave $0''.08$, with a change in the position angle that was consistent with the law of areas. Attempts to find other double stars by examination with the interferometer gave negative or doubtful results, and the work had presently to be discontinued.

Experiments made at the Lick and at the Yerkes Observatories did not prove satisfactory. At Catania, M. Maggini,[§] in 1922, applied an interferometer to the 12-in. equatorial and in the years immediately following made a considerable number of

* *A.N.* **139**, 353, 1896.
† *Contr. Mt. Wilson Obs.* **9**, 225, 1920.
‡ *Contr. Mt. Wilson Obs.* **11**, 203, 1922.
§ *Pub. R. Oss. Catania*, 1925.

measures of double stars with angular distances up to 0".25 and even greater.   These pairs were all within the measuring range of the micrometer attached to larger telescopes, and a comparison of actual measures could thus be made.   In the majority of cases, Maggini's results were in fair to good accord with those made with the micrometer, but in a number of cases, the disagreement was far beyond the error of micrometric measurement, and his values were entirely out of accord with the earlier (and later) micrometric results, though the pairs in question were as well suited to measurement by both methods as the others on his list.   It is clear that further investigation is required before the interferometer can be accepted as a standard instrument for double star observation.   We must know how to distinguish between genuine fringes and fringe disappearance and spurious effects of any kind whatever; and we must determine the limits of magnitude and angular separation within which the interferometer can be applied successfully with a telescope of given aperture and focal length.   It may be found that the number of pairs that can be measured with the interferometer is small, but, by way of compensation, these will, in general, be pairs that cannot be measured successfully by any other method unless the inclination of the orbit plane is high enough to permit measures of the relative radial velocities of the two components.   It is greatly to be desired that experiments with the interferometer be continued.

[The reader is referred to the second volume of the series *Stars and Stellar Systems* edited by Gerard P. Kuiper and Barbara M. Middlehurst.   Volume II, *Astronomical Techniques*, was edited by William A. Hiltner.   Chapter 19, "Techniques for Visual Measurements," by P. Muller, is a very fine discussion of instruments and their uses as related to visual binary stars.   Chapter 22, by W. H. van den Bos, "Orbit Determinations of Visual Binaries"; chapter 23, "Spectroscopic Binaries," by R. M. Petrie; and chapter 24, "Eclipsing Binaries," by John B. Irwin, are excellent treatments of their subjects.

Volume III of this same series, to be published soon, will also contain much relevant material.—J.T.K.]

CHAPTER IV

THE ORBIT OF A VISUAL BINARY STAR

We have seen that Sir William Herschel, by his analysis of the observed motion in *Castor* and other double stars, demonstrated that these systems are "real binary combinations of two stars, intimately held together by the bonds of mutual attraction." Later observation has shown that the apparent motion in such systems is on the arc of an ellipse and that the radius vector drawn from the primary star to its companion sweeps over areas which are proportional to the times. It has therefore been assumed from the beginning that the attractive force in the binary star systems is identical with the force of gravitation in our solar system, as expressed by Newton's law, and the orbit theories which we are to investigate in the present chapter are all based upon this assumption. Before taking up the discussion of these theories it is pertinent to inquire whether the fundamental assumption is justified.

It is supported by all of the available evidence, but rigorous mathematical proof of its validity is difficult because the motion which we observe in a stellar system is not the true motion but its projection upon a plane perpendicular to the line of sight. The apparent orbit is therefore, in general, not identical with the true orbit and the principal star may lie at any point within the ellipse described by the companion and not necessarily at either the focus or the center. Hence, in Leuschner's words, "mathematical difficulties are encountered in establishing a law of force which is independent of the angle θ, the orientation." In the article quoted, Leuschner, after pointing out that "Newton did not prove the universality of the law of gravitation, but by a happy stroke of genius generalized a fact which he had found to be true in the case of the mutual attraction of the Moon and the Earth," proceeds to show that the law does hold throughout the solar system, the question of orientation not entering. He then says that, in binary systems, "when the law is arbitrarily assumed to be independent of the orientation, as was found to be the case in the solar system, two possibilities arise, namely, either that the force is in direct proportion to the distance r between the two stars or that the Newtonian law applies. It can be shown, however, that when, in the case of an elliptic orbit, the force is proportional to r, the primary star must be in the center of the ellipse. As this has never been found to be the case, the only alternative is the Newtonian law."

It should be clearly understood that the difficulty in demonstrating the universality of the law of gravitation here pointed out is purely mathematical. No physical reason has ever been advanced for a dependence of an attracting central force upon the orientation, and until such dependence has been proved we may safely proceed with our investigation of binary star orbits under the action of the law of gravitation.

Until the relative masses of the two components are known it is impossible to determine the position of the center of gravity of the system and we are therefore unable to compute the orbits described by the two stars about that center. What our measures give us is the apparent orbit of one star, the companion, described about the other, the primary, which is assumed to remain stationary at the focus. It is clear that this relative orbit differs from the actual orbits of the two components only in its scale.

The problem of deriving such an orbit from the micrometer measures of position angle and distance was first solved by Savary,[*] in 1827, but Encke[†] quickly followed with a different method of solution which was somewhat better adapted to the needs of the practical astronomer, and Sir John Herschel[‡] communicated a third method to the Royal Astronomical Society in 1832. Since then the contributions to the subject have been many. Some consist of entirely new methods of attack, others of modifications of those already proposed. Among the more notable investigators are Villarceau, Mädler, Klinkerfues, Thiele, Kowalsky, Glasenapp, Seeliger, Zwiers, Howard, Schwarzschild, See, Russell, Innes, and van den Bos.

The methods of Savary and Encke utilize four complete measures of angle and distance and, theoretically, are excellent

[*] Savary, *Conn. des Temps*, 1830.
[†] Encke, *Berlin Jahrbuch*, 1832.
[‡] Herschel, *Memoirs R.A.S.*, **5**, 171, 1833.

solutions of the problem; Herschel's method is designed to utilize all the available data, so far as he considered them reliable. This idea has commended itself to all later investigators. Herschel was convinced, however, that the measures of distance were far less trustworthy than those of position angle, and his method therefore uses the measures of distance simply to define the semimajor axis of the orbit; all of the other elements depend upon measures of position angle. At the time this may have been the wisest course, but the distance measures of such early observers as W. Struve, Dawes, and Dembowski, and those of later observers working with modern micrometers, are entitled to nearly or quite as much weight as the measures of position angle and should be utilized in the entire orbit computation.

Whatever method is adopted, the investigator must, of course, begin by assuring himself that he has data sufficient for a satisfactory computation. In deciding this, he should consider both the length of the observed arc and its form. With strongly marked curvature, a comparatively short arc may suffice, provided the observations have a high degree of accuracy. Ordinarily, however, the arc should be long enough to cover *both ends* or elongation points of the apparent ellipse.

Satisfactory data being given, the problem before the computer evidently consists of two parts: first, the determination of the apparent ellipse, or the constant of areal velocity, from the data of observation; secondly, the derivation of the elements of the true orbit from the relations between an ellipse and its orthographic projection.

THE APPARENT ELLIPSE

Every complete observation of a double star supplies us with three data: the time of observation, the position angle of the companion with respect to the primary, and the angular distance between the two stars. It is clear, as Comstock pointed out many years ago, that the time of observation is known with far greater accuracy than either of the two coordinates of position. The relations between the times of observation and the motion in the ellipse should therefore be utilized; that is, the condition should be imposed that the law of areal velocities must be satisfied as well as the condition that the points of observation should fall approximately upon the curve of an ellipse. Elementary as this direction is, it is one that has been neglected in many a computation.

Theoretically, the first step in our computation should be the reduction of the measured coordinates to a common epoch by the application to the position angles of corrections for precession and for the proper motion of the system. The distance measures need no corrections. Practically, both corrections are negligibly small unless the star is near the Pole, its proper motion unusually large, and the time covered by the observations long. The precession correction, when required, can be found with sufficient accuracy from the approximate formula

$$\Delta\theta = +0\overset{s}{.}0056 \sin \alpha \sec \delta \ (t - t_0) \tag{1}$$

The formula for the correction due to the proper motion of the system is

$$\Delta\theta = -\mu'' \sin \delta \ (t - t_0) \tag{2}$$

where μ'' is the proper motion in right ascension expressed in seconds of arc.*

When the measures of any binary star have been tabulated (with the above corrections, if required), they will exhibit discordances arising from the accidental and systematic errors of observation and, occasionally, from actual mistakes. If they are plotted, the points will not fall upon an ellipse but will be joined by a very irregular broken line indicating an ellipse only in a general way. It will be advisable to investigate the measures for discordances before using them in the construction of the apparent ellipse and the simplest method is to plot upon coordinate paper first the position angles and then the distances, separately, as ordinates, against the times of observation as abscissae, using a fairly large scale. Well-determined points (for example, a point resting upon several accordant measures by a skilled observer and supported by the preceding and following observations) may be indicated by heavier marks. Smooth free-hand curves, interpolating curves, are now to be drawn to represent the general run of the measures and in drawing these curves more consideration will naturally be given to the well observed points than to the others. Obser-

---

* See "Note on the Effect of Proper Motion on Double Star Measures," by Alan Fletcher (*Mon. Not. R.A.S.* **92,** 119, 1931), for a more complete discussion.

vations that are seriously in error will be clearly revealed and these should be rejected if no means of correcting them is available. The curves will also show whether or not the measures as a whole are sufficiently good to make orbit computation desirable.

If the amount of available material warrants it, the question of the systematic or personal errors of the observers should also be considered at this time. No reliable determination of such errors is possible unless (a) measures by the same observer under essentially the same conditions in at least four or five different years are at hand, and (b) unless the total number of measures by many different observers is sufficient to establish the general character of the curves beyond reasonable question. If the second condition is satisfied, the average of the residuals from the curve for a given observer may be regarded as his personal error and the corresponding correction may be applied to all of his measures. Two further points should be noted: *First,* the residuals in position angle should be reduced to arc by multiplying by the factor $\rho/57.3$ before the mean is taken, to allow for the effect of variations in the angular separation; *second,* the corrections should not be considered as constant over too long a period of time. The application of such corrections has the effect of reducing the size of the residuals, but the principal advantage to be gained from it is that it lessens the danger of giving undue weight to measures seriously affected by systematic errors of observation.

After all corrections have been applied, the measures which are retained should be combined into annual means or into mean places at longer or shorter time intervals according to the requirements of the particular case. Several factors really enter into the question of the weights to be assigned to the individual observations in forming these means; for instance, the size of the telescope used, the observing conditions, the number of nights of observation, and the experience of the observer; but it will be wise, in general, to disregard all but the number of nights of observation, provided the telescope used is of adequate resolving power for the system in question and that the observer has not specifically noted some of his measures as uncertain. A single night's measure deserves small weight; mean results based upon from two to six nights' accordant measures may be regarded as of equal weight; means depending upon a much larger number of measures may be weighted higher. In general, a range in weights from one to three will be sufficient.

If, in addition to the visual measures, photographic measures have been made at several epochs, the combination of the measures by the two different methods merits special consideration. When, as, for example, in the case of ξ *Ursae Majoris*, many photographic measures of great accuracy are available, these should unquestionably be given high weight. If, on the other hand, only a few photographic measures have been made they may be weighted on the same basis as the visual observations.

Having thus formed a series of normal places, we may find the apparent ellipse that best represents them either graphically or by calculating the constants of the general equation of the ellipse with the origin at any point. This equation is

$$ax^2 + 2hxy + by^2 + 2gx + 2fy + c = 0 \qquad (3)$$

which may be written in the form

$$Ax^2 + 2Hxy + By^2 + 2Gx + 2Fy + 1 = 0 \qquad (4)$$

in which we must have $A > 0$, $B > 0$, and $AB - H^2 > 0$.

If we assume the position of the primary star as origin, we may calculate the five constants of this equation from five normal places by the relations

$$\left. \begin{array}{l} x = \rho \sin \theta \\ y = \rho \cos \theta \end{array} \right\} \qquad (5)$$

but it is advisable to make a least squares solution using all of the normal places.

The great objection to this method is that it entirely disregards the time of observation. Moreover, the errors of observation, small as they are numerically, are large in proportion to the quantities to be measured, a fact that makes it difficult to obtain a satisfactory ellipse without repeated trials. The graphical methods are therefore to be preferred.

The simplest method, and one that in most cases is satisfactory, is to plot the positions of the companion star in polar coordinates, the primary star being taken as the origin. With the aid of an ellipsograph or by the use of two pins and a thread, an ellipse is drawn through the plotted points and is adjusted by trial until it satisfies the law of areas. *This adjustment must be made with the greatest precision and the curve of the ellipse drawn with great care,* for the construction of the apparent ellipse is the critical part of the entire orbit determination. In my own practice I have found that the test for the law of areas can be made most rapidly by drawing radii to selected points which cover the entire observed arc and measuring the corresponding elliptic sectors with a planimeter. The comparison of the areal velocities derived from the different sectors at once indicates what corrections the ellipse requires. With a suitable ellipsograph a new ellipse is quickly drawn and the areas again measured. The process is repeated until a satisfactory ellipse has been obtained.

Some investigators prefer the mode of procedure in constructing the apparent ellipse first suggested by Sir John Herschel. An interpolating curve is drawn, in the manner described above, for the *position angles only,* using the mean or normal places. If the curve is carefully drawn, smoothly and without abrupt changes of curvature, it should give the position angle for any particular epoch more accurately than the measure at that epoch, for it rests upon all of the measures. From this curve read the times corresponding to, say, every 5° of angle, tabulate them, and take the first differences. Dividing these by the common angle difference will give a series of approximate values of $dt/d\theta$. But by the theory of elliptic motion $\rho^2 \dfrac{d\theta}{dt}$ must be a constant and hence $\rho = c\sqrt{\dfrac{dt}{d\theta}}$. Therefore a series of *relative* values of the distance (expressed in any convenient unit) corresponding to every fifth degree of position angle can be derived from the table of angles. Now plot the points representing corresponding angles and relative distances; if the interpolating curve has been correctly drawn and read off they will all lie upon the arc of an ellipse. If they do not, draw the best possible ellipse among them and use it to correct the interpolating curve, repeating the process until the result is satisfactory. Finally, convert the relative into true distances by comparing those distance measures which are regarded as most reliable with the corresponding values in the unit adopted in the plot.

There are at least two objections to this method: *First,* it does not make adequate use of the observed distances; and *second,* when the angle changes rapidly, as it does in many systems at the time of minimum apparent separation, it is almost impossible to draw the interpolating curve correctly. The former difficulty may in many cases be overcome by the following procedure: Read from the interpolating curve for position angles, normal values for every fourth year.* Regard each two consecutive values as the limiting radii of a circular sector, and as the radius of each sector adopt its mean observed distance, which may be derived, if desired, from an interpolating curve. Draw these circular sectors on coordinate paper and pass through them a free-hand curve, approximately the arc of an ellipse, giving sectors of equal area. In general, however, it is in my judgment most satisfactory to plot the positions of the companion star directly in polar coordinates, using normal places. From these the ellipse that best satisfies the law of areas must be found by the method of trial and correction.

THE TRUE ORBIT

After the apparent ellipse has been constructed graphically, or from the constants in the equation of the ellipse, it remains to derive the elements which define the form and size of the true orbit, the position of the orbit plane, the position of the orbit within that plane, and the position of the companion star in the orbit at any specified time. Three of the required elements have dynamic significance and are entirely independent of the space location of the system. These are the revolution period, the time of periastron passage, and the eccentricity. To these belongs the semimajor axis of the orbit when measured in linear units; measured in angular units it is, of course, also a function of the parallax of the system. The three remaining elements, the inclination of the orbit plane, the position of the line of nodes, and the angle between that line and the major axis are purely geometric and merely relate the orbit of the double star system to the orbit of the Earth.

The first four elements may be defined formally as follows: Let

P = the period of revolution expressed in mean solar years.

T = the time of periastron passage.

e = the eccentricity.

a = the semiaxis major expressed in seconds of arc.

* This will suffice for long-period systems; for systems of short period, readings at shorter intervals should be taken.

All authorities are agreed upon these definitions, but some confusion in the nomenclature and even in the systems used in defining the remaining elements has arisen from the fact that it is impossible to say, from the micrometer measures alone, on which side of the plane of projection (which is taken as the plane of reference) the companion star lies at a given time. In other words, we cannot distinguish between the ascending and the descending node, or between direct and retrograde motion in the ordinary sense. Further, in some systems the observed position angles *increase* with the times, in others they *decrease*.

The following is the classical system in the form most convenient when the requirements of the observer of radial velocities are considered as well as those of the observer with the micrometer. Let

Ω = the position angle of that nodal point which lies between 0° and 180°; that is, the position angle of the line of intersection of the orbit plane with the plane perpendicular to the line of sight. Call this merely "the nodal point," disregarding the distinction between ascending and descending nodes.

ω = the angle in the plane of the true orbit between the line of nodes and the major axis. It is to be measured from the nodal point to the point of periastron passage *in the direction of the companion's motion* and may have any value from 0° to 360°. It should be stated whether the position angles increase or decrease with the times.

i = the inclination of the orbit plane; that is, the angle between the orbit plane and the plane at right angles to the line of sight. Its value lies between 0° and $\pm 90°$ and may carry the double sign ($\pm$) or be left without sign until the indetermination has been removed by measures of the radial velocity.* When these are available, i is to be regarded as positive ($+$) if the orbital motion at the nodal point is carrying the companion star away from the observer; negative, if it is carrying the companion star toward the observer.

* Van den Bos, however, writes i in the second quadrant in all orbits in which the position angle decreases with the time ("A Table of Orbits of Visual Binary Stars," *B.A.N.* **3,** 149, 1926), and some later computers have followed this convention.

The symbol μ denotes the mean annual motion of the companion, expressed in degrees and decimals, *measured always in the direction of motion.*

The conventions of taking Ω always less than 180° and of counting ω (for which many computers use the symbol λ) always in the direction of the companion's motion were first suggested, I believe, by See, and have now been adopted generally. The definition of i (for which some computers write γ) is the usual one, also. Many computers prefer to count the mean annual motion in the direction of increasing position angles in all systems, and to consider the motion negative when the angles decrease with the times.

As early as 1883 T. N. Thiele* proposed a method of computation that would replace the geometrical elements i, ω, and Ω and the semiaxis major a by the polar coordinates, with respect to the center of the apparent ellipse, of the projections on the plane of the apparent orbit of the two points in the true orbit for which the eccentric anomalies are, respectively, 0° and 90°. More recently Innes independently worked out a system which is, in all essentials, the same as Thiele's. Innes' system, as formulated by van den Bos, is given on a later page and the relations between the Thiele-Innes constants and the elements as defined in the preceding paragraphs are there set forth.

When the elements are known, the apparent position angle θ and the angular distance ρ for the time t are derived from the following equations:

$$\left.\begin{aligned}
\mu &= \frac{360°}{P} \\
M &= \mu(t - T) = E - e \sin E \\
r &= a(1 - e \cos E) \\
\tan \tfrac{1}{2}v &= \sqrt{\frac{1 + e}{1 - e}} \tan \tfrac{1}{2}E
\end{aligned}\right\} \qquad (6)$$

$$\left.\begin{aligned}
\tan (\theta - \Omega) &= \pm \tan (v + \omega) \cos i \\
\rho &= r \cos (v + \omega) \sec (\theta - \Omega)
\end{aligned}\right\} \qquad (7)$$

Equations (6) are the usual ones for elliptic motion, the symbols M, E, and v representing respectively, the mean, eccentric, and true anomaly, and r the radius vector. Equations (7) convert the v and r of the companion in the true orbit

* *A.N.* **104**, 245, 1883.

into its position angle and distance in the projected, or apparent orbit. Position angles are generally recorded only to the nearest tenth of a degree in orbit computation, hence it is sufficiently exact to take the value of E corresponding to a given value of M from Åstrand's *Hülfstafeln*, which hold for all values of the eccentricity, or the value of v directly from the still more convenient *Allegheny Tables*,* provided the eccentricity does not exceed 0.77. If the latter tables are used, it is convenient to derive the value of r from the equation

$$r = \frac{a(1 - e^2)}{(1 + e \cos v)} \qquad (6a)$$

instead of from the third of Eqs. (6).

KOWALSKY'S METHOD

From the many methods of orbit computation that have been formulated, I have selected for presentation here those by Kowalsky, by Zwiers and by Innes. All three are of very general application and each one has its advocates among computers. Several other methods are useful and the student is advised to examine all those for which references are given at the end of this chapter†

Kowalsky's method‡ is essentially analytical and derives the orbit elements from the constants of the general equation of the apparent ellipse which is the orthogonal projection of the true orbit, the origin of coordinates being taken at S, the position of the primary star. This equation takes the form

$$Ax^2 + 2Hxy + By^2 + 2Gx + 2Fy + 1 = 0$$

The values of the constants A, H, B, G and F, may be computed by the method noted on page 75, but this is open to the serious objection that it takes no account of the law of areas. It is far better to follow the procedure proposed by Glasenapp§ and derive the values of the five constants from measures on the carefully drawn apparent ellipse, as follows:

* *Publ. Allegheny Obs.* **2**, 155–190, 1912.

† See particularly the methods of Russell (1933) and of Volet (1932).

‡ First published, according to von Glasenapp, in the *Proceedings of the Kasan Imperial University*, in 1873. This volume has not been accessible to me.

§ *Mon. Not. R.A.S.* **49**, 276, 1889.

In the general equation of the ellipse put $y = 0$; then the roots
of the roots of the resulting equation

$$Ax^2 + 2Gx + 1 = 0$$

will be the abscissae of the points of intersection of the ellipse and
the x-axis. Representing these roots by x_1 and x_2, we have

$$A = \frac{1}{x_1 x_2}, \qquad G = -\frac{x_1 + x_2}{2x_1 x_2} \tag{8}$$

Similarly, by putting $x = 0$, we obtain

$$B = \frac{1}{y_1 y_2}, \qquad F = -\frac{y_1 + y_2}{2y_1 y_2} \tag{9}$$

These four constants are thus obtained by direct measurements
of the distances from the principal star to the intersection points
of the ellipse with the x- and y-axes, in which care must be taken
to regard the algebraic signs. The fifth constant, H, is then
derived from the equation

$$H = -\frac{Ax^2 + By^2 + 2Gx + 2Fy + 1}{2xy} \tag{10}$$

Measure the coordinates of several well-distributed points on
the apparent ellipse, so chosen as to make the product xy as large
as possible and substitute each set of values successively in
Eq. (10). The accordance of the resulting values of H will
depend upon the care with which the ellipse has been drawn,
and the mean of all should be adopted.

The values of the coefficients $A, H \ldots F$ being known,
we proceed as follows, adopting the analysis recently given by
W. M. Smart:*

Construct a sphere (Fig. 3) with the principal star S as center,
and let SL, SM, SK be the rectangular axes to which the general
equation of the apparent ellipse, in the plane of the great circle
LNM (at right angles to the line of sight), is referred, SL defining
the direction to position angle 0°. Let the great circle $FNAB$
define the plane of the true orbit relative to the primary. Then
QSN is the line of nodes, and, assuming the position angles to
increase from L toward N, LN is the longitude of the nodal
point Ω, as defined in an earlier paragraph. Let P be the periastron point, and A the corresponding point on the sphere.

* W. M. Smart, On the Derivation of the Elements of a Visual Binary
Orbit by Kowalsky's Method, *Mon. Not. R.A.S.*, **90**, 534, 1930.

Then NA denotes ω, and ANM, the inclination, i, taken to lie between 0° and 90°.

Take rectangular axes SA, SB, and SC with reference to the plane of the true orbit, and let (ξ, η, o) be the coordinates of the companion at any time with respect to these axes. Since the

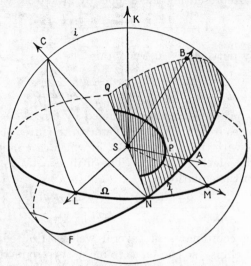

Fig. 3.—Diagram for Kowalsky's orbit method.

primary S is at a focus of the true orbit, the equation of the true ellipse is

$$\frac{(\xi + ae)^2}{a^2} + \frac{\eta^2}{b^2} = 1 \qquad (11)$$

where
$$b^2 = a^2(1 - e^2).$$

Let (l_1, m_1, n_1), (l_2, m_2, n_2), (l_3, m_3, n_3) denote the direction-cosines of SA, SB, and SC, respectively, with reference to the axes SL, SM, and SK. Then, drawing great circle arcs from each of A, B, and C in turn to L, M, and K, we can write

$$
\begin{aligned}
l_1 &= \cos AL & m_1 &= \cos AM, & n_1 &= \cos AK, \\
l_2 &= \cos BL & m_2 &= \cos BM, & n_2 &= \cos BK, \\
l_3 &= \cos CL, & m_3 &= \cos CM, & n_3 &= \cos CK,
\end{aligned}
$$

and from the appropriate spherical triangles we derive at once

$$
\left.
\begin{aligned}
l_1 &= \cos \Omega \cos \omega - \sin \Omega \sin \omega \cos i \\
m_1 &= \sin \Omega \cos \omega + \cos \Omega \sin \omega \cos i \\
n_1 &= \sin \omega \sin i
\end{aligned}
\right\} \qquad (12)
$$

$$l_2 = -\cos \Omega \sin \omega - \sin \Omega \cos \omega \cos i$$
$$m_2 = -\sin \Omega \sin \omega + \cos \Omega \cos \omega \cos i \qquad (13)$$
$$n_2 = \cos \omega \sin i$$

$$l_3 = \sin \Omega \sin i$$
$$m_3 = -\cos \Omega \sin i \qquad (14)$$
$$n_3 = \cos i$$

We require subsequently the following relations between the direction cosines:

$$l_1 m_2 - l_2 m_1 = n_3 \qquad (15)$$
$$l_1{}^2 + l_2{}^2 + l_3{}^2 = 1 \qquad (16)$$
$$m_1{}^2 + m_2{}^2 + m_3{}^2 = 1 \qquad (17)$$
$$l_1 m_1 + l_2 m_2 + l_3 m_3 = 0 \qquad (18)$$

Any point (ξ, η) on the true orbit projects into the point (x, y) on the apparent orbit. We have, consequently,

$$x = l_1 \xi + l_2 \eta$$
$$y = m_1 \xi + m_2 \eta$$

from which, using Eq. (15),

$$\xi = \frac{m_2 x - l_2 y}{n_3}$$

$$\eta = -\frac{m_1 x - l_1 y}{n_3}$$

Substituting these values of ξ and η in Eq. (11), we obtain

$$\frac{(m_2 x - l_2 y + aen_3)^2}{a^2 n_3{}^2} + \frac{(m_1 x - l_1 y)^2}{b^2 n_3{}^2} = 1. \qquad (19)$$

This is the equation of the apparent orbit and is therefore equivalent to Eq. (4) (page 75). The coefficients of the same powers of the variables in Eqs. (19) and (4) are therefore proportional. Denoting the common ratio by f, we have, considering the coefficients of x^2, y^2, . . . in turn,

$$A = \frac{f}{n_3{}^2}\left(\frac{m_2{}^2}{a^2} + \frac{m_1{}^2}{b^2}\right); \qquad B = \frac{f}{n_3{}^2}\left(\frac{l_2{}^2}{a^2} + \frac{l_1{}^2}{b^2}\right)$$

$$H = -\frac{f}{n_3{}^2}\left(\frac{l_2 m_2}{a^2} + \frac{l_1 m_1}{b^2}\right) \qquad (20)$$

$$G = \frac{fem_2}{an_3}; \qquad F = -\frac{fel_2}{an_3}$$

and, from the absolute terms,

$$1 = f(e^2 - 1)$$

or, writing

$$p = a(1 - e^2) \equiv \frac{b^2}{a}, \tag{21}$$

$$f = -\frac{a}{p} \tag{22}$$

This value of f can then be substituted in the expressions of Eq. (20).

We now derive the elements in terms of $A, B, \ldots F$. We have, firstly, using Eqs. (21) and (22),

$$
\begin{aligned}
F^2 - G^2 + A - B &= \frac{e^2}{p^2 n_3{}^2}(l_2{}^2 - m_2{}^2) - \frac{a}{p n_3{}^2}\left(\frac{m_2{}^2 - l_2{}^2}{a^2} + \frac{m_1{}^2 - l_1{}^2}{b^2}\right) \\
&= \frac{(l_2{}^2 - m_2{}^2)}{p^2 n_3{}^2}\left(e^2 + \frac{p}{a}\right) - \frac{(m_1{}^2 - l_1{}^2)}{p^2 n_3{}^2} \\
&= \frac{1}{p^2 n_3{}^2}(l_1{}^2 + l_2{}^2 - m_1{}^2 - m_2{}^2) \\
&= \frac{1}{p^2 n_3{}^2}(m_3{}^2 - l_3{}^2) \text{ by Eqs. (16) and (17).}
\end{aligned}
$$

Hence, using the values of l_3, m_3, n_3 given by Eq. (14), we obtain

$$F^2 - G^2 + A - B = \frac{\tan^2 i}{p^2}\cos 2\Omega \tag{23}$$

Again,

$$
\begin{aligned}
FG - H &= -\frac{e^2 l_2 m_2}{p^2 n_3{}^2} - \frac{a}{p n_3{}^2}\left(\frac{l_2 m_2}{a^2} + \frac{l_1 m_1}{ap}\right) \\
&= -\frac{1}{p^2 n_3{}^2}(l_1 m_1 + l_2 m_2) \\
&= \frac{l_3 m_3}{p^2 n_3{}^2}
\end{aligned}
$$

by (18). Hence, using Eq. (14),

$$FG - H = -\tfrac{1}{2}\frac{\tan^2 i}{p^2}\sin 2\Omega \tag{24}$$

From Eqs. (23) and (24) we obtain

$$(F^2 - G^2 + A - B)\sin 2\Omega + 2(FG - H)\cos 2\Omega = 0 \tag{25}$$

which determines Ω in terms of known quantities.

The value of $\tan^2 i/p^2$ can then be found from Eq. (23) or (24). Again, it is easily seen that

$$
\begin{aligned}
F^2 + G^2 - (A + B) &= \frac{1}{p^2 n_3{}^2}(l_1{}^2 + l_2{}^2 + m_1{}^2 + m_2{}^2) \\
&= \frac{1}{p^2 n_3{}^2}(2 - l_3{}^2 - m_3{}^2) \\
&= \frac{1}{p^2 \cos^2 i}(2 - \sin^2 i) \\
&= \frac{2}{p^2} + \frac{\tan^2 i}{p^2} \qquad (26)
\end{aligned}
$$

Since we already have the value of $\tan^2 i/p^2$, Eq. (26) enables us to calculate p, and therefore i.

Now, from Eqs. (13) and (20) we find

$$
-m_2 \equiv \sin \Omega \sin \omega - \cos \Omega \cos \omega \cos i = \frac{Gp \cos i}{e} \qquad (27)
$$

$$
-l_2 \equiv \cos \Omega \sin \omega + \sin \Omega \cos \omega \cos i = -\frac{Fp \cos i}{e} \qquad (28)
$$

Multiply Eqs. (27) and (28) by $\sin \Omega$ and $\cos \Omega$, respectively, and add. Then

$$
e \sin \omega = p(G \sin \Omega - F \cos \Omega) \cos i \qquad (29)
$$

Multiply Eqs. (27) and (28) by $\cos \Omega$ and $\sin \Omega$, respectively, and subtract. Then

$$
e \cos \omega = -p(G \cos \Omega + F \sin \Omega) \qquad (30)
$$

Hence,

$$
\tan \omega = -\frac{(G \sin \Omega - F \cos \Omega) \cos i}{(G \cos \Omega + F \sin \Omega)} \qquad (31)
$$

This equation, with Eqs. (29) and (30), determines ω without ambiguity.

The eccentricity e may now be obtained from Eq. (29) or (30) and the semimajor axis a, from Eq. (21)

$$
p = a(1 - e^2)
$$

To complete the solution analytically, the period P and the time of periastron passage T, are to be found from the mean anomalies M, computed from the observations by taking the ephemeris formulas on page 79 in reverse order. Every M will give an equation of the form

$$M = \frac{360°}{P}(t - T), \quad \text{or} \quad M = \mu t + \epsilon$$

where

$$\epsilon = -\mu T.$$

From these equations the values of M and T are computed by the method of least squares.

It is more convenient, however, to derive the values of P and T from measures on the apparent ellipse made with the aid of a planimeter, as follows: The diameter of the apparent ellipse drawn through the origin S is obviously the projection of the major axis of the true orbit, and the extremity of this diameter nearest the origin is therefore the projection of the point of periastron. Call it P'. Then, determine c, the constant of areal velocity, from planimeter measures of the entire portion of the ellipse covered by the observations, or, of that portion of this ellipse which seems to be most accurately defined by the observations; measure also the areas of two sectors $P'Sp$ and $P'Sp'$, p and p' being two observed positions on opposite sides of the point P'. Divide these areas by c and apply the quotients, with proper signs, to the times corresponding to the positions p and p', and thus derive two values of T, the time of periastron passage, which should agree closely. Several sets of points may, of course, be used and the mean of all values for T adopted. Similarly, the area of the entire ellipse may be measured, and the result divided by c to find P, the revolution period. It is not necessary to know the unit of area in making these measures, since all the areas are simply relative.

ZWIERS' METHOD*

Zwiers' method is essentially graphical, and assumes that the apparent orbit has been drawn. It may be well to insist again that the utmost care must be exercised in drawing this ellipse, for unless it gives a good geometrical representation of the observations *and satisfies the law of areas*, it is useless to proceed with the orbit computation.

The apparent ellipse being the projection of the true orbit, its diameter drawn through S, the position of the principal star, is the projection of the true major axis, and its conjugate, the

---

* *A. N.* **139**, 369, 1896. Prof. H. N. Russell independently worked out a method based upon the same geometric concept. *A. J.* **19**, 9, 1898.

projection of the true minor axis. Further, if P is that extremity of the diameter through S which is nearest S it will be the projection of the point of periastron passage in the true orbit. Therefore, letting C represent the center of the ellipse, the ratio CS/CP will be the eccentricity, e, of that orbit, since ratios are not changed by projection.

Let $K = 1/\sqrt{1 - e^2}$ be the ratio of the major to the minor axis in the true orbit; then, if all of the chords in this orbit parallel to the minor axis are increased in the ratio $K:1$, the ellipse will be transformed into Kepler's eccentric circle. Consequently, if in the *apparent* ellipse all ordinates parallel to the conjugate diameter, described above, are prolonged in the ratio $K:1$ we shall have another conic which may be called the *auxiliary ellipse*. It will evidently be the projection of the eccentric circle.

The major axis of the auxiliary ellipse will be a diameter of the eccentric circle and therefore equal to the major axis of the true orbit, and its position will define the line of nodes, since the nodal line must be parallel to the only diameter not shortened by projection. Designate the semimajor and semiminor axes of the auxiliary ellipse by α and β, respectively; then the ratio $\beta:\alpha$ is the cosine of the inclination of the orbit plane to the plane of projection. Again, the angle ω' between the major axis of the auxiliary ellipse and the diameter $PSCP'$ of the apparent orbit is the projection of the angle ω, the angle between node and periastron in the true orbit. Therefore

$$\tan \omega = \frac{\tan \omega'}{\cos i} = \frac{\alpha}{\beta} \tan \omega' \qquad (32)$$

Finally P and T are found by areal measures in the apparent ellipse in the manner already described.

The conjugate diameter required in Zwiers' construction may be found most easily by first drawing *any* chord of the ellipse parallel to $PSCP'$, the projected major axis. The diameter through the middle point of this chord is the conjugate required. If desired, advantage may also be taken of the fact that the conjugate diameter is parallel to the tangents to the ellipse at the points P and P', and the rectangular axes of the auxiliary ellipse found by trial or by the following construction: Let

$$\frac{x^2}{(a')^2} + \frac{y^2}{(b')^2} = 1$$

be the equation of the apparent ellipse referred to its conjugate diameters. The equation of the auxiliary ellipse referred to the same axes will be

$$\frac{x^2}{(a')^2} + \frac{y^2}{(Kb')^2} = 1$$

The axes are therefore also conjugate diameters of the auxiliary ellipse. At the extremity P of the diameter a' $(PSCP')$, erect two perpendiculars, PA and PB, to the tangent to the ellipse at this point and make each equal in length to Kb'. Through the extremities of the two perpendiculars and the center C of the apparent ellipse pass a circle. It will cut the tangent in two points, A' and B'. The lines $A'C$ and $B'C$ will give the directions of the two rectangular axes required, the major axis lying in the acute, the minor axis in the obtuse angle between the diameters a' and Kb'.

Instead of actually constructing the auxiliary ellipse it will generally be easier to derive the elements directly from measures of the apparent ellipse with the aid of simple formulas based upon the analytical solution of the construction. Thus:

Let e, a', and b' again represent, respectively, the eccentricity, and the projected major and minor axes of the orbit, and let x_1 and x_2 be the position angles of a' and b'. To avoid ambiguity, let x_1 be the position angle of the principal star as viewed from the center of the apparent ellipse and let x_2 be so taken that $(x_1 - x_2)$ is an acute angle. Also, compute as before, $K = 1/\sqrt{1 - e^2}$ and $b'' = Kb'$. Then the relations between the rectangular axes 2α and 2β of the auxiliary ellipse and the conjugate diameters $2a'$ and $2b''$ are given by the equations

$$\alpha^2 + \beta^2 = a'^2 + b''^2$$
$$\alpha\beta = a'b'' \sin(x_1 - x_2) \qquad (33)$$

the sine being considered positive.

The coordinates of any point on the auxiliary ellipse with respect to the axes 2α and 2β may be written in the form $\alpha \cos \phi'$, $\beta \sin \phi'$. Let $\alpha \cos(\omega)$, $\beta \sin(\omega)$ be the coordinates of the extremity of the a' diameter; then we shall have

$$a'^2 = \alpha^2 \cos^2(\omega) + \beta^2 \sin^2(\omega) \qquad (34)$$

and

$$\tan(\omega) = \pm\sqrt{\frac{\alpha^2 - a'^2}{a'^2 - \beta^2}} \qquad (35)$$

in which the sign of tan (ω) is to be the same as that of $(x_1 - x_2)$. But ω', the projection of ω is related to (ω) by the equation

$$\tan \omega' = \frac{\beta}{\alpha} \tan (\omega) \qquad (36)$$

that is $(\omega) = \omega$ and $\Omega = (x_1 - \omega')$.

The angle ω obviously may have either of two values differing by 180°; that value is to be taken which will make Ω less than 180°.

Zwiers counts all angles in these formulas in the direction of increasing position angles.

The practical procedure may therefore be stated as follows: Construct the apparent ellipse and the diameter b' conjugate to a'; measure e, a', b', x_1 and x_2; compute $K = 1/\sqrt{1 - e^2}$, $b'' = Kb'$, and find α and β from

$$(\alpha \pm \beta)^2 = a'^2 + b''^2 \pm 2a'b'' \sin (x_1 - x_2)$$

the sine being taken positive.   Then

$$a = \alpha$$
$$\cos i = \frac{\beta}{\alpha}$$
$$\tan \omega = \pm \sqrt{\frac{\alpha^2 - a'^2}{a'^2 - \beta^2}},$$

the sign of tan ω being taken the same as that of $(x_1 - x_2)$, and of the two values of ω that one which makes Ω less than 180°.

Next we have

$$\tan \omega' = \frac{\beta}{\alpha} \tan \omega \qquad \Omega = (x_1 - \omega'),$$

and finally deduce the values of P and T from area measurement, as in the Glasenapp-Kowalsky method.

THE THIELE METHOD AND THE THIELE-INNES CONSTANTS

In 1883,[*] T. N. Thiele published a method of orbit computation depending upon three observed positions and the constant of areal velocity, and substituting for the elements a, i, ω, and Ω, the polar coordinates (a, A) and (b, B), referred to the center of the apparent ellipse as origin, of two points, P' and R', the projections upon the apparent ellipse of the points P and R in

[*] *A. N.* **104**, 245, 1883.

the true orbit having, respectively, the eccentric anomalies 0° and 90°. The three observed positions should, of course, be normal places carefully selected to represent as long an arc as convenient of the well-observed part of the apparent ellipse, for the success of the computation depends upon the skill with which this selection is made, and the accuracy with which the areal constant, defined later, is determined.

Although the method has a wide range of applicability, it did not come in to extensive use until quite recently, when it was revived by Innes and van den Bos. Innes,* in 1926, seeking a simpler method than those in common use for correcting the preliminary elements of an orbit differentially, independently developed a method of orbit computation which differs from Thiele's only in that he used rectangular instead of polar coordinates and for Thiele's points R and R' substituted Q, the point on the auxiliary circle drawn on the major axis of the true orbit that corresponds to R and Q' its projection on the plane of the apparent ellipse. If A, B, F, and G, represent these coordinates, the relations between them and Thiele's are:

Innes	Thiele
A	$a \cos A$
B	$a \sin A$
F	$b \sec \varphi \cos B$
G	$b \sec \varphi \sin B$

where $\sin \varphi = e$.

It will be convenient to treat the two methods together, and to follow Innes and van den Bos† rather than Thiele in the development of the formulas.

The data assumed as known are the three normal places corresponding to the times t_1, t_2, t_3 and C, the double constant of areal velocity. Each observation gives

$$\left. \begin{aligned} x &= \rho \cos \theta \\ y &= \rho \sin \theta \end{aligned} \right\} \tag{37}$$

These are connected with the usual orbit elements by

$$\left. \begin{aligned} \rho \cos (\theta - \Omega) &= r \cos (v + \omega) \\ \rho \sin (\theta - \Omega) &= r \sin (v + \omega) \cos i \end{aligned} \right\} \tag{38}$$

---

* W. H. van den Bos, Orbital Elements of Double Stars, *Union Obs. Circ.* **68**, 354, 1926; **86**, 261, 1932.

† *Loc. cit.*

Removing Ω to the right-hand number, and separating v from ω, we have

$$
\left.\begin{aligned}
x = \; & r \cos v \, (\cos \omega \cos \Omega - \sin \omega \sin \Omega \cos i) + \\
& r \sin v \, (-\sin \omega \cos \Omega - \cos \omega \sin \Omega \cos i) \\
y = \; & r \cos v \, (\cos \omega \sin \Omega + \sin \omega \cos \Omega \cos i) + \\
& r \sin v \, (-\sin \omega \sin \Omega + \cos \omega \cos \Omega \cos i)
\end{aligned}\right\} \quad (39)
$$

It is to be noted that in all the Thiele-Innes formulas *the inclination i, for retrograde motion, is taken between 90° and 180°.*

Put

$$
\left.\begin{aligned}
X = \frac{r}{a} \cos v = \cos E - \sin \varphi \\
Y = \frac{r}{a} \sin v = \cos \varphi \sin E
\end{aligned}\right\} \quad (40)
$$

where $\sin \varphi = e$
and

$$
\left.\begin{aligned}
A &= a \, (\cos \omega \cos \Omega - \sin \omega \sin \Omega \cos i) \\
B &= a \, (\cos \omega \sin \Omega + \sin \omega \cos \Omega \cos i) \\
F &= a \, (-\sin \omega \cos \Omega - \cos \omega \sin \Omega \cos i) \\
G &= a \, (-\sin \omega \sin \Omega + \cos \omega \cos \Omega \cos i)
\end{aligned}\right\} \quad (41)
$$

Then we have

$$
\left.\begin{aligned}
x = AX + FY \\
y = BX + GY
\end{aligned}\right\} \quad (42)
$$

Equations (41) show the relations between Innes' constants and the elements a, i, ω and Ω, while Eqs. (42) are his fundamental equations. It is also clear that the points (A, B), $(F \cos \varphi, G \cos \varphi)$, with the center of the apparent ellipse, define a pair of conjugate axes which are the projections of the major and minor axes of the true orbit.

The double areal constant is, obviously, twice the area of the entire ellipse divided by the period. Since the area of an ellipse is π times the product of its semiaxes, and the area of the rectangle constructed on the axes equals the area of the parallelogram constructed on any pair of conjugate axes, we have

$$
C = \frac{2\pi}{P}(AG - BF) \cos \varphi = \mu(AG - BF) \cos \varphi \quad (43)
$$

where $\mu = 2\pi/P = 6.28319/P$ is the mean annual motion expressed in radians. Let $\Delta_{p,q}$ represent the double area of the triangle formed by the position of the primary and the positions of the companion at the times t_p and t_q. Then

$$\Delta_{p,q} = x_p y_q - x_q y_p = (AG - BF)(X_p Y_q - X_q Y_p),$$

or, introducing values from Eqs. (40) and (43),

$$\frac{\Delta_{p,q}}{C} = \frac{1}{\mu} [\sin (E_q - E_p) - \sin \varphi(\sin E_q - \sin E_p)] \qquad (44)$$

From Kepler's equation, $E - \sin \varphi \sin E = M = \mu(t - T)$, we find

$$t_q - t_p = \frac{1}{\mu}[(E_q - E_p) - \sin \varphi(\sin E_q - \sin E_p)]$$

ana, subtracting Eq. (44), we obtain

$$t_q - t_p - \frac{\Delta_{p,q}}{C} = \frac{1}{\mu} [(E_q - E_p) - \sin (E_q - E_p)] \qquad (45)$$

This, in different notation, is Thiele's fundamental equation. Let us put $E_2 - E_1 = u$, $E_3 - E_2 = v$, $E_3 - E_1 = u + v$, and write Eq. (45) for $(t_2 - t_1)$, $(t_3 - t_2)$, and $(t_3 - t_1)$. We have

$$\left.\begin{aligned}
t_2 - t_1 - \frac{\Delta_{1,2}}{C} &= \frac{1}{\mu} (u - \sin u) \\
t_3 - t_2 - \frac{\Delta_{2,3}}{C} &= \frac{1}{\mu} (v - \sin v) \\
t_3 - t_1 - \frac{\Delta_{1,3}}{C} &= \frac{1}{\mu} [(u + v) - \sin (u + v)]
\end{aligned}\right\} \qquad (45a)$$

The left hand members of the three equations are known from the three normal places and the double areal constant.

If the observations extend over a full revolution, so that the period is approximately known, the approximate value of μ will be known and we may proceed at once to derive the values of e ($= \sin \varphi$) and E_2. If this is not the case, we assume the most plausible value for μ, and, with the help of a table for $(x - \sin x)$, compute u, v and $(u + v)$. By successive approximations a value for μ should readily be found which will make the values of u and v check with the value of $(u + v)$. Then

$$P = \frac{2\pi}{\mu} = \frac{6.28319}{\mu}, \quad \text{and} \quad n = 57.2958\mu$$

From Eq. (44) we have, by introducing u, v, $(u + v)$, $\Delta_{1,2}$, $\Delta_{2,3}$ and $\Delta_{3,1}$ successively, and combining,

$$\Delta_{1,2} + \Delta_{2,3} - \Delta_{1,3} = \frac{C}{\mu}[\sin u + \sin v - \sin (u + v)]$$

and

$$\Delta_{2,3} \sin u - \Delta_{1,2} \sin v = \frac{C}{\mu} \sin \varphi[\sin v(\sin E_2 - \sin E_1) - \\ \sin u(\sin E_3 - \sin E_2)].$$

Substituting $(E_2 - E_1)$ and $(E_3 - E_2)$ for u and v in the right-hand member of this equation, removing all parentheses, and recombining and substituting, we finally derive

$$\Delta_{2,3} \sin u - \Delta_{1,2} \sin v = \frac{C}{\mu} \sin \varphi \sin E_2 [\sin u + \sin v - \sin (u + v)] \tag{46}$$

Similarly, from

$$\Delta_{2,3} \cos u + \Delta_{1,2} \cos v - \Delta_{1,3} = \frac{C}{\mu} \sin \varphi[\sin E_3 - \sin E_1 \\ - \cos u(\sin E_3 - \sin E_3 - \cos v(\sin E_2 - \sin E_1)]$$

we derive

$$\Delta_{2,3} \cos u + \Delta_{1,2} \cos v - \Delta_{1,3} = \frac{C}{\mu} \sin \varphi \cos E_2 \\ [\sin u + \sin v - \sin (u + v)] \tag{47}$$

and from Eqs. (46) and (47)

$$\left.\begin{array}{l} \sin \varphi \sin E_2 = \dfrac{\Delta_{2,3} \sin u - \Delta_{1,2} \sin v}{\Delta_{1,2} + \Delta_{2,3} - \Delta_{1,3}} \\[2mm] \sin \varphi \cos E_2 = \dfrac{\Delta_{2,3} \cos u + \Delta_{1,2} \cos v - \Delta_{1,3}}{\Delta_{1,2} + \Delta_{2,3} - \Delta_{1,3}} \end{array}\right\} \tag{48}$$

These equations give E_2 and $e = \sin \varphi$; then E_1, E_3 follow from $(E_2 - u)$ and $(E_2 + v)$. For each time, t_1, t_2, t_3, we next derive the mean anomaly from Kepler's equation and thus three values of T, the time of periastron passage, which should agree closely. The values for X and Y follow from Eq. (40) and, finally, those of the four constants, A, F, B, G, from the normal places by the use of Eqs. (42).

Whatever method of orbit computation is adopted, it is recommended that the Thiele-Innes constants as well as the elements in the usual notation be given. The formulas, to convert from the one system to the other, in convenient form for logarithmic computation are:

To derive the Thiele-Innes constants

$$\left.\begin{aligned}
A + G &= 2a \cos (\omega + \Omega) \cos^2 \frac{i}{2} \\
A - G &= 2a \cos (\omega - \Omega) \sin^2 \frac{i}{2} \\
B - F &= 2a \sin (\omega + \Omega) \cos^2 \frac{i}{2} \\
-B - F &= 2a \sin (\omega - \Omega) \sin^2 \frac{i}{2}
\end{aligned}\right\} \qquad (49)$$

For the inverse process,

$$\left.\begin{aligned}
\tan (\omega + \Omega) &= \frac{B - F}{A + G} \\
\tan (\omega - \Omega) &= \frac{-B - F}{A - G} \\
\tan^2 \frac{i}{2} &= \frac{A - G}{A + G} \cdot \frac{\cos (\omega + \Omega)}{\cos (\omega - \Omega)} = \frac{-B - F}{B - F} \cdot \frac{\sin (\omega + \Omega)}{\sin (\omega - \Omega)}.
\end{aligned}\right\} \qquad (50)*$$

It may again be pointed out that in these formulas i, in the case of retrograde motion, is taken in the second quadrant.

The practical procedure, then, is first to form the three normal places and find the value of C the double areal constant. Thiele employs processes of numerical integration for this purpose, but it is better, as well as more convenient, to utilize the carefully drawn apparent ellipse, or interpolating curves for position angles and distances against the times. It is hardly necessary to say that the normal places must conform to the law of areas, and, that, if they are derived from interpolating curves, care must be taken that they fall upon the curve of the apparent ellipse; but it may be well to note that $C \left(= \rho^2 \dfrac{d\theta}{dt} \right)$ has the negative sign when the position angles decrease with the time and that the units for ρ and $d\theta/dt$ are, respectively, seconds of arc, and radians per annum.

---

* [The $\tan^2 \dfrac{i}{2}$ formulas are awkward. A better method of solution for a, i, ω, and Ω, is:

$$a(1 + \cos i) = (A + G) \sec (\omega + \Omega) = (B - F) \csc (\omega + \Omega)$$
$$a(1 - \cos i) = (A - G) \sec (\omega - \Omega) = (-B - F) \csc (\omega - \Omega),$$

from which a and i may be computed easily.—J.T.K.]

Having the required data, we first find P through the value of μ derived from Eq. (45a), then e and T, from Eq. (48) and Kepler's equation, and finally X and Y and the four constants A, B, F, G, from Eqs. (40) and (42). In other words, the three purely dynamic elements are derived first, and then values of the four constants (representing the geometric elements) to correspond.

ILLUSTRATIVE EXAMPLES

In the first edition of this book, I used my computations of the orbit of A88 (*ADS*, 11520) to illustrate the Glasenapp-Kowalsky

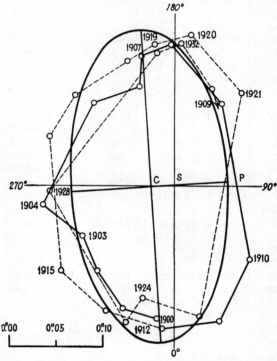

Fig. 4.—The apparent orbit of A 88. The solidly drawn broken line connects the positions used in the computation of the orbit; the dashed and dotted lines connect the positions given by later measures.

method and the method of Zwiers. The period of the system is 12.12 years, and the observations now available show that the companion has described more than 2½ revolutions about the primary since discovery. These later observations, when compared with an ephemeris based on the orbit, give residuals comparable to those obtained for the observations on which the orbit was based. I have therefore not revised the elements, but retain the original computations which were made in 1912,

MEASURES AND RESIDUALS FOR A88

Date	θ_0	ρ_0	n	Obs.	$(O - C)$		
						$\Delta\theta$	$\Delta\rho$
1900.46	353°.2	0″.14	3	......	− 1°.3	−0″.004	−0″.03
1901.56	338.3	0.14	3	......	− 0.8	−0.002	−0.02
1902.66	318.1	0.12	3	......	+ 0.7	+0.002	−0.01
1903.40	293.6	0.11	3	......	− 0.2	−0.000	0.00
1904.52	278.4	0.14	4	......	+20.8	+0.040	+0.03
1905.53	224.8	0.12	4	......	− 0.2	−0.000	+0.01
1906.48	199.1	0.13	4	......	− 7.4	−0.020	−0.03
1907.30	193.5	0.14	1	......	− 0.8	−0.002	−0.03
1908.39	178.1	0.15	3	......	+ 0.1	+0.000	0.00
1909.67	150.4	0.10	2	......	+ 3.3	+0.006	+0.01
1910.56	47.0	0.11	2	......	− 0.6	−0.001	+0.03
1911.55	18.7	0.15	1	......	+ 7.0	+0.017	+0.01
1912.57	356.1	0.15	3	......	+ 0.9	+0.003	−0.02
1914.55	331.2	0.14	4	......	+ 9.2	+0.022	0.00
1914.55	330.2	<0.20	1	Rabe	+ 8.2	+0.020	
1915.52	306.4	0.15	3	......	+10.6	+0.020	+0.04
1916.24	277.2	0.13	1	VBs	− 9.8	−0.017	+0.03
1916.63	243.0	0.16	2	Lv	−12.1	−0.023	+0.05
1916.76	248.8	0.14	2	......	− 2.3	−0.004	+0.03
1917.62	222.5	0.10	1	VBs	− 3.6	−0.008	+0.03
1917.64	228.1	0.14	2	......	+ 2.1	+0.008	+0.01
1918.52	200.4	0.14	3	......	− 7.4	−0.021	−0.02
1918.76	196.9	0.14	1	VBs	− 7.1	−0.020	−0.02
1919.62	188.4	0.15	3	......	− 3.1	−0.009	−0.02
1920.37	173.6	0.16	2	......	− 7.4	−0.020	0.00
1920.67	172.6	0.16	5	Btz	− 2.6	−0.007	+0.01
1921.52	143.5	0.15	1	BtF	− 6.9	−0.011	+0.06
1921.53	144.4	0.12	4	......	− 6.0	−0.009	+0.03
1922.62	Too close		1				
1923.57	10.9	0.14	4	......	− 2.9	−0.007	0.00
1923.76	11.8	0.18	4	Mag	+ 1.9	+0.005	+0.03
1924.51	354.9	0.15	1	VBs	− 2.9	−0.009	−0.02
1924.65	344.2	0.12	1	......	−11.6	−0.034	−0.05
1925.61	340.6	0.15	3	......	− 1.5	−0.004	−0.01
1928.63	272.2	0.14	2	......	+12.8	+0.025	+0.03
1931.66	187.5	0.14	2	......	− 6.9	−0.020	−0.03
1932.78	177.7	0.15	2	......	+ 2.4	+0.006	0.00
1933.60	159.3	0.11	4	......	+ 6.6	+0.012	+0.01

The average residual in angle expressed in radians, $\Delta\theta(\rho/57.3)$, is ±0″.012; and in distance, $\Delta\rho$, ±0″.022.

adding, however, the later measures and the corresponding residuals.

All of the measures to date are given in the table on page 96. The dates, observed position angles, and observed distances are recorded in the first three columns. The fourth column shows the number of measures (on different nights) on which each position rests. Almost all of the measures were made by me, with the 36-in. refractor; for the others, the name or an abbreviation of the name of the observer is entered in the fifth column. (VBs = Van Biesbroeck, Lv = Leavenworth, Btz = Bernewitz, Mag = Maggini.) The last three columns give the residuals, observed minus computed, for the position angles and distances, the former entered both in degrees and reduced to stricter comparison with the distance residuals by multiplying by the factor $\rho/57.3$.

All of the measures to 1912 inclusive were plotted, using a scale of 3 in. to $0''.1$, and, after repeated trials, the ellipse shown in the diagram on page 95 was drawn. It represents the observation points fairly and satisfies the law of areas closely. Applying the Glasenapp-Kowalsky method, we first measure the intercepts of the ellipse with the axes of coordinates, and the coordinates of two selected points for the value of H, counting the end of the x-axis at $0°$, and of the y-axis at $90°$, positive. The measures are (in inches on the original drawing):

$$x_1 = +4.98, \quad y_1 = +1.77, \quad x_a = -2.55, \quad y_a = -2.86$$
$$x_2 = -4.73, \quad y_2 = -3.12. \quad x_b = +3.17, \quad y_b = -2.49$$

Therefore we have

$$x_1 x_2 = -23.5554, \quad y_1 y_2 = -5.5224, \quad x_a y_a = +7.2930,$$
$$x_1 + x_2 = +0.25, \quad y_1 + y_2 = -1.35, \quad x_b y_b = -7.8933,$$
$$x_a{}^2 = 6.5025, \quad y_a{}^2 = 8.1796$$
$$x_b{}^2 = 10.0489, \quad y_b{}^2 = 6.2001$$

from which to compute the five constants of the equation of the ellipse. We find

$$A = \frac{1}{x_1 x_2} = -0.04245$$

$$B = \frac{1}{y_1 y_2} = -0.18108$$

$$F = -\frac{y_1 + y_2}{2 y_1 y_2} = -0.12223$$

$$G = -\frac{x_1 + x_2}{2x_1x_2} = +0.00531$$

From these values and the coordinates x_a, y_a, we obtain

$$H = -\frac{Ax^2 + By^2 + 2Gx + 2Fy + 1}{2xy} = +0.00584,$$

and, similarly, from the coordinates x_b, y_b,

$$H = +0.00590,$$

and adopt the mean, $+0.00587$.

Combining these constants, we have,
$FG = -0.00065$; $F^2 = +0.01494$; $G^2 = +0.00003$;
$-2(FG - H) = +0.01304$; $F^2 - G^2 + A - B = +0.15354$;
$F^2 + G^2 - (A + B) = +0.23850$.

The solution of Eqs. (24), (23), (26), (29), (30), and (21) then proceeds as follows:

$\log \dfrac{\tan^2 i}{p^2} \sin 2\Omega$	8.11528
$\log \dfrac{\tan^2 i}{p^2} \cos 2\Omega$	9.18622
$\log \tan 2\Omega$	8.92906
2Ω	4°85
Ω	2°42
$\log \cos 2\Omega$	9.99844
$\log \dfrac{\tan^2 i}{p^2}$	9.18778
$\dfrac{\tan^2 i}{p^2}$	+0.15409
From Eq. (26) $\dfrac{2}{p^2} + \dfrac{\tan^2 i}{p^2}$	+0.23850
$\dfrac{2}{p^2}$	+0.08441
$\dfrac{1}{p^2}$	+0.04220
$\log \dfrac{1}{p^2}$	8.62536
$\log p^2$	1.37464
$\log p$	0.68732
$\log \tan^2 i$	0.56242
$\log \tan i$	0.28121
$180° - i = 62°22'30'' = 62°4$	

$$i \qquad 117°6$$
$$\log \cos i \qquad 9.66586$$

$\log F$	9.08718_n		$\log G$	7.72509
$\sin \Omega$	8.62557		$\sin \Omega$	8.62557
$\cos \Omega$	9.99962		$\cos \Omega$	9.99962
(1) $\log F \cos \Omega$	9.08680_n		(3) $\log G \sin \Omega$	6.35066
(2) $\log F \sin \Omega$	7.71275_n		(4) $\log G \cos \Omega$	7.72470
(1)	-0.12212		(3)	$+0.00022$
(2)	-0.005161		(4)	$+0.005305$
(3) $-$ (1)	$+0.12234$		(2) $+$ (4)	$+0.000144$
$\log [(3) - (1)]$	9.08757	$\log - [(2) + (4)]$		6.15836_n
$\cos i$	9.66586	p		0.68732
$\log p$	0.68732			
$\log e \sin \omega$	9.44075	$\log e \cos \omega$		$6.84568n$
$\log \tan \omega$	2.59507_n			
ω	$90°1$			
$\sin \omega$	0.00000			
$\log e$	9.44075			
e	0.276			
e^2	0.07618			
$1 - e^2$	0.92382			
$\log (1 - e^2)$	9.96559			
$\log p$	0.68732			

$$\log \frac{p}{(1 - e^2)} = \log a \qquad 0.72173$$

$$a \qquad 5.269 \text{ in.}$$
$$= 0''176$$

From the diagram (Fig. 4) it is obvious that the companion passed its periastron point between the dates of observation 1909.67 and 1910.56; but the measures made in 1908 and 1912 were regarded as more reliable than these and were accordingly used to determine the time of periastron passage. The constant of areal velocity (in units of the planimeter scale) had been found to be 0.205. Drawing radii to the points P and 1908.39 and 1912.57, the areas of the two resulting sectors were, in terms of the same unit, respectively, 0.34440 and 0.50225. Hence the time intervals between these two dates and the date of periastron passage were, respectively, $+1.68$ years, and -2.45 years, giving for T, the two values, 1910.07 and 1910.12. The mean, 1910.1, was adopted. The planimeter measures gave as the area of the entire ellipse, 2.4848, and the period, **12.12** years.

To solve the orbit by Zwiers' method, we begin by finding the axis b' conjugate to a' ($PSCP'$). Draw the chord cc parallel to $P'CSP$ and then draw the diameter through its middle point. This will be the required conjugate.

We now measure $CS = 0.67$, $CP = 2.45$, $a' = 2.445$, $b' = 5.050$; and the angles $x_1 = 92°6$ and $x_2 = 3°6$.

The ratio $CS:CP$ gives at once the value of the eccentricity, $e = 0.273$, and from this we compute the value of $K = 1/\sqrt{1 - e^2}$ (in logarithms) 0.01682. Thence we find $b'' = Kb' = 5.2494$.

The computation then proceeds as follows:

log a'	0.38828
log b''	0.72011
log 2	0.30103
log sin $(x_1 - x_2)$	9.99993
log $2a'b''$ sin $(x_1 - x_2)$	1.40935
$2a'b''$ sin $(x_1 - x_2)$	25.6653
$(a')^2 + (b'')^2$	33.5342
$(\alpha + \beta)^2$	59.1995
$(\alpha - \beta)^2$	7.8689
$(\alpha + \beta)$	7.6942
$(\alpha - \beta)$	2.8052
2α	10.4994
2β	4.8890
α	5.2497
β	2.4445
log β	0.38819
log α	0.72014
log cos i	9.66805
$\therefore i =$	62°25
$a = \alpha =$	5.25 in.
$=$	0″175
$(a')^2$	5.9780
$(b'')^2$	27.5562
$[(a')^2 + (b'')^2]$	33.5342
α^2	27.5600
β^2	5.9756
$\alpha^2 - (a')^2$	21.5820

$$(\alpha')^2 - \beta^2 \qquad 0.0024$$
$$\log [\alpha^2 - (\alpha')^2] \qquad 1.33409$$
$$\log [(\alpha')^2 - \beta^2] \qquad 7.38021$$
$$\log \tan^2 \omega \qquad 3.95388$$
$$\log \tan \omega \qquad 1.97694$$
$$\therefore \omega = 89°\!.4$$
$$\log \cos i \qquad 9.66805$$
$$\log \tan \omega' \qquad 1.64499$$
$$\omega' \qquad 88°\!.7$$
$$\therefore \Omega = (x_1 - \omega') = 3°\!.9$$

Assembling the elements we have the following:

Glasenapp's Method	Zwiers' Method
$P =$ 12.12 years	12.12 years
$T =$ 1910.10	1910.10
$e =$ 0.276	0.273
$a =$ 0″.176	0″.175
$\omega =$ 269°.9	270°.6
$i =$ 117°.6	117°.75
$\Omega =$ 2.4	3.9

Angles decreasing with the time.

In the formulas, all angles are counted in the direction of increasing position angles, whereas in the notation given on page 78, ω is counted from node to periastron *in the direction of motion of the companion.* Therefore, when as in this system the observed position angles decrease with advancing time, the value for ω derived from the formulae must be subtracted from 360°. In applying the formulas for computing the ephemeris of such a system, the anomalies are counted positive after periastron passage and negative before, just as in the case of direct motion (angles increasing with the time); $\cos i$ is counted as positive, and the angles $(\theta - \Omega)$ are taken in the quadrant $360° - (v + \omega)$. I have found this to be the simplest and most satisfactory method of procedure in every case where the angles decrease with the time. In orbits with direct motion the value of ω is used as given directly by the formulas and the angles $(\theta - \Omega)$ are taken in the same quadrant as the angles $(v + \omega)$.

The orbit of 24 *Aquarii** has been selected as an illustration of Thiele's method, as it is a beautiful example of the power of that

* 24 Aqr = B 1212 = BDS 11125 = ADS 15176.

method in dealing with a rather recalcitrant case. The orbit was computed by W. S. Finsen and is published in *Union Observatory Circular* **81,** 112, 1929. In the list of measures on page 103 the columns give respectively the date, the position angle, the distance, the number of nights, the aperture, the observer, and the residuals (observed minus computed) in angle and in distance. An asterisk attached to the date denotes measures overlooked in Finsen's compilation or not available at the time.

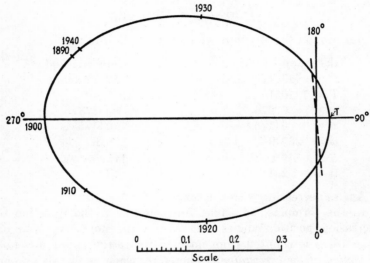

FIG. 5.—The apparent orbit of 24 *Aquarii*.

The angles and distances were plotted against the time and interpolation curves drawn. In the years 1922–1924 the measures are discordant and uncertain; they were therefore disregarded, the areal constant being based on the arc 1891–1918 alone and the three normal places required being taken sufficiently far away from the unreliable part of the interpolation curves.

The angles and distances were read for every second year as shown in the table on page 104.

The numbers in the column headed $d_1 d_2 \Delta\rho$, giving the products of two successive distances and the sector-angle between them, may be considered sufficiently close approximations to the double areas of the sectors (provided that the distance does not vary too greatly within the sector) and should therefore be constant.

MEASURES AND RESIDUALS FOR 24 *Aquarii*

Date	θ_0	ρ_0	n	Tel.	Obs.	$O - C$	
						$\Delta\theta$	$\Delta\rho$
1890.75	254°.5	0″.45	3	36	β	− 2.0	−0″.08
1.75	261.0	0.55	4	36	β	+ 4.0	+0.01
2.40	256.2	0.38	2	19	Sp	− 3.0	−0.16
3.68	260.5	0.55	3	16	HCW	− 0.6	0.00
3.88	262.8	0.59	1	36	Bar	+ 1.4	+0.04
4.82	264.7	0.52	7	36	Bar	+ 1.9	−0.03
4.86	261.5	0.45	3	19	Sp	− 1.3	−0.10
7.81	263.5	0.65	3	36	A	− 3.6	+0.09
7.89	267.4	0.73	1	26	SBn	+ 0.2	+0.17
8.78	269.0	0.49	3	36, 12	A	+ 1.7	−0.07
8.84	269.0	0.54	1	40	β	+ 0.4	−0.02
9.98	282.6	0.5e	1	26	SBn	......	......
1900.67	205.1	0.5e	1	6	Sola	......	......
0.74	271.9	0.55	2	14	Dob	+ 0.7	−0.01
1.54	269.4	0.49	10	28	GrO	− 3.0	−0.07
1.79	274.0	0.55	2	36	A	+ 1.2	−0.01
2.00	273.0	0.57	11	18	Doo	− 0.1	+0.01
3.86	273.8	0.54	2	15	VBs	− 1.9	−0.01
4.54*	273.0	0.48	5	15½	Com	− 3.7	−0.07
4.67	278.6	0.49	1	36	A	+ 1.7	−0.06
8.35	282.6	0.52	3	15½	Com	− 0.1	0.00
8.47	285.5	0.49	4	15	VBs	+ 2.7	−0.03
8.72	279.6	0.68	2	26	Ol	− 3.6	+0.16
8.72	284.8	0.56	2	26	RW	+ 1.6	+0.04
8.73	286.4	0.72	2	26	Neff	+ 3.2	+0.20
9.85	281.1	0.58	3	18	Doo	− 4.1	+0.07
1910.40	282.2	0.51	3	15½	Com	− 3.9	+0.01
0.72	278.2	0.43	5	28	GrO	− 8.5	−0.07
1.20	291.9	0.52	3	6	Dob	+ 4.3	+0.02
1.68	286.8	0.50	3	15	VBs	− 1.6	+0.01
4.00	292.5	0.47	8	28	GrO	− 0.5	+0.01
4.63	291.3	0.47	2	36	A	− 2.7	+0.02
4.65	294.6	0.48	2	15½	Com	+ 0.6	+0.03
4.66*	293.5	0.51	1	40	Lv	− 0.5	+0.06
4.79*	298.1	0.45	3	10½	Lv	+ 3.6	0.00
4.94	311.1	0.41	5	8	Rabe	+16.0	−0.04
6.42	296.5	0.53	3	26	Ol	− 2.0	+0.11
6.62	293.1	0.46	3	12, 40	Lv	− 5.9	+0.04
6.65	301.9	0.41	3	15½	Com	+ 2.9	−0.01
7.69	305.9	0.40	3	15½	Com	+ 3.9	0.00
7.74	294.7	0.42	1	40	VBs	− 7.5	+0.01
1921.66	321.1	0.22	3	36	A	+ 3.3	−0.07
2.81	40 ?	<0.1	1	36	A	......	......
3.62	341.8	0.20	2	40	VBs	+11.3	−0.01
3.85	6.0	0.57	4, 3	30	Bail	......	......
3.88	333.5	0.15	3	13	Mag	+ 0.3	−0.05
4.55	55	0.12	1	36	A	......	−0.04
4.71	6.9	0.22	1	30	Plq	......	+0.07
4.82	350.0	0.16	1	40	VBs	+ 2.1	+0.02
1926.64	190.7	0.20	1	26½	B	−10.0	+0.05
6.69	204.2	0.19	1	36	A	+ 2.9	+0.03
7.74	211.0	0.21	3	26½	B	− 3.6	−0.02
7.74	218.7	0.23	1	26½	φ	+ 4.1	0.00
8.73*	224.6	0.26	1	36	A	+ 2.9	−0.01
8.75	221.2	0.27	4	26½	B	− 0.6	0.00
8.75	222.6	0.26	4	26½	φ	+ 0.8	−0.01
9.46*	228.8	0.28	4	23½	V	+ 3.1	−0.02
9.63*	230.2	0.27	1	36	A	+ 3.8	−0.04
9.86*	227.8	0.26	3	26½	B	+ 0.3	−0.05
1930.48*	234.3	0.29	3	23½	V	+ 4.3	−0.04
1.66*	236.0	0.37	2	36	A	+ 1.6	0.00
2.79*	236.9	0.35	4	26½	B	− 0.9	−0.04
2.79*	238.3	0.30	1	26½	φ	+ 0.5	−0.09

The actual figures show the need of further adjustment. As this can be made both for Δp and for d, it is advisable to plot the polar coordinates as a check that the adjusted positions show a smooth elliptic arc. In general it is found that the major part of the adjustment has to be made in the distances.

The columns on the right of the double rule show the result of the adjustment, which may be regarded as satisfactory.

t	p	Δp	d	$d_1 d_2 \Delta p$	p	Δp	d	$d_1 d_2 \Delta p$
1890	255°5		0″47		255°4		0″53	
		+3°1		+0.71		+3°2		+0.92
2	258.6		0.49		258.6		0.54	
		2.9		0.74		3.0		0.89
4	261.5		0.52		261.6		0.55	
		2.5		0.70		2.9		0.89
6	264.0		0.54		264.5		0.56	
		2.0		0.59		2.8		0.89
8	266.0		0.55		267.3		0.57	
		3.0		0.92		2.7		0.88
1900	269.0		0.56		270.0		0.57	
		3.0		0.94		2.8		0.91
2	272.0		0.56		272.8		0.57	
		3.6		1.15		2.9		0.92
4	275.6		0.57		275.7		0.56	
		2.6		0.85		3.0		0.92
6	278.2		0.57		278.7		0.55	
		3.5		1.14		3.2		0.93
8	281.7		0.57		281.9		0.53	
		3.6		1.11		3.4		0.92
10	285.3		0.54		285.3		0.51	
		3.0		0.84		3.6		0.90
12	288.3		0.52		288.9		0.49	
		3.9		0.99		4.0		0.90
14	292.2		0.49		292.9		0.46	
		4.8		1.06		4.6		0.91
16	297.0		0.45		297.5		0.43	
		6.1		1.10		5.5		0.92
18	303.1		0.40		303.0		0.39	
				Mean +0.917				Mean +0.907

The mean value of $d_1 d_2 \Delta p$, +0.907, has now to be divided by the interval in time, here 2, and by 57.3 to reduce Δp to radians. We obtain for the double areal constant: $c = +0.007914$.

As the result of a similar adjustment Finsen found $c = +0.00781$ which he supplemented by the three normal places

1892.00	258°6	0.″54
1910.00	285°3	0.″51
1928.00	217°0	0.″24

The above adjustment, which is equivalent to, though experts in the method regard it as considerably simpler than, the construction of the apparent orbit in the graphical methods, has been given rather fully, for, as noted in describing the method, it is the crux of the problem. It is at this stage that the computer's judgment, experience, and knowledge of the reliability of the heterogeneous observational material come into play; once the three normal places and the double areal constant have been found, the derivation of the orbital elements is simple and straightforward.

It sometimes happens that the period is known *a priori* (from the recurrence of position angle) while the character of the apparent orbit, or large gaps in the observed arc, cause difficulties in the determination of c. It is therefore worth remembering that in Thiele's fundamental formula

$$t_q - t_p - \frac{\Delta_{p,q}}{c} = \frac{1}{\mu}[E_q - E_p - \sin(E_q - E_p)]$$

we may regard either μ or c as unknown.

Adopting Finsen's normal places and c so as to obtain his elements, the computation proceeds as follows:

$t_1 = 1892.00$ $x_1 = -0.107$ $y_1 = -0.529$ $\Delta_{1,2} = +0.1240$
$t_2 = 1910.00$ $x_2 = +0.135$ $y_2 = -0.492$ $\Delta_{2,3} = -0.1139$
$t_3 = 1928.00$ $x_3 = -0.192$ $y_3 = -0.144$ $\Delta_{1,3} = -0.0862$

$$\frac{\Delta_{1,2}}{c} = +15.88 \qquad u - \sin u \qquad = 2.12\mu$$

$$\frac{\Delta_{2,3}}{c} = -14.58 \qquad v - \sin v \qquad = 32.58\mu$$

$$\frac{\Delta_{1,3}}{c} = -11.04 \qquad (u+v) - \sin(u+v) = 47.04\mu$$

In the approximations on page 106 for μ the table for $x - \sin x$ given in *Union Observatory Circular* No. 86 is used; it is helpful to plot the differences found in the last row against the values of μ in the first row, as after three approximations have been made the resulting differences frequently define the curve so well, that the fourth approximation becomes final.

As we expect the period to be of the order of 50 years ($\mu = 0.126$), we try $\mu = 0.12$ and $\mu = 0.13$:

μ	0.12	0.13	0.122	0.1224
$u - \sin u$	0.2544	0.2756	0.2586	0.2595
$v - \sin v$	3.9096	4.2354	3.9748	3.9878
$(u + v) - \sin(u + v)$	5.6448	6.1152	5.7389	5.7577
u	67.51	69.43	67.90	67.98
v	202.27	212.17	204.22	204.61
Sum	269.78	281.60	272.12	272.59
$(u + v)$	266.25	301.54	271.53	272.66
Difference	+3.53	−19.94	+0.59	−0.07

and find

$$\mu = 0.1224 \qquad u = 67°98 \qquad v = 204°61$$

Finsen, working to another decimal place, obtained:

$$\mu = 0.12241 \qquad u = 68°022 \qquad v = 204°642 \qquad \begin{array}{l} \text{Final difference} \\ -0°002 \end{array}$$

and hence for period and mean motion:

$$P = 51.33 \text{ years} \qquad n = 7°0134$$

Further

$$e \sin E_2 = -0.5598 \qquad e \cos E_2 = -0.7178$$
$$e = 0.9102 \qquad E_2 = 217°95$$
$$E_1 = E_2 - u = 149°93 \qquad E_3 = E_2 + v = 62°59$$

From Kepler's equation, $\begin{cases} M_1 \ 123°80 \\ M_2 \ 250°02 \\ M_3 \ 16°29 \end{cases}$

all giving $T = 1925.68$.

$$X_1 = -1.7754 \qquad Y_1 = +0.2078$$
$$X_2 = -1.6985 \qquad Y_2 = -0.2550$$
$$X_3 = -0.4492 \qquad Y_3 = +0.3679$$

From the first and third normal places

$$A = -0''0011, \ B = +0''2939, \ F = -0''5233, \ G = -0''0317.$$

These values give

$$x_2 = +0''135 \qquad y_2 = -0''491$$

for the second normal place, a satisfactory check.

Though the conflicting results obtained in the years 1922–1924 were entirely disregarded in deriving the orbit, partly because it was not even possible to assign the quadrants with certainty, the residuals show that the measures by Aitken in 1921, Maggini in 1923, and van Biesbroeck in 1923 and 1924 are satisfactorily represented. This success of the orbit in bridging the large gap from 300° to 200°, a sector of 260° in all, inspires confidence in the elements found.

$$A = -0.0011 \qquad B = +0.2939$$
$$G = -0.0317 \qquad F = -0.5233$$
$$A + G = -0.0328 \qquad B - F = +0.8172$$
$$A - G = +0.0306 \qquad -B - F = +0.2294$$

$$\cos (\omega + \Omega) \text{ negative, sine positive}$$
$$\cos (\omega - \Omega) \text{ positive, sine positive}$$

$$\tan (\omega + \Omega) = \frac{+0.8172}{-0.0328} = -24.9 \qquad \text{second quadrant}$$

$$\tan (\omega - \Omega) = \frac{+0.2294}{+0.0306} = + 7.49 \qquad \text{first} \qquad ''$$

$$\omega + \Omega = \ 92°30$$
$$\omega - \Omega = \ 82.40$$

$$\omega = 87°35 \qquad \Omega = 4°95 \qquad \qquad 2\omega = 174.70$$
$$2\Omega = \quad 9.90$$

If Ω were found to be in the third or fourth quadrant, 180° should be added to (or subtracted from) both ω and Ω.

$$\cos (\omega + \Omega) = -0.0401 \qquad \sin (\omega + \Omega) = +0.9992$$
$$\cos (\omega - \Omega) = +0.1323 \qquad \sin (\omega - \Omega) = +0.9912$$

$$\tan^2 \frac{i}{2} = \frac{+0.2294}{+0.8172} \cdot \frac{+0.9992}{+0.9912} = +0.2830 \qquad \tan \frac{i}{2} = \pm 0.5320$$

$$\frac{i}{2} = \pm 28°01 \qquad i = \pm 56°02 \qquad \cos \frac{i}{2} = +0.8828$$

$$a = \frac{B - F}{2 \sin(\omega + \Omega)\cos^2 \frac{i}{2}} = \frac{0.8172}{2 \times 0.9992 \times 0.7793} = 0''525$$

Assembling the elements in the usual notation and the Thiele-Innes constants, we have:

$$P = 51.33 \text{ years}$$
$$T = 1925.68$$
$$a = 0''.525$$
$$e = 0.9102$$
$$\omega = 87°.35$$
$$i = \pm 56°.02$$
$$\Omega = 4°.95$$
$$A = -0.0011$$
$$B = +0.2939$$
$$F = -0.5233$$
$$G = -0.0317$$

CONSTRUCTION OF THE APPARENT ELLIPSE FROM THE ELEMENTS

It is sometimes desirable to be able to construct the apparent ellipse from the elements of the true orbit. This construction is easily and quickly effected in the following manner:

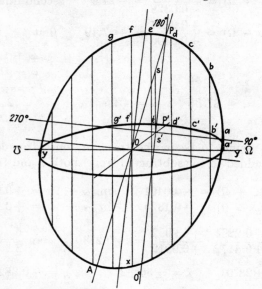

FIG. 6.—The true and apparent orbits of a double star. (*After See.*)

Take the point O (Fig. 6), at the intersection of two rectangular axes, OX and OY, as the common center of the true and projected orbits. Draw the line $O\Omega$ making an angle equal to Ω with the line OX, counting from 0°. Lay off the angle ω from the line $O\Omega$, starting from the extremity Ω between 0° and 180°

and *proceeding in the direction of the companion's motion* (clockwise, that is, if the position angles decrease with the time, counterclockwise, if they increase with the time). This will give the direction of the line of apsides, AOP, in the true orbit. Upon this line lay off OS, equal to ae, the product of the eccentricity and the semiaxis of the orbit, using any convenient scale, and OP and OA, each equal to a. The point S lies between O and P, and P is to be taken in the quadrant given by applying ω to Ω as described above. Having thus the major axis and the eccentricity, the true ellipse is constructed in the usual manner.

Now divide the diameter $\mho O\Omega$ of this ellipse into any convenient number of parts, *making the points of division symmetrical with respect to O*, and draw chords $b\beta b'$, etc., perpendicular to the line of nodes. Measure the segments βb, $\beta b'$, etc., and multiply the results by $\cos i$. The products will evidently be the lengths of the corresponding segments βb_1, βb_2, etc., in the projected ellipse, and the curve drawn through the points b_1, c_1, d_1, . . . will be the desired apparent orbit.

To find the position of the principal star in the apparent ellipse draw through S a line perpendicular to the line of nodes, and on it lay off the length $ae \sin \omega \cos i$ from the line of nodes. This will give S', the point required. Lines through S' parallel to OX and OY will be the rectangular axes to which position angles in the apparent orbit are referred, and the position angle of the companion at any particular epoch may be obtained by laying off the observed position angle. The line OS' extended to meet the ellipse defines P', the projection of the point of periastron passage.

DIFFERENTIAL CORRECTIONS

If sufficient care is exercised in the construction of the apparent ellipse, methods like those described will, as a rule, give a preliminary orbit that will satisfy the observed positions within reasonable limits and that will approximate the real orbit closely enough to serve as the basis for a least squares solution. It should be emphasized that a satisfactory representation of the observed positions does not necessarily imply a correct orbit when the arc covered by the observations is comparatively small. The percentage of error inherent in double star measures is so great that, if the observed arc is less than 180°, it will generally be possible to draw several very different ellipses each of which will satisfy the data of observation about equally well. *In general, it is not worth while to compute the orbit of a double star until the observed arc not only exceeds 180°, but also defines both ends of the apparent ellipse.*

It may not be amiss to add a few words on the practice, all too common, of giving a fictitious appearance of accuracy to the values of the preliminary elements by the use of unwarranted decimals. To give the angular elements, the eccentricity, or the semimajor axis to three or four decimals when even the first decimal is uncertain, or the period and time of periastron passage to the second or third decimal when the latter may be in doubt by years and the former by decades, or in extreme cases, by centuries, adds nothing to the real accuracy of the results and does not inspire confidence in them.

Many computers are content with a preliminary orbit; but it is advisable to correct these elements by the method of least squares whenever the data are sufficient for an investigation of the systematic errors of observation.

The position angle is a function of the six elements

$$\Omega, i, \omega, e \, (= \sin \phi), T \text{ and } \mu = \frac{360°}{P}$$

and the required differential coefficients for the equations of condition can be computed with all necessary accuracy from the approximate formula

$$A\Delta\Omega + B\Delta\omega + C\Delta i + D\Delta\varphi + F\Delta M + G\Delta\mu + (C - O) = 0 \quad (51)$$

where $\Delta\Omega$, $\Delta\omega$, etc., are the desired corrections to the elements, and $(C - O)$ is the difference between the position angle computed from the preliminary elements and the observed angle and A, B, etc., are the partial differential coefficients. The eccentric angle φ, defined by $\sin \varphi = e$, and the mean anomaly $M \, [= \mu(t - T)]$ are substituted for the eccentricity (e) and the time of periastron passage (T).

The corresponding equation for the distances may be written

$$h\Delta a + b\Delta\omega + c\Delta i + d\Delta\varphi + f\Delta M + g\Delta\mu + (C - O) = 0 \quad (52)$$

the difference between the computed and observed distance forming the absolute term.

The values of the partial differential coefficients are derived from the equations for θ and ρ (pages 79, 80). It has been the common practice to base the corrections to all the elements except the semimajor axis, solely upon the residuals for position angle, but it is sounder, theoretically at least, and in many cases practically as well, to utilize the residuals both in angle and in distance for the corrections to the five elements ω, i, φ, M and μ by combining the two sets of equations of condition after eliminating $\Delta\Omega$ from the first set and Δa from the second. If this combination is made, the term $(C - O)$ in the equations for position angle must be expressed in circular measure, which is accomplished by multiplying the angle residuals by the factor $\rho/57.3$.

Comstock has put the expressions for the differential coefficients into the form given below. The residuals in angle are assumed to be expressed in circular measure, and the expressions are so formulated that the solution of the equations of condition by the method of least squares will give the correction to the semimajor axis in seconds of arc, and those to the other elements in degrees.

Introduce the auxiliary quantities m, k and σ defined by

$$m = \rho/57.3 = (8.2419)\rho,$$

$$k = (2 + \sin \varphi \cos v) \sin E, \quad \text{and}$$

$$\sigma = -m \tan i \sin (\theta - \Omega) \cos (\theta - \Omega).$$

The differential coefficients for the terms given in the central column are:

Angle	Terms	Distance
$A = +m$	$\Delta\Omega$	
$B = +m\left(\dfrac{r}{\rho}\right)^2 \cos i$	$\Delta\omega$	$b = +\sigma \sin i$
$C = +\sigma$	Δi	$c = +\sigma \tan (\theta - \Omega)$
$D = +B\left(\dfrac{a}{r}\right)k$	$\Delta\varphi$	$d = +b\left(\dfrac{a}{r}\right)k - m\left(\dfrac{a}{r}\right) \cos \varphi \cos v$
$F = -B\left(\dfrac{a}{r}\right)^2 \cos \varphi$	ΔM	$f = -b\left(\dfrac{a}{r}\right)^2 \cos \varphi - m\left(\dfrac{a}{r}\right)^2 \sin \varphi \sin E$
$G = -F(t - T)$	$\Delta\mu$	$g = -f(t - T)$
	Δa	$h = +\dfrac{\rho}{a}$

If the Thiele-Innes constants A, B, F, G, have been computed, the following method will be found convenient, particularly if tables for X and Y are available.* The equations of condition take the form

$$\left.\begin{array}{l} \Delta x = X\Delta A + Y\Delta F + P_x\Delta e + Q_x n\Delta T + R_x\Delta n \\ \Delta y = X\Delta B + Y\Delta G + P_y\Delta e + Q_y n\Delta T + R_y\Delta n \end{array}\right\} \quad (53)$$

where

$$P_x = +A\frac{dX}{de} + F\frac{dY}{de}$$

$$P_y = +B\frac{dX}{de} + G\frac{dY}{de}$$

$$Q_x = -A\frac{dX}{dM} - F\frac{dY}{dM}$$

$$Q_y = -B\frac{dX}{dM} - G\frac{dY}{dM}$$

$$R_x = -(t - T)Q_x$$

$$R_y = -(t - T)Q_y$$

From the formulas already given,

$$M = E - e \sin E$$

$$X = \cos E - e$$

$$Y = \sqrt{1 - e^2} \sin E \left(= \frac{r}{a} \sin v \right)$$

$$e = \sin \varphi, \qquad \sqrt{1 - e^2} = \cos \varphi$$

we have, by differentiation,

$$\left.\begin{array}{l} \dfrac{dX}{de} = -0.01\left[1 + \dfrac{Y^2}{\cos^2 \varphi(\cos^2 \varphi - X \sin \varphi)}\right] \\[2mm] \dfrac{dY}{de} = +0.01\dfrac{XY}{\cos^2 \varphi(\cos^2 \varphi - X \sin \varphi)} \\[2mm] \dfrac{dX}{dM} = -0.017453\dfrac{Y}{\cos \varphi(\cos^2 \varphi - X \sin \varphi)} \\[2mm] \dfrac{dY}{dM} = +0.017453\dfrac{\cos \varphi(X + \sin \varphi)}{\cos^2 \varphi - X \sin \varphi} \end{array}\right\} \quad (54)$$

the units being 0.01 for Δe and $1°$ for ΔM.

The question of algebraic sign is always an important one in computing differential coefficients. For the present formulas van den Bos gives the following rules:

dX/de is always negative,

---

* Such tables have been issued, in an Appendix to *Un. Obs. Circ.* 71. The method described is given in *Circs.* 68 and 86.

dY/de is positive when X and Y have the same sign, negative when they have opposite signs,

dX/dM has the sign contrary to that of Y,

dY/dM is negative only when X is negative and numerically greater than e.

These rules follow from the fact that $\cos \varphi$ and the expression $(\cos^2 \varphi - X \sin \varphi)$—which is simply a transformation of the expression $1 - e \cos E$ derived by differentiating Kepler's equation—are always positive, and, for the last two formulas, from simple geometrical considerations. The sign of X is given directly in the tables referred to; that of Y is always the same as that of M, the mean anomaly.

The special advantage of the method arises from the fact that the values of dX/de, etc., can be read off directly from the tables of X and Y, for the value of the differential coefficient differs from the mean of the preceding and following first difference, in the tables (taken horizontally, for de and vertically for dM), by only one-sixth of the third difference, a negligible quantity. If these tables are not available, the differential expressions dX/de etc., may be computed from the formulas given above, special attention being given to the units for Δe and ΔM and to the algebraic signs.

SPECIAL CASES

All methods based upon the construction of the apparent ellipse fail when the inclination of the orbit plane is (within the limit of error of observation) 90°; for the apparent ellipse is then reduced to a straight line and the observed motion is entirely in the distance, the position angle remaining constant except for the change of 180° after each occultation or apparent merging of the two components into a single image. Such a limiting case is actually presented by 42 *Comae Berenices* ($\Sigma 1728$). Many other pairs are known in which the orbit inclination is only slightly smaller.

In the limiting case, the elements, except Ω which is obviously given by the observed position angle, and i (90°), must be derived entirely from the observed distances; in other cases special methods may be devised which will vary with the peculiarities of the observed motion but which will depend in large part upon the observed distance.

The first orbit for 42 *Comae Berenices* was published by Otto Struve in 1875,* but his paper contains no statement as to the methods used in obtaining his preliminary set of elements, and, in 1918, I was unable to find in print any solution of the problem. Simple graphical methods for finding the elements P, T, and e from the curve of observed distances at once suggested themselves; but methods for deriving the values of a and ω were not immediately apparent. In the first edition of this book I outlined a method for obtaining them which Prof. F. R. Moulton had kindly sent me in manuscript. More recently other methods have been published by Prof. Kurt Laves,† Dr. F. C. Henroteau‡

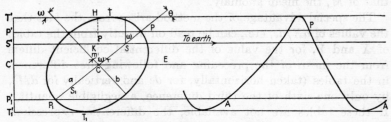

Fig. 7.—Apparent and true orbits and interpolating curve of observed distances for a binary system in which the inclination is 90°.

and Prof. R. T. Crawford.§ The methods by Laves and by Crawford are the simplest ones, and the latter will be given here in conjunction with the methods for deriving the elements P, T, and e.

In Fig. 7 let the ellipse represent the true orbit and the line $T'C'T_1'$, its projection upon the plane perpendicular to the line of sight. Let the curve APA be the interpolating curve of observed distances, obtained in the usual way by plotting the distances against the times and drawing the most probable smooth curve to represent the plotted points.

The revolution period may be read directly from this curve and the accuracy of its determination will increase with the number of observed revolutions.

In the true orbit, let S be the position of the primary star and C, the center of the ellipse. Then the points C' and S' on the projected orbit are known for $T'C'$ ($= T_1'C'$) must be half the

* *Mon. Not. R.A.S.*, **35**, 367, 1875.

† *A.J.* **37**, 97, 1926.

‡ *Handbuch der Astrophysik*, **6**, 338, 1928.

§ *Lick Obs. Bull.* **14**, 6, 1928.

amplitude of the curve of distances and S' must be the apparent position of the primary star.

The points on the curve of distances which correspond to the points P and P_1 of the true orbit must be separated by exactly half of the revolution period and their distances from the line $C'CE$ must be equal in length and of opposite sign. The point corresponding to periastron, P, must lie on the same side of this line as S', and on the steeper branch of the curve as the rate of change of distance is greater near periastron than near apastron. In practice these two points are readily found by cutting a rectangular slip of paper to a width equal to half that of the period on the adopted scale and sliding it along the curve until the edges, kept perpendicular to the line $C'CE$, cut equal ordinates (with respect to $C'CE$) on the curve; or we may adopt Laves's suggestion to "draw the central axis of the graph and make a tracing of the time graph of distances, turn it through 180° about the central time axis and then advance the tracing by half the period of the orbit. Of the four points of intersection of graph and tracing it is easy to find that pair which is separated by half the period." In either of these ways the positions of the points P' and P_1' are obtained.

Since ratios are not altered in the projection we have

$$e = \frac{C'S'}{C'P'}. \tag{55}$$

To obtain the two remaining elements a and ω, Crawford makes use of a relation involving the perpendicular from the center of the ellipse on a tangent to the ellipse. In the figure let CH be such a perpendicular and call its length p. Let ω (which is here our element ω) be the angle the tangent line makes with the minor axis. Then, if a and b are the major and minor semiaxes, respectively, from the properties of the conic it can be shown that

$$p^2 = a^2 \cos^2 \omega + b^2 \sin^2 \omega$$

which can be written

$$p^2 = a^2 - (a^2 - b^2) \sin^2 \omega = a^2 - a^2 e^2 \sin^2 \omega. \tag{56}$$

But, from the figure,

$$CK \equiv m = CS \cos \omega = ae \cos \omega$$

Hence

$$\cos \omega = \frac{m}{ae} \qquad (57)$$

and

$$\sin^2 \omega = 1 - \frac{m^2}{a^2 e^2} \qquad (58)$$

Substituting (58) into (56) and solving for a, we have

$$a = \sqrt{\frac{p^2 - m^2}{1 - e^2}} \qquad (59)$$

p is $C'T'$, and m is $C'S'$, both of which are known.

The order of solution is, then, Eqs. (55), (59), and (57) which give e, a, and ω, respectively.

If the major axis is directed toward the Earth, the points C', P', and S' coincide and $\omega = 90°$. Equation (55) then becomes indeterminate, but at the same time $p = b$ and $m = 0$. Hence, from Eq. (59) we have

$$a = \sqrt{\frac{b^2}{1 - e^2}}. \qquad (60)$$

To determine e, let τ be the ratio of the intervals of time from elongation to elongation such that $\tau < 1$. Then from the law of areas we have τ equal to the ratio of the area described by the radius vector in the true orbit in the shorter interval to the area described by the radius vector in the longer interval, or

$$\tau = \frac{\frac{1}{2}\pi ab - abe}{\frac{1}{2}\pi ab + abe} = \frac{\frac{1}{2}\pi - e}{\frac{1}{2}\pi + e}$$

whence

$$e = \frac{\pi}{2} \cdot \frac{1 - \tau}{1 + \tau} \qquad (61)$$

The time of periastron passage, T, is the middle instant of the shorter interval between two consecutive elongation times. If the intervals are all equal, $\tau = 1$, $e = 0$, and the orbit is a circle, in which case the elements ω and T lose significance.

When a preliminary set of elements has been derived, improved values may be computed by the method of least squares, using

Comstock's expressions for the differential coefficients in the equation for distance.

THE ORBIT OF ε EQUULEI

An excellent example of an orbit whose computation was made possible by taking advantage of the special features of the observed motion is that of ε *Equulei,* published by Russell in 1917.* The apparent orbit of this system is an extremely narrow and elongated ellipse. Fortunately the double star was discovered by Struve in 1835, when the angular separation was only 0″.35. In later years the companion moved out to a maximum elongation of 1″.05 and then in again until, in 1917, the pair could not be resolved by any existing telescope. Plotting the distances (using mean places) against the times, Russell noted that the curve was practically symmetrical with respect to the maximum separation point. It follows that the line of apsides in the true orbit must be approximately coincident with the line of nodes, or that $\omega = 0$. Further, the mean of the position angles for a few years on either side of the time of elongation gives a preliminary value for the angle Ω, and the elongation time itself is the epoch of apastron passage, which may be taken in place of the epoch of periastron as one of the orbit elements. It is also apparent that the inclination of the orbit is very high and a preliminary value for this element may be assumed. This leaves the three elements, a, e, and P, which Russell finds as follows: Let

y_1 = the maximum elongation distance
T'' = the corresponding epoch (*i.e.,* apastron)
y'' = the distance at any other time t''
E = the corresponding eccentric anomaly in the true orbit.

Then we have

$$a(1 + e) = y_1, \qquad a(\cos E - e) = -y''$$
$$M = E - e \cos E, \qquad \text{and} \qquad (t'' - T) = 180° - M$$

which determine a and P in terms of e.

Assume values of e and compute a and P, repeating the process until those values result which represent the curve of the observed distances.

The preliminary elements obtained by these processes Russell corrected differentially, a, e, T and μ from the observed distances,

* *A.J.* **30**, 123, 1917.

i and Ω from the observed angles; ω (= 0) being assumed as definitely known,*

SYSTEMS IN WHICH ONE COMPONENT IS INVISIBLE

Luminosity, Bessel said long ago, is not a necessary attribute of stellar mass, and it may happen that one component of a double star system is so feebly luminous as not to be visible in existing telescopes. If the orbit is one of short period and the inclination of its plane sufficiently high, the system may be detected by the spectroscope, by the methods to be discussed in the following chapter. In other instances the companion's presence may be revealed by a periodic variation in the bright star's proper motion, the path described by it upon the celestial sphere becoming a cycloid instead of the arc of a great circle. A system of the latter type is most readily detected when the proper motion is large, and it is of course essential that the motion be accurately determined.

Variable proper motion was actually recognized in the stars *Sirius* and *Procyon*, nearly a century ago, and was explained by Bessel as the effect of the attraction of such invisible companions. Orbits, referring the motion of the bright star to the center of gravity of a binary system, were thereupon computed for these stars by C. A. F. Peters and A. Auwers. Bessel's hypothesis was proven to be correct by the subsequent discovery of a faint companion to *Sirius* by Alvan G. Clark (in 1861), and of a still fainter companion to *Procyon* by Schaeberle (in 1896). The relative orbit of the companion to *Sirius* has been computed from the micrometer measures, and the elements are consistent with those determined from the proper motion of the bright star. There is no question but that this will also prove to be the case in the system of *Procyon* when the micrometer measures permit an independent determination of its orbit.

Dark companions to β. *Orionis*, α *Hydrae*, and α *Virginis* have also been suspected from supposed irregularities in the proper motions, but closer examination of the data has not verified the suspicion. Since cases of this kind will probably always be very exceptional, the formulas for their investiga-

---

* More recent observations indicate the need of revision of Russell's elements.

tion will not be considered here. Those who are interested in their development are referred to the original memoirs.*

The presence of invisible companions in several well-known double star systems has also been revealed by the observed periodic variations in the motion of one of the visible components. In one of these, ε *Hydrae*, the primary star was later found to be a very close pair whose components complete a revolution in about fifteen years, and Seeliger† has shown that the orbital motion in this close pair fully accounts for the irregularities observed in the motion of the more distant companion. Another of these systems, ζ *Cancri*, consists of three bright stars, two of which revolve about a common center in a period of approximately 60 years, while the third star revolves with this binary system in a much larger orbit. Seeliger has shown that the irregularities observed in the apparent motion of this third star may be explained on the hypothesis that it is accompanied by an invisible star, the two revolving about a common center in circular orbits with a period of 18 years. The system then, would, be a quadruple one.

Again, Nörlund, in the course of his investigation of the orbit of ξ *Ursae Majoris*, in 1905, discovered a perturbation of 1.8 years period with an amplitude of 0."05. He attributed this to the presence of an invisible companion to the brighter component, the two bodies revolving in an orbit inclined nearly 90° to the plane of projection. Such a companion had, as a matter of fact, been discovered by Wright, *five years earlier*, from the variable radial velocity of the bright star, but Nörlund was unaware of the discovery when he announced his result. Van den Bos‡ has made a complete investigation of this triple system,§ utilizing

---

* Bessel, *A. N.* **22**, 145, 169, 185, 1845.
  Peters, *A. N.* **32**, 1, 17, 33, 49, 1851.
  Auwers, *A. N.* **63**, 273, 1865 and *Untersuchungen über veränderliche Eigenbewegung*, 1. Theil, Königsberg, 1862; 2. Theil, Leipzig, 1868. See also *A. N.* **129**, 185, 1892.

  † *A. N.* **173**, 321, 1906.

  ‡ *Mem. de l'Acad. Roy. des Sciences et des Lettres de Danemark. Sec. des Sci.* 8ᵐᵉ Serie, **12**, No. 2, 1928.

  § It is really a quadruple system, for an invisible companion to the fainter visual component was discovered in 1918 from spectrograms taken at the Lick Observatory. Berman's orbit (*Lick Obs. Bull.* **15**, 109, 1931), however, shows that the revolution period of this pair is only 3.98 days. No sensible perturbation in the visual orbit can be produced by it.

both the micrometric and photographic measures of the bright pair and the spectrographic observations of the primary star and its invisible companion. There are irregularities in the observed motion of 70 *Ophiuchi* which have been regarded as due to the perturbations produced by a third body, but a really satisfactory solution of the orbit has not yet been published. Finally, we may refer to Comstock's investigation* of the orbital motion in the system ζ *Herculis* from which he concludes that small irregularities in the areal velocity of the bright pair may be represented as the effect of an invisible companion to one component, having a periodic time of 18 years and an amplitude less than 0."1. Comstock, however, points out that when the systematic errors of the observers are determined and allowed for, the orbit, without the assumption of a third body, "satisfies the observations within the limits of error commonly deemed satisfactory." The paper is an excellent example of the method by which systematic errors should be investigated in the computation of a definitive double star orbit.

It is probable that the invisible companion in such a system as that of ζ *Herculis* revolves, like the bright components, in an elliptic, rather than a circular orbit; and it is not at all improbable that the plane of this orbit is inclined at a greater or less angle to the plane of the orbit of the visible system. To determine the eccentricity and the inclination, however, would greatly complicate the problem and the precision of the observational data is not sufficient to warrant such refinements unless, as in the case of ξ *Ursae Majoris*, spectrographic observations are also available. In practice, it has been found satisfactory, in general, to assume that the invisible body moves in a circle in the plane of the orbit of the visible stars of the system. This assumption leaves but two elements to be determined, the period and the radius or semiamplitude, and the formulas for these are quite simple. Comstock's formulas for the companion in the system of ζ *Herculis*, for example, are as follows:

Let θ, ρ, represent the polar coordinates of the visible companion referred to the primary star; ψ, r the corresponding coordinates of the center of gravity of the assumed system (*i.e.*, the system comprised of the secondary bright star and its dark companion) referred to the same origin; and v, a, the coordinates of the visible companion referred to the center of

* *A. J.* **30**, 139, 1917.

mass of itself and its dark companion. Then we shall have from the geometrical relations involved,

$$\rho^2 = r^2 + a^2 + 2ar \cos (v - \psi)$$

$$\theta = \psi + \frac{a}{\rho} \sin (v - \psi) \tag{62}$$

If we assume that a/r and r/ρ are quantities whose squares are negligibly small, we have by differentiation

$$\rho^2 \frac{d\theta}{dt} = r^2 \frac{d\psi}{dt} + ar \cos(v - \psi)\left(\frac{dv}{dt} + \frac{d\psi}{dt}\right) - a \sin(v - \psi)\frac{dr}{dt} \tag{63}$$

Since the assumed system is circular, a and dv/dt are constant quantities. $r^2 \dfrac{d\psi}{dt}$ is also a constant, and a is so small that, in the second member of the equation, we may write θ for ψ and ρ in place of r without sensible error. If, further, for brevity, we put $d\psi/dt = K/\rho^2$ and $k = dv/dt$, the equation takes the form

$$\rho^2 \frac{d\theta}{dt} = K + a\left(k\rho + \frac{K}{\rho}\right)\cos(v - \theta) - a \sin(v - \theta)\frac{d\rho}{dt} \tag{64}$$

RECTILINEAR MOTION

The relative motion in some double stars is apparently rectilinear and it is desirable to have criteria which shall enable us to decide whether this results from the fact that the orbit is a very elongated ellipse, or from the fact that the two stars are unrelated and are changing their relative positions by reason of the difference in their proper motions. One excellent test, which has been applied by Lewis to many of the Struve stars, is to plot the path of the companion relative to the primary and note whether its motion *along that path* is uniform or whether it becomes more rapid as the distance between it and the primary diminishes. In the former case the two stars are independent, in the latter, they are physically related.

A more rigorous test is the one applied, for example, by Schlesinger and Alter* to the motion of 61 *Cygni*. If the motion is uniform and in a straight line, the position angles and distances of the companion referred to the primary may be represented by the equations

* *Publ. Allegheny Obs.* **2**, 13, 1910.

$$\left. \begin{aligned} \rho^2 &= a^2 + (t - T)^2 m^2 \\ \tan(\theta - \phi) &= \frac{m}{a}(t - T) \end{aligned} \right\} \quad (65)$$

in which a is the perpendicular distance from the primary, considered as fixed, to the path of the companion; ϕ is the position angle of this perpendicular; T, the time when the companion was at the foot of the perpendicular, and m, the annual relative rectilinear motion of the companion. Approximate values for these four quantities may be obtained from a plot of the observations and residuals may then be formed

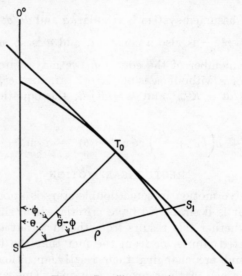

FIG. 8.—Rectilinear motion.

by comparing the positions computed from the formulas with the observations. If these residuals exhibit no systematic character, rectilinear motion may be assumed; if they show a systematic course a closer examination is in order to decide whether this is due to chance or to orbital motion. In the latter case, the indicated curve must be concave to the primary and the systematic run of the residuals should be quite uniform. In any event, a least squares solution may be made to obtain more precise values for the quantities a, ϕ, T and m. For this purpose, differentiate Eqs. (65) and introduce the values $\sin(\theta - \phi) = \dfrac{m(t - T)}{\rho}$, $\cos(\theta - \phi) = \dfrac{a}{\rho}$ (see Fig. 8); we thus obtain the equations of condition in the form given by Schlesinger and Alter:

$$\left.\begin{array}{l} -\cos (\theta - \phi_0)\Delta a - \sin (\theta - \phi_0)(t - T_0)\Delta m \\ \qquad\qquad + \sin (\theta - \phi_0)m_0\Delta T + \Delta\rho = v_\rho \\ +\sin (\theta - \phi_0)\Delta a - \cos (\theta - \phi_0)(t - T_0)\Delta m \\ \qquad\qquad + \cos (\theta - \phi_0)m_0\Delta T - \rho\Delta\phi + \rho\Delta\theta = v_\theta \end{array}\right\} \quad (66)$$

in which the subscript $_0$ indicates the preliminary values of the elements, $\Delta\rho$ and $\Delta\theta$ the deviations from the approximate straight line, and v_ρ and v_θ the residuals from the definitive values of the elements.

References

In addition to the papers cited in the footnotes to the chapter, the student of double star orbit methods will find the following of interest:

KLINKERFUES: Über die Berechnung der Bahnen der Doppelsterne, *A.N.* **42**, 81, 1855.

———: Allgemeine Methode zur Berechnung von Doppelsternbahnen, *A.N.*, **47**, 353, 1858.

THIELE: Über einen geometrischen Satz zur Berechnung von Doppelsternbahnen, u. s. w., *A.N.*, **52**, 39, 1860.

———: Undersøgelse af Omløbsbevaegelsen i Dobbelstjernesystemet γ Virginis, Kjøbenhavn, 1866.

———: Neue Methode zur Berechnung von Doppelsternbahnen., *A.N.*, **104**, 245, 1883.

SEELIGER: Untersuchungen über die Bewegungsverhältnisse in dem dreifachen Stern-system ζ Cancri, Wien, 1881.

———: Fortgesetzte Untersuchungen über das mehrfache Stern-system ζ Cancri, München, 1888.

SCHORR: Untersuchungen über die Bewegungsverhältnisse in dem dreifachen Stern-system ξ Scorpii, München, 1889.

SCHWARZSCHILD: Methode zur Bahnbestimmung der Doppelsterne, *A.N.*, **124**, 215, 1890.

RAMBAUT: On a Geometrical Method of Finding the Most Probable Apparent Orbit of a Double Star, *Proc. Roy. Dublin Society*, **7**, 95, 1891.

HOWARD: A Graphical Method for Determining the Apparent Orbits of Binary Stars, *Astronomy and Astrophysics*, **13**, 425, 1894.

HALL: The Orbits of Double Stars, *A.J.*, **14**, 89, 1895.

SEE: Evolution of the Stellar Systems, Vol. 1, 1896.

LEUSCHNER: On the Universality of the Law of Gravitation, *University of California Chronicle*, **18**, No. 2, 1916.

ANDRÉ: Traité d'Astronomie Stellaire, Vol. 2.

Also the chapters on double star orbits in such works as Klinkerfues-Buchholz, *Theoretische Astronomie;* Bauschinger, *Die Bahnbestimmung der Himmelskörper;* Crossley, Gledhill, and Wilson, *A Handbook of Double Stars.*

DOBERCK, W.: On the Orbit of ξ *Bootis, A.N.* **214**, 89, 1921.

COMSTOCK, G. C.: On the Determination of Double Star Orbits from Incomplete Data, *A.J.*, **33**, 139, 163, 1921.

MEYERMANN, B.: Eine neue graphische und eine halbgraphische Methode zur Bestimmung von Doppelsternbahnen, *A.N.* **215**, 179, 1922.

————: Zur Bestimmung von Doppelsternbahnen, *A.N.* **228**, 49, 1926.

DAWSON, B. H.: Provisional Elements of the Binary Star h5011 with a Note on the Method Employed, *A.J.* **36**, 181, 1926.

NASSAU, J. J., and P. D. WILKINS: Graphical Determinations of Orbits of Visual Binary Stars, *A.J.* **38**, 56, 1928.

HENROTEAU, F. C.: Double and Multiple Stars, *Handbuch der Astrophysik*, Bd. VI, 2ter Teil, Chapter 4, 1928.

PARVULESCO, C.: Méthode nouvelle pour calculer des Orbites d'Étoiles doubles, *Bull. Lyon Obs.* **10**, 49, 1928.

————: Contribution à la détermination de l'orbite apparente d'une Étoile double, d'après la variation de l'angle de position, *Bull. Lyon Obs.* **12**, 122, 1930.

VAHLEN, TH.: Doppelsternbahn aus sieben Beobachtungen, *A.N.* **233**, 217, 1928.

KERRICH, J. E.: A Method for the Computation of the Orbital Elements for Certain Binary Stars, *Union Obs. Circ.* **82**, 123, 1930.

VOLET, CH.: Application de la méthode des moindres carrées au calcul des orbites d'étoiles doubles, *C.R.* **192**, 482, 1931.

————: Méthode pour le Calcul des Orbites d'Étoiles Doubles Visuelles, Application à l'Orbite du Compagnon de Sirius, *Bull. Astron.*, Ser. 2, **7**, 13, 1931.

RUSSELL, H. N.: A Rapid Method for Determining Visual Binary Orbits, *Mon. Not. R.A.S.* **93**, 599, 1933.

DE SITTER, W.: On the Solution of Normal Equations, *Ann. Cape Obs.* **12**, Pt. 1. 160–173.

CHAPTER V

THE RADIAL VELOCITY OF A STAR

By J. H. Moore

The observations treated in the preceding chapters concern only that part of the star's actual motion in space, which appears as change of position in a plane perpendicular to the line joining the observer and star. Of the component directed along the *line of sight,* called the star's *radial motion,* the telescope alone gives no indication. In fact, the possibility of detecting radial motion was recognized less than a century ago, and the methods of its measurement belong distinctly to another and newer branch of astronomy, known as astrophysics. Moreover, observations of the rate of change of position of a star on the celestial sphere can be translated into linear units, such as kilometers per second, only if the star's parallax is known, while measures of radial velocity by the method to be described, are expressed directly in kilometers per second and are independent of the star's distance.

The determination of the radial velocity of a light source, such as a star, is made possible by two well-known properties of light; *viz.,* that it is propagated as a wave motion, and with a definite and finite velocity. We are not concerned with the properties of the hypothetical medium, called the ether, in which these waves move, nor with the nature of the disturbance in the ether, whether it be mechanical or electromagnetic. For our purpose it is sufficient to know that in this medium, or in interstellar space, the velocity of light is about 299,796 km/sec. and that the well-known laws of wave motion hold for light waves.

In 1842, Christian Doppler called attention to an effect upon the apparent length of a wave which should result from a relative motion of the source of the waves and the observer. This result was independently reached and further developed, especially with reference to light waves, some six years later by the great French physicist, Fizeau. According to the

125

Doppler-Fizeau principle, when the relative motion of the light source and the observer is such, that the distance between the two is increasing or decreasing, the length of the waves received by the observer will be longer or shorter, respectively, than the normal length of these waves.

It is readily shown that the change in wave length is directly proportional to the normal length of the wave and to the ratio of the relative velocity of source and observer to the velocity of propagation of the waves. Moreover, for light waves the change is the same whether the source, or observer, or both are moving and depends only upon the relative velocity of the two.

Let us denote by v the relative radial velocity in kilometers per second of a star and observer, where v is considered positive when the distance between the two is increasing and negative when this distance is decreasing. Call λ' the wave length of a monochromatic ray reaching the observer, whose normal wave length, as emitted by the star, is λ.

Then from the Doppler-Fizeau principle, $\lambda' - \lambda : \lambda : : v : 299{,}796$; or $\lambda' - \lambda = \lambda v / 299{,}796$ (if v is $+$, λ' is greater than λ); or, writing $\Delta\lambda$ for the change in wave length $(\lambda' - \lambda)$, we have for the relative radial velocity of star and observer

$$v = \frac{299{,}796\Delta\lambda}{\lambda} \qquad (1)*$$

The determination of the radial velocity of a star rests then upon a knowledge of the velocity of light and of the wave lengths of certain definite rays emitted by a source at rest, and the measurement of the apparent wave lengths of those same rays received from a star. In short, the problem reduces to one of measuring $\Delta\lambda$ with the greatest possible precision. For this purpose the micrometer, with which we have become familiar, is replaced by the spectroscope. This wonderful instrument originating in the physical laboratory has developed a whole new science, spectroscopy, with an extensive and technical literature of its own. In this chapter we shall only call attention to some of the elementary principles of spectroscopic analysis and give a very brief survey of the spectrographic method

---

* It may be shown from the theory of relativity that this formula holds for the relative velocity of source and observer where this is small in comparison with the velocity of light. This condition is fulfilled by the stellar light sources with which we are here concerned.

as applied to the determination of stellar radial velocities. The student who wishes to pursue the subject further will find a list of references to extended treatment of the various topics at the end of this chapter.

Since stellar light sources are very faint in comparison with those available in the laboratory, it is necessary to employ for this special problem the spectroscope which is the least wasteful of light. For this reason the prism spectroscope is the only one of the various laboratory forms which is at present generally applicable to stellar spectroscopy* and therefore we limit our discussion to this particular type.

The essential parts of a laboratory spectroscope and their principal functions are briefly as follows: Light from the source to be studied is brought to a focus by a *condensing lens* on the narrow *slit* of the spectroscope. After passing through the slit, the rays are rendered parallel by an achromatic converging lens, called the *collimator lens*. The rays then strike a *glass prism*, placed with its apex parallel to the length of the slit, by which they are bent from their original direction. It is here that we obtain the separation of the rays, since the amount by which each ray is deviated by the prism is a function of its wave length. The direction of the long red waves is changed the least, while the shorter violet ones suffer the greatest deviation. After each set of rays is collected and brought to its corresponding focus by a second achromatic converging lens, we shall have an orderly array of images of the slit, each image formed by light of a definite wave length. Such a series of images is called a *spectrum* of the source. The spectrum may be viewed with an ordinary eyepiece, or the second lens may be used as a *camera lens*, and the spectrum be recorded on a photographic plate placed in its focal plane. When the spectroscope is employed photographically, as it is in practically all stellar work, it is called a *spectrograph*, and the photograph obtained with it is a *spectrogram*.

If the slit is made extremely narrow, there will be very little overlapping of the images and the spectrum is then said to be

---

* In recent years, grating spectrographs of high dispersion have been successfully employed with large telescopes for studies of the spectra of the brighter stars. This instrument has also proved more efficient for the investigation of the spectra of the red stars on account of the greater dispersion given by the grating in the region of longer wave length.

pure. It can be shown that the purest spectrum is obtained when the incident rays fall upon the prism at such an angle that they will be least deviated from their original direction by the prism. It is well known that this position of *minimum deviation* is also the one of maximum light transmission by the prism; and it has the further advantage that any accidental displacement of the prism produces the minimum displacement of the spectrum line. The prism or prisms of stellar spectrographs are therefore always set at the angle of minimum deviation for the approximate center of the region of spectrum to be studied.

Attention was called in an earlier chapter to two factors which define the optical efficiency of a telescope for the separation of close double stars, *viz.:* (*a*) the resolving power of the objective, (*b*) the magnification or linear distance between the two images at the focus of the objective. These same factors form a convenient basis for the comparison of the resolving powers of two spectrographs. Here, however, we are concerned with the separation of two images of the slit formed by light of different wave lengths. The resolving power of a spectrograph is, therefore, defined as *the minimum difference of wave length between two lines for which the lines will just be separated.* It is a function of the width of slit, the wave length, and the difference between the maximum and minimum lengths of path of the rays in the prism. The magnification, called the *linear dispersion* of the spectrograph, is expressed, as the number of wave length units per unit length of spectrum and depends upon the wave length of the ray, the optical constants for the prism system and the focal length of the camera lens.

When the slit of a spectroscope is illuminated by the light from an incandescent solid, such as the filament of an incandescent lamp, or from an incandescent gas under high pressure, the spectrum consists of an unbroken band of color; that is, a *continuous spectrum.* An incandescent gas or vapor under low pressure gives a spectrum consisting of isolated bright line images of the slit, a *bright line spectrum,* the bright lines indicating that radiations of certain definite wave length are emitted by the gas. Each chemical element, in the gaseous state, when rendered luminous in the electric arc, electric spark, flame, or vacuum tube, gives its own set of bright lines which are characteristic of this element alone and whose wave lengths remain constant for a source at rest under the same conditions of temperature, pressure, etc.

An incandescent gas has the property not only of radiating light of certain definite wave lengths, but also of absorbing, from white light passing through it, the rays of precisely those same wave lengths. If the temperature of the incandescent gas is lower than that of the source behind it, the continuous spectrum will be crossed by relatively dark lines whose positions agree exactly with the bright line spectrum characteristic of the gas. This relation existing between the emission and absorption of a gas is known as Kirchhoff's law, and the type of spectrum described is termed an *absorption spectrum*.

The three principles just stated obviously lead to a simple and direct method of analyzing the chemical constituents of gaseous light sources and of furnishing information as to their physical conditions. Nebulae of a certain class, for example, give bright line spectra, indicating that they are masses of luminous and extremely rarefied gases. Most of the stars, including our own Sun, give absorption spectra, showing that the light emitted by a central glowing core has passed through a surrounding atmosphere of cooler vapors. The presence in the atmospheres of the Sun and stars of most of the known chemical elements has been recognized from the lines in the spectra of these objects. In addition, there occur in these spectra many lines, which have not yet been identified with those of any known element.

The length of the light wave for each line is such a minute fraction of a millimeter that spectroscopists have adopted as the unit of wave length, the Ångström, equal to 0.0000001 mm. for which A is the symbol. Thus the wave length of the hydrogen radiation in the violet is 0.0004340 mm. or 4340A.

Measures of the wave lengths of the lines in a star's spectrum secured with the prism spectrograph, are readily effected by a comparison of the positions of the stellar lines with those from a source the wave lengths of whose lines are known. To accomplish this the light from a suitable source (for example, the iron arc) is made to pass over very nearly the same path in the spectrograph as that over which the star's light travels, and the spectrum of this source, termed the *comparison spectrum*, is recorded on each side of the star spectrum.

When the spectra of a number of stars are examined, it is found that they exhibit a great variety in the number and character of their lines. From an examination of several hundred stars by means of a visual spectroscope, Secchi, about 1866–1867, was able to arrange their spectra under four types. While exhibiting very well the most prominent characteristics of stellar spectra, his system is insufficient for portraying the finer gradations, which the photographic method has brought to light. The classification now in general use among astrophysicists was formulated by Prof. Pickering, Miss Maury, and Miss Cannon from the very extensive photographic survey of stellar spectra made at the Harvard College Observatory and at the Harvard station at Arequipa, Peru. It is based upon the observed fact that certain groups of lines have a common behavior. They make their appearance and increase or decrease in intensity at the same time, so that a more or less orderly sequence of development from one type of spectrum to another is indicated.

A condensed outline of this system will serve to indicate its chief features. The main divisions are represented by the letters, O, B, A, F, G, K, M (R, N, S). Classes B to M, in the order given, form a continuous sequence, and types intermediate between the main ones are indicated by numbers 1 to 9 inclusive. Class O undoubtedly precedes Class B, but its subdivisions are still provisional and are indicated by small letters a to e. Classes R and N appear to form a branch from the main sequence beginning at Class K, while Class S seems to be still another such offshoot.

In Class O, subdivisions Oa to Oe show faint continuous spectra upon which are superposed bright bands. The lines of hydrogen and helium are bright in the beginning of the class but dark in the later subdivisions. Characteristic lines of the class are those of ionized helium,* and doubly and trebly ionized oxygen, nitrogen,

* On the basis of the atomic model that considers the atom to consist of a positively charged nucleus about which revolve negatively charged units called electrons, it is possible to picture the manner in which the atoms radiate energy of definite frequencies corresponding to the different spectral lines. Each atom in the neutral state has a definite number of electrons— hydrogen 1, helium 2, lithium 3, etc.—and to the atom of each element in this state there corresponds a characteristic spectrum. If one electron is removed from the atom, the latter is said to be singly ionized, if two are removed, doubly ionized. Thus the atoms of ionized helium and doubly ionized lithium have only one electron and give entirely different spectra from those given by their neutral atoms. In the laboratory it is found

and silicon. Prominent features of Class B are the dark lines of hydrogen and neutral helium. Near the end of the class the helium lines weaken and they are absent in A0, while the lines given by the ionized atoms of the metals magnesium, calcium, iron, etc., begin to appear. The hydrogen lines reach their maximum intensity early in Class A and steadily decrease in strength through the remainder of the spectral sequence. The lines of ionized calcium, H and K, and those of the metals increase in prominence through this class and the subdivisions of Class F. In Class G, which includes stars whose spectra closely resemble that of the Sun, the H and K lines and the numerous metallic lines are conspicuous features, whereas hydrogen has become less prominent. Class K spectra show a further weakening of the enhanced lines of the metals and strengthening of the arc lines, especially those which appear in the laboratory at lower temperatures. In Class M these low-temperature lines are still further strengthened as the high-temperature lines decrease in intensity. This class is characterized by the absorption bands of titanium oxide which first make their appearance at K5 and increase in intensity through the subdivisions of Class M. Stars of Class Me show, in addition, bright hydrogen lines. To classes R and N belong stars whose spectra of metallic lines are similar to those of M but which are particularly characterized by bands of carbon and cyanogen. Spectra of Class S are likewise similar to M in the strengthening of the low temperature lines of the metals, but in this class the bands of zirconium oxide are present in addition to those of titanium oxide.

Stars of classes O and B are bluish white in color; those of Class A, white; of F and G, yellow; of K, orange; of M, R, and S, red; while the N stars are a deep red.

In Plate III are reproduced four stellar spectrograms secured with the three-prism spectrograph of the D. O. Mills Expedition, at Santiago, Chile, which illustrate the different appearance of the spectra in the blue-violet region of classes B8, F, G, and K5. On all of the spectrograms the bright line spectrum

---

that the lines from the ionized atom are stronger in the spark (enhanced) as compared with their intensities in the electric arc, while in the latter the lines of the neutral atom are stronger. The lines of the ionized atom are therefore frequently referred to as *enhanced* and those of the neutral atom as *arc* lines.

of the iron arc was photographed above and below the star spectrum. The spectrum of v_4 *Eridani* (Figure *a*) of Class B8, shows only the hydrogen line Hγ (4340.477A) and the magnesium

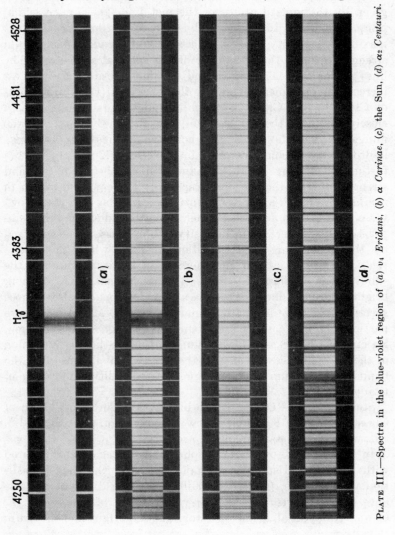

4528
4481
4383
Hγ
4250

(*a*)   (*b*)   (*c*)   (*d*)

PLATE III.—Spectra in the blue-violet region of (*a*) v_4 *Eridani*, (*b*) α *Carinae*, (*c*) the Sun, (*d*) α_2 *Centauri*.

line (4481.228A), as the very faint metallic lines, some of which appear on the original negative, are lost in the process of reproduction. This star is a spectroscopic binary, and the spectra of both stars are visible, so that each of the two lines mentioned above is double.   The strengthening of the metallic lines and the decrease in intensity of Hγ are shown in the spectrum of α *Carinae* of Class F (Fig. *b*), while in the solar spectrum (Fig. *c*), of Class G, and in that of α₂ *Centauri* (Fig. *d*), of Class K5, a further decrease in Hγ, the disappearance of 4481A and a considerable increase in the number and strength of the absorption lines of other elements are noticeable.

The four spectrograms illustrate also the displacement of the lines in star spectra as effects of motion in the line of sight. The iron lines in the solar spectrum are practically coincident with the corresponding lines of the iron arc, since the relative radial velocity of the Sun and the observer is very small.   The iron lines in the spectrum of α *Carinae* are clearly displaced from their normal positions, as given by the lines of the comparison spectrum.   This displacement is toward the red end of the spectrum, and corresponds, therefore, to an increase in the wave lengths of the star lines.   Interpreted on the Doppler-Fizeau principle, this change is produced by a recession of the star with respect to the Earth at the rate of +18.0 km/sec. In the case of α₂ *Centauri*, the displacement of the lines is toward the violet and corresponds to a velocity of approach of −35.0 km/sec.   As an example of the Doppler-Fizeau effect, the spectrogram of the spectroscopic binary ν₄ *Eridani*, is perhaps the most striking.   The two stars revolve about their common center of mass in a period of 5.01 days, as shown by an extended series of plates similar to this one.   Due to their orbital motion, the velocity of each star in the line of sight is continually changing, giving rise to a continuous variation in the separation of the lines of the two spectra.   The spectrogram reproduced here was taken at the time of maximum velocity of approach of one, and the corresponding velocity of recession of the other component. It shows, therefore, the maximum separation of the lines of the two spectra.   The relative radial velocity of the two stars was 132 km/sec.   Obviously, the lines of the two spectra will be coincident when the motion of the two components is across the line of sight, which occurs at intervals of 2.5 days.

It is well known that the wave lengths of spectral lines are affected by other causes than that arising from radial motion of the source.   For example, it is found that an increase in pressure of the emitting or absorbing vapor will in general shift the lines toward the red.   This effect, even with considerable pressures, is small and is moreover not the same for all lines. Of the many conditions which displace spectrum lines, radial motion is the only one of which measures of stellar spectra have furnished reliable evidence.*

Displacements of the stellar lines, with reference to those of the comparison spectrum, may arise wholly or in part from causes which are purely instrumental. Thus, if the starlight and the artificial light do not pass over equivalent paths in the spectrograph, or if a change in the relative positions of the parts of the instrument occurs between the times of photographing the stellar and the reference spectra, a relative displacement of the lines of the two spectra will result. The first-named source of error is an optical condition, to be met for all spectroscopic measures, that is easily satisfied. With the conditions of a fixed mounting and approximately constant temperature, under which the spectrograph is used in the laboratory, the second source of error need not be considered. When, however, the spectrograph is applied to stellar observation, it is necessary, in order to avoid undue loss of light, to mount it on a moving telescope, and hence to subject the instrument to the varying component of gravity and the changing temperature of a well-ventilated dome. The spectrograph must be so designed and constructed that it will be free from appreciable differential flexure in any two positions of the telescope, and provision must be made against the disturbing effects of temperature changes in the prisms and the metal parts of the instrument. Further, in addition to the obvious requirement that the prisms and lenses shall give good definition, they must be so chosen and arranged as to give satisfactory resolving power with efficiency in light transmission.

The earlier determinations of stellar radial velocities were made entirely by the visual method. Although made by such skilled observers as Huggins, Vogel, and others, the errors of observation, except for a very few of the brightest stars, often exceeded the quantities to be measured. After the introduction of the photographic method of studying stellar spectra, Vogel and Scheiner, at Potsdam, and later Belopolsky, at Pulkowa, were able to measure the radial velocities of the

---

* A possible exception is the lengthening of the light waves in a strong gravitational field, evidence of which has been found in the spectrum of the companion of *Sirius*.

brightest stars with an average probable error of ± 2.6 km/sec. In 1895–1896 the problem was attacked by Campbell, who employed a specially designed stellar spectrograph—the Mills Spectrograph—in conjunction with the 36-in. refractor of the Lick Observatory. For the brighter stars, the probable error of his measures was about ± 0.5 km and for bright stars whose spectra contain the best lines, the probable error was reduced to ± 0.25 km. Many improvements in stellar spectrographs have, of course, been made in the succeeding years, but the standard of precision, set by his measures nearly 40 years ago, represents that attained today for the same stars. The advances which have been made in this time relate more to the increased accuracy of the results for fainter stars.

Now this remarkable advance in the precision of the measures made by Campbell was due not to the use of a great telescope but to the fact that his spectrograph was designed in accordance with the important requirements mentioned in the foregoing—excellence of definition and maximum light transmission, rigidity, and temperature control of the spectrograph—and to improved methods of measuring and reducing the spectrograms.

In order to understand more clearly the manner in which the optical and mechanical requirements are met in practice, a detailed description will be given of a modern spectrograph which was designed to have maximum efficiency for the particular problem of determining stellar radial velocities. A view of the new Mills spectrograph attached to the 36-in. refractor of the Lick Observatory is presented in Plate IV. The essential parts of this instrument are the same as those described for the simple laboratory spectrograph; namely, the slit, collimator lens, prism, and camera lens, except that here *three* 60° prisms of flint glass are employed. The prisms, set at minimum deviation for 4500A, produce a deviation of this ray of 176°. A rectangular box constructed of saw-steel plates, to which are connected respectively the slit mechanism, the prism box, and the plate holder, by three light steel castings, forms the main body of the spectrograph. In the casting to which the prism box is attached are mounted the collimator and camera lenses, both of which are achromatic for the region of 4500A. The spectrograph has an entirely new form of support, designed by Campbell, to incorporate the suggestion made

by Wright, that such an instrument should be supported *near
its two ends,* like a bridge truss or beam, in order to give minimum
flexure. The support is a frame work of T-bars extending down
from the telescope, the form and arrangement of which are such
as to hold the instrument rigidly in the line of collimation of the

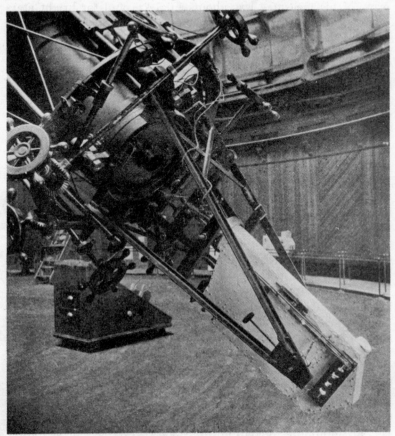

PLATE IV.—The Mills spectrograph of the Lick Observatory.

large telescope. The lower support is a bar passing through a
rectangular opening in the casting carrying the prism box.
This bar is pivoted at the center of the casting and connected at
its two ends to the supporting frame. The upper support
consists of a cylindrical ring firmly attached to the frame work.
In this cylinder fits a spherical flange of the spectrograph casting,
the two forming a universal joint. Any strains originating

in the supporting frame cannot, with this form of mounting, be communicated to the spectrograph. Careful tests of this instrument and of the spectrograph of the D. O. Mills Expedition to Chile, which has the same form of mounting, show that the effects of differential flexure have been eliminated. This method of support permits, further, of a very convenient mode of moving the spectrograph as a whole in order to bring the slit into the focal plane of the large telescope, since it is only necessary to provide sliding connections on the frame, for the lower support.

Nearly all modern stellar spectrographs are provided with reflecting slit plates inclined at a small angle to the collimation axis, which enable the observer to view the star image directly on the slit. This is accomplished through the aid of a total-reflection prism, placed above the slit and outside of the cone of rays from the telescope objective, which receives the light from the slit and sends it to the guiding eyepiece. By placing the slit parallel to the celestial equator, small errors of the driving clock cause the star image to move along the slit, which is desirable in order to obtain width of spectrum. *Constant and careful guiding is necessary to insure that the star's image be kept exactly on the slit and that its motion along the slit be such as to give a uniform exposure.*

With a prism spectrograph and a straight slit the spectrum lines are curved. The amount of the curvature depends upon the optical constants of the instrument and the wave length of the line. This source of trouble in measuring the spectrograms may be eliminated for a short range of spectrum by employing a slit of the proper curvature to make the spectrum lines straight. Both three-prism instruments referred to above are provided with curved slits.

As a source for the comparison spectrum, it is necessary to select one giving a number of well-distributed lines in the part of the spectrum to be studied. For example, for the new Mills spectrograph in which the region 4400 to 4600A is utilized, the spark spectrum of titanium is used. In the southern instrument, arranged for the region 4200 to 4500A, the comparison source is the iron arc.

In order to eliminate the effects of any possible change in the instrument during an exposure on the star, several impressions of the comparison spectrum are made at regular intervals. This is accomplished very conveniently and without

danger of changing the adjustment of the comparison apparatus
by a simple device due to Wright. Two small total-reflection
prisms are placed just above the slit, so that their adjoining
edges define the length of the slit. Two light sources are then
so arranged that the beam of each is brought to a focus on the
slit by a small condensing lens after total reflection in its respec-
tive prism.

The optical parts of the spectrograph should, of course, be
mounted so that they cannot move, but care must be taken
that they are not cramped. This caution is especially pertinent
with regard to the large prisms. In the Mills spectrographs
the prisms rest upon hard-rubber blocks and are firmly clamped
to one of the side plates of the prism box by light steel springs
which press against their upper surface. Small hard-rubber
stops prevent lateral motion of the prisms.

In order to prevent the effects of changing temperature, the
principal parts of the spectrograph are surrounded by a light
wooden box, lined with felt. Over the felt surface are strung
a number of turns of resistance wire. The regulation of the
heating current is effected by means of a very sensitive mer-
cury-in-glass thermostat by which the temperature inside of
the prism box is held constant during the night's work to within
a few hundredths of a degree centigrade.

The function of the telescope objective, for observations of
stellar spectra, is that of a condensing lens and the brightness
of the point image in the focal plane is directly proportional to
the area of the lens and its transmission factor. If we had
perfect seeing, we should receive in the slit of the spectrograph, with the widths generally employed, about 90 per cent
of the light in the star image. Due to atmospheric disturbances
the image of a star under average conditions of seeing, is a
circular *tremor* disk whose diameter is four or five times the
width of the slit, so that the brightness of the spectrum is not
proportional to the *area* of the objective but more nearly to its
diameter. For example, the relative intensities of stellar spectra
obtained with the same spectrograph respectively upon the
36-in. and 12-in. refractors of the Lick Observatory would be
(allowing for the difference of transmission of the two), about
as two to one, since, for the photographic rays, the loss of light is
for the former about 50 per cent and for the latter about 25 per
cent. When a visual refractor is used for spectroscopic work,

it is necessary to render it achromatic for the photographic rays. This is accomplished for the 36-in. refractor by a correcting lens of 2½-in. aperture placed one meter inside the visual focus of the telescope. This lens introduces an additional loss of light of fully 10 per cent.

Since a silver-on-glass mirror has, under the best conditions, a high reflecting power, and since it is also free from chromatic aberration, it would seem that the reflector should be the more efficient telescope to use in connection with a stellar spectrograph. The reflector, however, possesses its own disadvantages, one of which is that it is very sensitive to changes of temperature. Our experience with the 36-in. refractor at Mount Hamilton and the 37½-in. reflector in Chile, when used with high dispersion spectrographs, indicates that the relative light efficiency of the two is about equal in the region of Hγ. For apertures up to 36 in. one is inclined to favor the refractor for high dispersion work, while for low dispersion, where considerable extent of spectrum is desired, the reflector is, of course, preferable.

The focal lengths of both refracting and reflecting telescopes vary with change in temperature of the lens or mirror. It is, therefore, necessary before beginning the night's work, and, with the reflector, frequently during the night, to bring the slit into the focal plane of the telescope, which, as noted above, is effected by moving the spectrograph as a whole in the line of collimation of the instrument.

It is well known that all high dispersion spectrographs are very wasteful of light, though to what extent is perhaps not always appreciated. When stellar spectrographs of three-prism dispersion are used in conjunction with large refractors or reflectors, the combined instrument delivers to the photographic plate probably less than 2 per cent of the light incident upon the telescope objective. Half of the light is lost, as we have noted, before it reaches the slit. The remaining losses occur at the slit, in the prisms and in the collimator and camera lenses of the spectrograph. In order to avoid unnecessary losses of light, the obvious conditions must be satisfied, that the angular apertures of the collimator lens and object glass are the same, and that the prisms and camera lens are of sufficient aperture to admit the full beam from the collimator. The most serious losses occur at the narrow slit and in the prism train. Indeed, one of the most important factors in the design of stellar spectrographs, for maximum light efficiency, is the proper balancing of these two conflicting elements, the transmission at the slit and the transmission of the prisms. Thus, in the new Mills spectrograph, by using a collimator of slightly greater focal length than the present one (28½ in.) with corresponding increase in aperture of the lens and prisms, a wider slit could be employed and still maintain the present purity of spectrum. After allowing for the increased absorption of the prism train, there would remain a small gain in light transmitted. Although theoretically possible, this gain would probably be more than offset by the inferior definition of the larger prisms and the added difficulty of eliminating flexure. It is necessary here, as at so many points in the spectrograph, to sacrifice a little in order to gain more elsewhere. In fact, the most efficient design of spectrograph may be described as the one in which the wisest compromises have been made between the various conflicting interests.

The decision as to the resolution and dispersion to be employed is governed by several considerations: the type of stellar spectrum to be studied, the size of the telescope at one's disposal, and the brightness of the source whose spectrum can be photographed with reasonable exposure times. With the spectrograph here described two lines in the region of 4500A whose wave lengths differ 0.2A are resolved, while the linear dispersion for 4500A is 1 mm = 11A. In order to obtain a spectrogram of suitable density of a star whose photographic magnitude is 5.0, an exposure time of an hour and a half is required. For stars of photographic magnitudes 6.0 to 6.5 the width of the slit is increased, thus sacrificing to some degree the purity of spectrum, but not enough to interfere seriously with the accuracy of the measures. In the case of early-type stars whose spectra contain single lines, the question of resolution is not important, and where these lines are also broad, it is preferable to employ lower dispersion. The adjustments of the various parts of the spectrograph call for continual attention. It is necessary that the instrument be placed with its axis of collimation accurately in that of the large telescope and frequent tests should be made to be sure that it remains so. The comparison source must be adjusted so that its light follows very nearly the same path as the starlight in the spectrograph. Care must be exercised at every point in the process of obtaining and measuring the spectrogram.

THE MEASUREMENT AND REDUCTION OF SPECTROGRAMS

For the measurement of spectrograms any one of the usual forms of laboratory measuring microscopes will suffice. This is merely a microscope on the stand of which is mounted a carriage, movable by an accurate micrometer screw, in a direction at right angles to that of the microscope axis.

In order to fix ideas, we shall assume that it is required to measure and reduce a spectrogram of α_2 *Centauri*, similar to the one whose positive is reproduced in Plate III. The spectrogram is first clamped on the carriage of the microscope, and the usual adjustments of focus and alignment of the plate are made. Great care should be taken that the illumination of the field of the microscope is uniform. Beginning with the comparison line 4250A, settings are made continuously along the plate on good star lines and comparison lines as they chance to occur. The plate is then reversed and the settings are repeated. It has been shown by several investigators that the effects of errors due to personal equation are practically eliminated by taking the mean of the measures in the two positions. In the reversal of the plate the spectrum is also inverted, which may so change the appearance of the lines as to interfere with the elimination of personal equation. Especially is this true if the lines are curved. The effects of accidental errors in setting are reduced by employing a number of lines.

The table on page 143 contains the data of the measure and reduction of this plate. Column I gives the wave lengths in terms of the International Ångström (I.A.) of the lines in the iron comparison and the normal wave lengths of the star lines, taken from the *The Revision of Rowland's Preliminary Table of Solar Wave Lengths*. In columns IV and V are recorded respectively the settings on the comparison and star lines (in revolutions of the micrometer screw). The displacements of the iron lines in the star are evidently given directly in amount and sign by the differences, star minus comparison, and these are entered at once in column VII (Displ.). We cannot enter the displacements for the other star lines until the normal positions of these lines have been obtained from those of the

iron comparison, by interpolation. This is effected in the
following manner:

A smooth curve drawn by plotting, for the comparison lines,
the reading on each line and its corresponding wave length,
respectively as ordinates and abscissae, will evidently represent for this spectrogram the relation existing between wave
length and micrometer readings. From this curve—called a
dispersion curve—either the zero readings or the observed
wave length of the stellar lines could be obtained. This curve
was found by Cornu and later by Hartmann to be nearly of
the form of an equilateral hyperbola so that it is approximately
represented by the equation

$$x - x_0 = \frac{c}{\lambda - \lambda_0} \tag{2}$$

where x is the micrometer reading on a line whose wave length
is λ and λ_0, x_0, and c are constants. Since it is not practicable
to plot the dispersion curve, the Cornu-Hartmann formula
furnishes a very convenient means of obtaining it. The values
of the three constants are determined from three equations
formed by substituting the micrometer readings and wave
lengths of three lines, selected, one at each end of the region
of spectrum and the other near the middle. Micrometer readings of all other comparison and star lines are then computed
from the formula. The departure of this computed curve from
the true dispersion curve is furnished by a plot of the differences between the observed and calculated readings of the
comparison lines. The computed normal positions of the star
lines are then corrected for the difference between the computed and observed dispersion curve. The decimal portions of
the results would be entered in column VI (Sup'd).*

As before, the difference, star line minus zero line, gives the
displacement in revolutions of the screw. In order to express
this as $\Delta\lambda$, that is in units of wave length, it is necessary to
know r, the number of Ångström units in one revolution of the
screw. The value of r for any point in the spectrum is evidently the slope of the dispersion curve at that point, and is
equal to $(\lambda - \lambda_0)/(x - x_0)$. Finally, in accordance with the

---

* The figures actually entered in this column in the example were obtained
by a different method of reduction which is explained in the paragraphs
following.

* α_2 Centauri ft.   * Plate No. 3791 III a 14^h 32.8^m
Date 1911 Feb. 27

λ	Table	Co-Ta	Comp.	*	Sup'd.	Displ.	rV_s	v_s
4250.132	54.886	0	54.886	54.758	...	−0.128	319	−40.8
4250.799	55.031	3	55.034	54.909	...	−0.125	320	−40.0
4282.413	61.819	13	61.832	61.710	...	−0.122	335	−40.9
4283.016	61.944	...	......	61.831	958	−0.127	335	−42.5
4294.147	64.250	16	64.266	64.140	...	−0.126	338	−42.6
4299.252	65.295	20	65.315	65.190	...	−0.125	340	−42.5
4312.877	68.039	...	......	67.944	061	−0.117	349	−40.8
4313.633	68.190	...	......	68.090	212	−0.122	349	−42.6
4318.660	69.185	...	......	69.105	220	−0.115	352	−40.5
4325.000	70.431	...	......	70.355	469	−0.114	356	−40.6
4325.777	70.584	40	70.624	70.502	...	−0.122	356	−43.4
4327.919	71.001	...	......	70.928	041	−0.113	357	−40.3
4337.057	72.767	43	72.810	72.692	...	−0.118	360	−42.5
4340.477	73.421	...	......	73.350	467	−0.117	362	−42.4
4359.625	77.027	...	......	76.970	082	−0.112	372	−41.7
4369.781	78.896	...	......	78.844	957	−0.113	376	−42.5
4375.946	80.018	...	......	79.972	083	−0.111	378	−42.0
4379.240	80.612	...	......	80.571	680	−0.109	380	−41.4
4383.559	81.388	70	81.458	81.352	...	−0.106	382	−40.5
4399.780	84.257	...	......	84.228	337	−0.109	390	−42.5
4404.763	85.126	86	85.212	85.105	...	−0.107	392	−41.9
4406.654	85.453	...	......	85.432	539	−0.107	394	−42.2
4415.137	86.913	93	87.006	86.898	...	−0.108	397	−42.9
4425.446	88.664	...	......	88.662	759	−0.097	402	−39.0
4428.551	89.198	...	......	89.194	296	−0.102	404	−41.2
4430.624	89.536	...	......	89.535	636	−0.101	404	−40.8
4434.969	90.270	...	......	90.270	372	−0.102	406	−41.4
4435.690	90.380	...	......	90.378	482	−0.104	406	−42.2
4442.351	91.482	108	91.590	91.491	...	−0.099	411	−40.7
4443.814	91.724	...	......	91.732	831	−0.099	412	−40.8
4447.730	92.365	...	......	92.375	473	−0.098	413	−40.5
4459.140	94.216	114	94.330	94.238	...	−0.092	417	−38.4
4476.023	96.906	127	97.033	96.940	...	−0.093	426	−39.6
4482.217	97.872	131	98.003	97.905	...	−0.098	428	−41.9
4494.575	99.782	138	99.920	99.820	...	−0.100	434	−43.4

$$35)\overline{1449.9}$$

$$-41.43$$

Scale = + 0.13
va = +21.82
vd = − 0.07
Observed V $\overline{-19.55 \text{ km}}$

relation deduced on page 126, *v* the observed radial velocity is obtained by multiplying Δλ for each line by its corresponding factor $V_s = 299,796/\lambda$.

Each spectrogram may be reduced in the manner outlined above, and some observers prefer to follow this method rigorously for each stellar spectrogram. When this is done the process is simplified by carrying through the computation in wave lengths, so that the displacement is expressed at once in Ångströms.

Since for the same spectrograph the form of the dispersion curve differs but slightly for different temperatures, a simple and practical method of reduction is offered by the following procedure: A standard dispersion curve is computed once for all, according to the method described above, from measures of a solar spectrogram. With the aid of this all other spectrograms taken with the spectrograph may be quickly and easily reduced. It is convenient to put this standard curve in the form of a dispersion table in which are entered the normal wave lengths of the comparison and stellar lines used for stars of different spectral classes, and the micrometer readings corresponding to these wave lengths. In this standard table are given also the values of rV_s for each line. Columns I, II, and VIII, in the example, are taken from such a table.

It is now only necessary to reduce the readings of the standard table to the dispersion of the plate, by plotting the differences between the observed and table readings of the comparison lines (recorded in column III in the example). From this curve the difference to be applied to the table reading for each star line is read off. In the sixth column are given the new table readings (for zero velocity) after this difference has been applied. When there are comparison lines corresponding to star lines some observers follow rigorously the process outlined, while others (as in the present example) take the difference between the readings of the two as the displacements. The last three columns contain, respectively, the displacements (∗ minus Comp. or Sup'd), the factor rV_s, and the products of these two values, which are the relative radial velocities of star and observer as supplied by the lines measured. The mean of the measures for 40 lines gives as the observed radial velocity −41.43 km/sec. It will be noticed that the dispersion of the star plate is about 0.3 per cent greater than that of the standard table, and consequently the factor r (computed for the table) is too large, and the numerical value of this velocity must be reduced by this amount. This is allowed for, in the example, as scale correction. In practice, it is convenient to have several standard tables corresponding to the dispersion of the spectrograph at different temperatures. The one whose dispersion is nearest that of the star plate is selected for use. Experience has shown that the results obtained by the very simple method just described are of the same accuracy as those derived by the longer process of computing a dispersion curve for each plate.

If the spectrograph is not provided with a curved slit, it is necessary to introduce a correction for the curvature of the lines. This correction may be computed from Ditscheiner's formula* or determined empirically from lines on a spectrogram of the Sun, on the assumption that the curve of each line is a parabola. The better method is to eliminate the source of this correction by the use of a curved slit.

The observed radial velocity of a star is made up of the star's velocity, V, with reference to the solar system, and the velocity of the observer in the solar system. The latter consists of three components, which arise from (1) the revolution of the Earth around the Sun; (2) the rotation of the Earth on its axis; (3) the revolution of the Earth around the center of mass of the Earth-Moon system. This last component never exceeds ± 0.014 km/sec and may be neglected. The correction for the annual and diurnal motions of the Earth are readily computed from the formulas given by Campbell in Frost-Scheiner's *Astronomical Spectroscopy* (pages 338–345). The values for these in the example are given respectively under v_a and v_d. Hence, the observed radial velocity of α_2 *Centauri* with reference to the Sun on 1911, February 27.883 (Greenwich Mean Time) was $- 19.55$ km/sec.

Methods of reduction which depend upon dispersion formulas require an accurate knowledge of the wave lengths of the lines used in both the comparison and stellar spectra. Accurate values of the *absolute* wave lengths are not required but their *relative* values must be well determined. For example,

---

* Uber die Krümmung der Spectrallinien, *Sitz. Ber. d. Math. Klasse d. k. Akad. Wien*, Bd. LI, Abth. II, 1865; also Frost-Scheiner, *Astronomical Spectroscopy*, p. 15, 1894.

a relative error of ± 0.01A in the wave length of any line would produce an error in the velocity for that line of nearly a kilometer. Interferometer measures of the wave lengths in the spectra of a number of elements are now available, but for the wave lengths of solar lines it is still necessary to use the determinations by Rowland. Fortunately, we now possess accurate wave lengths of the lines in the spectra of most of the elements, and the *Revision of Rowland's Preliminary Table of Solar Wave Lengths* has furnished a homogeneous set of data for the lines of the Sun's spectrum. A serious difficulty, however, arises for stellar lines, from the fact that stellar spectrographs have not sufficient resolution to separate lines which were measured as individual lines in the solar spectrum with the more powerful instruments employed by Rowland and his successors. It is the practice of many observers, where two lines merge to form one line in the star spectrum, to take the mean of the wave lengths of the component lines, weighted according to the intensities given by Rowland for those lines in the Sun. Wave lengths based on estimates of intensity should naturally be regarded with suspicion, and in fact we do not know, until the entire plate has been reduced, whether we have chosen an erroneous wave length or not. It is well known that various stellar lines and blends behave differently for stars of different types. The lines in solar type stars are assumed to have the same wave lengths as similar lines in the Sun. In the case of stars of other spectral classes, the solar lines which occur can be used in determining the wave lengths of the nonsolar lines and blends. In this manner special tables are constructed for stars of different types.

When spectrographs of lower dispersion and resolution than those of three prisms are employed for the measurement of solar and later-type spectra, the effect of uncertainties in wave length of the stellar lines, due to blends, becomes very serious. The two methods of measurement and reduction which follow eliminate the sources of error incident to the use of blends, and erroneous wave lengths as far as it is possible to do so. The first is that due to Prof. R. H. Curtiss and is called by him the *velocity standard method*. In principle it amounts to a determination of the wave lengths of the lines in the spectrum of a source whose radial velocity is known made with the particular spectrograph which is to be used for measures of stellar spectra of this same class. Thus for the measures of spectra of the solar type, a table similar to the one we have described is formed. The micrometer readings in this table, however, are not computed from assumed wave lengths, but are the mean of the actual settings, on comparison and solar lines, obtained on several spectrograms of the Sun. These standard plates are produced as nearly as possible under the same conditions as the stellar plates to be measured. The procedure in the reduction of the measures by means of this table is then the same as that described. It is necessary, of course, to correct the measured stellar velocity for the radial velocity of the source when the standard spectrograms were taken. Standard tables for the reduction of measures of stars of other spectral classes may be formed in a similar manner, using as the standard sources stars whose radial velocities are well determined.

The second method is due to Prof. Hartmann and is in principle the same as the preceding one, except that the star plate is referred directly to the standard plate on a special measuring microscope, known as the spectrocomparator. The instrument is provided with two plate carriages, one of which is movable. On one of the carriages the star plate is placed and on the other, which is provided with a fine micrometer screw, is a standard plate of the Sun (taken with the stellar spectrograph). The microscope has two objectives so arranged that the images of portions of the two plates are brought, by means of total reflection prisms and a reflecting surface, to focus in the same plane and in the field of one eyepiece. By means of a silvered strip on the surface of one prism, the central portion of the Sun's spectrum is cut out and the star spectrum thrown into its place. In a similar manner, central strips of the comparison spectra of the Sun plate are replaced by those of the comparison spectra of the star plate. An ingenious arrangement of the microscopes permits of equalizing the scale of the two plates, by changing the relative magnifying powers of the two objectives. The method of measurement is, then, after proper alignment of the plates, to bring corresponding sections of the two plates into the field of the microscope, and by means of the micrometer screw set the corresponding lines of the comparison spectra in the same straight line. A setting is then made with the corresponding lines of the solar and star spectra in the same straight line. The difference between the micrometer readings in the two positions is the displacement of the star lines relative to the solar lines. In practice it is found sufficient to divide the length of the spectrum into about 15 sections, for each of which these comparative settings are made. The mean of the displacements, obtained with the plates in the direct and reverse positions, when multiplied by the rV_s for each section, gives for each the value $V^* - V_0$, where V^* is the radial velocity of the star and V_0 that of the Sun. Theoretically, the values of $V^* - V_0$ should receive weights proportional to $1/rV_s$ in taking the mean. Although this correction is negligible, except where an extent of spectrum of 400 or 500A is used, its introduction leads to a very simple method of computation. Take the sum of the displacements in the direct and reverse measures and multiply by a factor $f = \dfrac{1}{2\sum \dfrac{1}{rV_s}}$. The product is equal to the weighted mean of the values $V^* - V_0$ for each section. This, corrected for the velocity of the original Sun plate (V_0), gives the radial velocity of the star relative to the observer. The reduction to the Sun is made in the usual way. The factor f is a constant so long as the same regions are used, and its values may be computed for all combinations of the regions that are used. The great advantage of the method, aside from those which it possesses in common with the velocity standard method, is that we are able to measure and reduce in an hour a plate of a star rich in lines, and practically utilize all the material on the plate. With the older methods, to make such a comprehensive measure and reduction, *i.e.*, to utilize all of the lines on the plate, would require one or two days.

For the measures of spectra of a type other than the solar it is necessary to select for the standard plate a spectrogram of a star of that particular spectral class. In order to obtain the velocity for this standard spectrogram, it should be measured and reduced, either by the method first described or perhaps preferably by the velocity standard method. The adopted value should be the mean of the measures made by several different observers.

The spectrocomparator offers a very efficient method for determining the differences in velocities of the same star, by measuring a series of plates of the star with reference to one of these selected as a standard.

Five of the six elements of a spectroscopic binary orbit depend only upon the accurate determination of the relative radial velocities given by the series of spectrograms. One of the most important applications of the Hartmann comparator is, therefore, to the measurement of plates of a spectroscopic binary.

For the measure and reduction of spectrograms of stars of the earlier spectral classes, the use of the Cornu-Hartmann dispersion formula will suffice, inasmuch as the spectra of such stars consist of lines due to the simple gases, the wave lengths of which have been accurately determined in the laboratory.

The measure and reduction of spectrograms of stars of the solar and later classes of spectra are accomplished with great saving of time and labor, and by a method free from some of the uncertainties of wave lengths, by the use of the spectro-comparator. If the observer is not provided with such an instrument the velocity standard method is preferable to the use of the dispersion formulas, at least until a system of stellar wave lengths of the requisite accuracy is available.

To the reader who has followed the long and intricate process of determining the radial velocity of a star, the question will naturally occur, how do we know that the final result represents the star's velocity? Obviously, the final test of the method is its ability to reproduce known velocities. Fortunately, we have at hand a means of making such a test. Since the orbital elements of the inner planets of the solar system are well determined, we can readily compute the radial velocity of one of these with reference to the Earth at any given time. It is only necessary, then, to observe the relative radial velocity of the planet and the Earth and compare this with the computed value at the time of observation. At the Lick Observatory spectrograms of *Venus* and of *Mars* are secured at frequent intervals with the stellar spectrograph and measured by the observers in the regular course of measuring stellar plates. With the three-prism spectrograph, described above, the observed and computed velocities of these two planets generally agree to within ± 0.5 km, or the unavoidable error of measure. When the spectrograms are measured by several observers, the effects of personal equation are to some extent eliminated in the mean, and an agreement within a few tenths of a kilometer is to be expected. A continual check is thus afforded on the adjustments of the spectrograph and the measurement of the spectrograms.

References

GENERAL

CAMPBELL, W. W.: *Stellar Motions*, Yale University Press, 1913.

EBERHARD, G.: Sternspektrographie und Bestimmung von Radialgeschwindigkeiten, *Handbuch der Astrophysik*, I, chap. 4, 1933.

INSTRUMENTS AND DESIGN

CAMPBELL, W. W.: The Mills Spectrograph, *Ap. Jour.* **8**, 123, 1898.

FROST, E. B., The Bruce Spectrograph, *Ap. Jour.* **15**, 1, 1902.

HARTMANN, J.: Remarks on the Construction and Adjustment of Spectrographs. *Ap. Jour.* **11**, 400, 1900; **12**, 31, 1900.

KEELER, J. E.: Elementary Principles Governing the Efficiency of Spectrographs for Astronomical Purposes, *Sidereal Messenger* **10**, 433, 1891.

NEWALL, H. F.: On the General Design of Spectrographs to be Attached to Equatorials of Large Aperture, Considered Chiefly from the Point of View of Tremor-discs, *Mon. Not. R.A.S.* **65**, 608, 1905.

PLASKETT, J. S.: Spectrograph of the Dominion Astrophysical Observatory, *Publ. Dominion Astroph. Obs.* **1**, 81, 1920.

VOGEL, H. C.: Description of the Spectrographs for the Great Refractor at Potsdam, *Ap. Jour.* **11**, 393, 1900.

WRIGHT, W. H.: Description of the Instruments and Methods of the D. O. Mills Expedition, *Publ. Lick. Obs.* **9**, 25, 1905.

METHODS OF MEASUREMENT AND REDUCTION

CAMPBELL, W. W.: The Reduction of Spectroscopic Observations of Motions in the Line of Sight, *Astronomy and Astrophysics*, **11**, 319, 1892. Also, Frost-Scheiner, *Astronomical Spectroscopy*, p. 338.

CURTISS, R. H.: A Proposed Method for the Measurement and Reduction of Spectrograms for the Determination of the Radial Velocities of Celestial Objects, *Lick Obs. Bull.* **3**, 19, 1904; *Ap. Jour.* **20**, 149, 1904.

HARTMANN, J. F.: Über die Ausmessung und Reduction der Photographischen Aufnahmen von Sternspectren, *A.N.* **155**, 81, 1901.

————: A Simple Interpolation Formula for the Prismatic Spectrum, *Ap. Jour.* **8**, 218, 1898.

————: The Spectro-comparator. *Ap. Jour.* **24**, 285, 1906; *Publ. Astroph. Obs., Potsdam*, **18**, 5, 1908.

[For a modern discussion of spectrum analysis see: J. A. Hynek, ed., *Astrophysics*, pp. 12–258, 1951; R. H. Garstang, Peculiar Stars, *R. A. S. Occasional Notes* **3**, 21, Nov. 1959; and Helmut A. Abt, A Discussion of Spectral Classification, *Ap. Jour. Supplement Series* **8**, 75, Apr. 1963.—J.T.K.]

CHAPTER VI

THE ORBIT OF A SPECTROSCOPIC BINARY STAR

The problem of determining the orbit of a binary system from measures of radial velocity, made in the manner described in the previous chapter, differs in several important particulars from that of computing an orbit from micrometric measures of position angle and distance. It has been shown that micrometer measures provide the data from which the projection of the orbit of the companion star with respect to its primary can be drawn, the true relative orbit following, correct in proportions but of unknown linear dimensions. The radial velocities, on the other hand, when plotted against the times, produce a periodic curve, having the general appearance of a distorted sine curve; from this curve we are to find the elements of the true orbit of the star with respect to the center of gravity of the system of which it forms one component.*

Figure 9 illustrates the conditions of the problem. Let the XY-plane be tangent to the celestial sphere at the center of motion, and let the Z-axis, perpendicular to the XY-plane, be parallel to the line of sight along which the radial velocities are measured. *The velocities are considered positive $(+)$ when the star is receding from, and negative $(-)$ when it is approaching the observer.* The orientation of the X- and Y-axes remains unknown. Let PSA be the true orbit of the star with respect to the center of motion and let the orbit plane intersect the XY-plane in the line NN'.

Then, when the star is at any point S in its orbit, its distance z from the XY-plane will be

$$z = r \sin i \sin (v + \omega)$$

* It is here assumed that the spectrum of only one component is visible; when both components give spectra, we may determine the relative orbit of one with respect to the other, using the same formulas but changing the value of the constant of attraction. The relative and absolute orbits are, of course, similar in every respect.

the symbols in the right-hand member of the equation having the same significance as in the case of a visual binary star.

The spectrograph, however, does not give us the *distances* of the star from the XY-plane, but the *velocities of its approach*

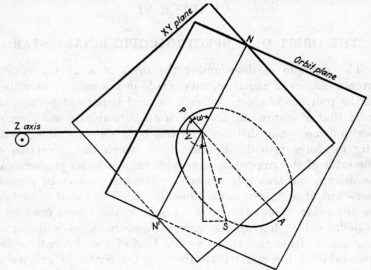

Fig. 9.—The spectroscopic binary star problem.

to, or recession from this plane, generally expressed in kilometers per second. The radial velocity at point S is equal to dz/dt, and is therefore expressed by

$$\frac{dz}{dt} = \sin i \sin (v + \omega)\frac{dr}{dt} + r \sin i \cos (v + \omega)\frac{dv}{dt}$$

From the known laws of motion in an ellipse we have

$$r\frac{dv}{dt} = \frac{\mu a(1 + e \cos v)}{\sqrt{1 - e^2}}, \qquad \frac{dr}{dt} = \frac{\mu a e \sin v}{\sqrt{1 - e^2}}$$

and therefore

$$\frac{dz}{dt} = \frac{\mu a \sin i}{\sqrt{1 - e^2}}[e \cos \omega + \cos (v + \omega)] \qquad (1)$$

which is the fundamental equation connecting the radial velocities with the elements of the orbit.*

* In place of $(v + \omega)$ the symbol u (= the argument of the latitude) is often used, the expressions for $\frac{dr}{dt}$ and $r\frac{du}{dt}$ written

The observed velocities evidently contain the velocity, V, of the center of mass of the system, which is a constant quantity for any given simple binary system,* as well as the variable velocities due to the star's orbital motion and the quantity V must therefore be subtracted from the observed values to make them purely periodic. In other words, the velocity curve is purely periodic only with respect to a line representing the velocity of the system as a whole. This line is called the V-axis.

Equation (1) applies only to the velocities counted from the V-axis. If $d\zeta/dt$ represents the velocity as actually observed (*i.e.*, the velocity referred to the zero-axis) we shall have the relation†

$$\frac{d\zeta}{dt} = V + \frac{dz}{dt} = V + \frac{\mu a \sin i}{\sqrt{1 - e^2}}[e \cos \omega + \cos (v + \omega)] \quad (1a)$$

Methods of determining the position of the V-axis will be given later; for the present we shall assume it to be known.

Five constants enter the right hand member of Eq. (1), *viz.*, $a \sin i$, e, μ, ω, and (through v) T. These express the five orbit elements which it is possible to determine by measures of radial velocity.

Since the inclination of the orbit plane is not determinable, the value of a, the semimajor axis, must also remain unknown. It is therefore customary to regard the function $a \sin i$ as an

$$\frac{dr}{dt} = \frac{f}{\sqrt{p}}e \sin (u - \omega), \quad \text{and} \quad r\frac{du}{dt} = \frac{f\sqrt{p}}{r} = \frac{f}{\sqrt{p}} [1 + e \cos (u - \omega)]$$

and hence the fundamental equation in the form

$$\frac{dz}{dt} = \frac{f}{\sqrt{p}} \sin i \, (\cos u + e \cos \omega).$$

In these equations $p \; [\equiv a(1 - e^2)]$ is the semi-parameter of the true ellipse and f denotes the constant of attraction, which, when the spectrum of only one component is visible, and the motion is determined with reference to the center of mass of the system, takes the form $km^{3/2}/(m + m_1)$, k being the Gaussian constant; when both spectra are visible and the motion of one star with respect to the other is determined, $f = k\sqrt{m + m_1}$. It is clear that the form of the fundamental equation will be the same whatever value we may assign to f and the constant of attraction may therefore be disregarded until the question of the relative masses in the system comes up for discussion.

* In a triple or multiple system, this quantity will itself be variable.

† The symbol γ is often used for the velocity of the system instead of V.

element. Further, it is clear that the position of the line of nodes cannot be determined, though we can find the times when the star passes through each of the nodal points. The various elements have the same definitions as in the case of visual binary star orbits (see page 78), except that the angle ω in spectroscopic binary orbits is always measured from the ascending node, *the node at which the star is moving away from the observer.* It will be seen later that the radial velocity has its maximum positive value at this node and its minimum positive value (or maximum negative value) at the descending node. It should also be noted that the unit of time for μ (and therefore for P) is the day, not the year as in visual binary orbits.

Theoretically, values of the radial velocity at five different times suffice for the complete solution of Eq. (1); practically, no computer undertakes an orbit until a considerable number of measures is available which give the velocities at short intervals throughout the entire revolution period. To secure a satisfactory distribution of the observations a preliminary value of the period is necessary and such a value can ordinarily be obtained without difficulty by plotting the early observations on coordinate paper, taking the times, expressed in Julian days and decimals of a day, as abscissas and the velocities, expressed in kilometers per second, as ordinates. A convenient epoch as origin for the period is selected near the beginning of the series, preferably one corresponding to a point of maximum or minimum velocity. If later measures indicate that the period is in error, a new period which is a submultiple of the original one will often prove satisfactory. In difficult cases, the following artifice may be found helpful.* Copy on transparent paper from one-third to one-half of the series of observed points, choosing the time interval best covered by observation; slide the copy along the original plot, keeping the time axis in coincidence, until some point on the copy falls approximately upon a different point in the original at which the velocity is changing in the same direction. The time interval between the

---

* This was suggested to me by Dr. R. K. Young who said that it had been used with good results by several computers of binary star orbits at the Dominion Observatory. No prior mention of the device has been found in print and its author is unknown to me. Its usefulness arises from the fact that, in effect, it doubles the number of observations for a given time interval.

two points is evidently equal to the period or a multiple of the period.

Schlesinger* has published a criterion that may be applied to advantage in cases where an observer has accumulated many plates of a star which apparently shows variable radial velocity without being able to determine any period. It consists in constructing a frequency curve for the velocities by "dividing the total range exhibited by the measured velocities into successive groups of equal extent, say 3 km each, and then counting the number of velocities that fall within these groups. Regarding these numbers as ordinates, we plot them and join the ends by a smooth curve." This curve is compared with the well-known error curve; if the two are the same, within reasonable limits, we may conclude that the differences in the measured velocities are due to errors of observation, and afford no support for the assumption that the star is a spectroscopic binary. If the two curves differ, the star is a binary and the form of the frequency curve will give an idea as to the general character of the orbit and frequently furnish a clew to the period. For Schlesinger shows that circular orbits, elliptic orbits with periastron at descending node, elliptic orbits with periastron at ascending node, and elliptic orbits with periastron removed 90° from the nodes, all have characteristic frequency curves which differ in form from the error curve. When the nature of the frequency curve has shown to which of these classes the orbit in question belongs, it becomes very much easier to decide upon the epochs for the various observed velocities, and thus upon an approximate value for the period.

When the period is approximately known all of the observations may be reduced to a single revolution by subtracting

* *Ap. Jour.* **41**, 162, 1915. In his paper on the "Orbit of the Spectroscopic Binary χ *Aurigae*" (*Jour. R.A.S.C.* **10**, 358, 1916), Young shows that the errors of measurement may affect the expected distribution in such a manner as to mask to a considerable degree the presence of the orbital variation. If possible, all of the spectrograms used in the determination of a particular orbit should be secured with the same instrument and measured by the same person, to avoid the effect of systematic errors of observation and of the personal equation in measurement. The small systematic differences between the radial velocities of stars made at different observatories have been discussed by several investigators. See, for example, Dr. J. H. Moore's Introduction to his *General Catalogue of the Radial Velocities of Stars, Nebulae, and Clusters* (*Publ. Lick Obs.* **18**, 1932).

multiples of the period from the later dates. A preliminary curve is drawn to represent the plotted positions as closely as possible. The deviations from the curve at points near the mean of the maximum and minimum velocities, where a change in the periodic time will have the greatest effect, will indicate advisable changes in the assumed period and these are readily found by dividing the deviations of such critical observations, expressed in time, by the number of revolutions elapsed. A second curve is then drawn whose periodic time will generally be very close to the true value. In practice it will frequently happen that two or three measures of the radial velocity of a star are available which were made (perhaps at another observatory) several years before the series of spectrograms for the orbit computation is begun. When a fairly good value of the period has been found from the later series, these early plates will determine its true value with high precision. Generally they are not used in finding the other orbit elements.

When the period has been determined as accurately as possible and a series of spectrograms has been accumulated giving the velocities at points well distributed throughout the entire period, the most probable curve is drawn, by estimation, through the points as plotted, and, if the ingenious methods of superposition devised by Schwarzschild and Zurhellen are to be used, the curve should be prolonged through a revolution and a half. The plotted points used for this curve should represent normal positions, formed by combining several velocities observed at very nearly the same orbit phase, whenever the number of observations is sufficient to permit such combinations. In making the combinations, the question of weights arises, and here the practice of computers varies considerably, for several factors enter. The character of the lines on the spectrograms, broad or narrow, sharp or ill-defined, strong or weak, is one factor; the number of lines is another; if the plates have been taken with different telescopes and spectrographs, a third factor is introduced. These must all be considered in assigning the weights to each plate. The only direction that can be given is the general one to use a rather simple system of weighting. It will rarely be of advantage to assign fractional weights, or to use a range of weights greater than, say, four units. The weights should, of course, be assigned to each plate, at the time of measurement.

The errors in drawing the most probable curve have considerable effect upon the accuracy of the determination of the elements. At best the curve is not likely to be a perfect representation of the elliptic motion which caused it since it is natural to bend the curve slightly in or out at different points to satisfy the more or less exact observations. This difficulty is inherent and for it there is apparently no remedy other than that of testing the first orbit by a trial ephemeris and making the small changes in the elements which are indicated by the residuals.*

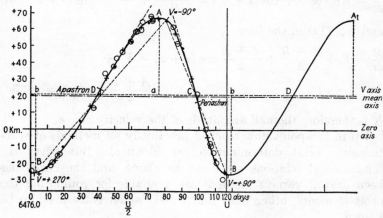

FIG. 10.—Velocity curve of κ *Velorum.*

If Fig. 10 represents a velocity curve, it is evident from Eq. (1) that the points A and B correspond respectively to the ascending and descending nodes of the star's orbit, for at the times of nodal passage we have $(v + \omega) = 0°$, and $(v + \omega) = 180°$, respectively, and therefore $\cos (v + \omega) = \pm 1$. The radial velocity thus reaches its maximum and minimum values at the nodal points.

Taking A and B as the magnitudes of the curve ordinates at the points of maximum and minimum reckoned from the V-axis, regarding B as a positive quantity and writing for brevity $K = \mu a \sin i/\sqrt{1 - e^2}$, we have

$$A = K(1 + e \cos \omega)$$
$$B = K(1 - e \cos \omega)$$

* King's method affords a graphical test of the first orbit found, see page 170.

and therefore

$$\left.\begin{array}{c} \dfrac{A+B}{2} = K \\[2ex] \dfrac{A-B}{2} = Ke\cos\omega \\[2ex] \dfrac{A-B}{A+B} = e\cos\omega \end{array}\right\} \qquad (2)$$

Hence we may write Eq. (1) in the form

$$\frac{dz}{dt} = K[e\cos\omega + \cos(v+\omega)] = \frac{A-B}{2} + \frac{A+B}{2}\cos(v+\omega) \qquad (3)$$

and Eq. (1a) in the form

$$\frac{d\zeta}{dt} = V + \frac{A-B}{2} + \frac{A+B}{2}\cos(v+\omega) = V_1 +$$
$$\frac{A+B}{2}\cos(v+\omega). \qquad (3a)$$

K is therefore the half amplitude of the velocity curve.

Up to the point now reached practically all methods of spectroscopic orbit determination are identical. But when the fundamental relations are given as above, and the curve has been drawn, various methods are available for computing the orbit elements, other than the period, which is assumed to be known.

Of these, the method devised by Lehmann-Filhés will first be presented, essentially in full; other methods will then be treated in less detail. The student who desires to study the various methods more fully is referred to the important papers given in the references at the end of the chapter.

METHOD OF LEHMANN-FILHÉS

Given the observations, and the velocity curve drawn with the value of P assumed as known, the first step is to fix the V-axis, the line defining the velocity of the center of gravity of the system. This is found by the condition that the integral of dz/dt, that is, the area of the velocity curve, must be equal for the portions of the curve above and below the V-axis. By far the easiest method of performing this integration is to use a planimeter. A line, approximately correct, is first drawn by estimation; the areas contained between it and the curve above and below are measured, and the difference between the two is taken. The position of the axis is then shifted to eliminate this difference, and the measures are repeated. It will rarely be necessary to make more than one correction to secure an accurate value of the position of the V-axis, which, by this method, depends upon the entire curve.

If a planimeter is not available, the areas above and below the axis may be equalized by using coordinate paper for the plot of the curve and counting the small squares in each area. Approximate mechanical integration, as advised by Lehmann-Filhés, may also be resorted to, by those who enjoy this form of recreation.

Having found the V-axis, the ordinates to it are next drawn from the points of maximum and minimum velocity, A and B. It is at this point, as Curtis says, that the method is weakest, for slight errors in fixing the position of A and B may easily arise. It is well to apply the check afforded by the requirement that area AaC (Fig. 10) must equal CbB and DaA equal BbD. Since C and D lie on the V-axis the velocities at these points are zero, hence from Eqs. (3) and (2) we have for dz/dt at these points

$$\cos (v + \omega) = - \frac{A - B}{A + B} = - e \cos \omega \tag{4}$$

If v_1 is the true anomaly corresponding to the point C, which is traversed by the star on the way from the ascending to the descending node, and v_2, the true anomaly for the point D, $\sin (v_1 + \omega)$ will be positive, $\sin (v_2 + \omega)$ negative, and we shall have

$$\left.\begin{array}{ll} \cos (v_1 + \omega) = - \dfrac{A - B}{A + B}, & \cos (v_2 + \omega) = - \dfrac{A - B}{A + B} \\[2mm] \sin (v_1 + \omega) = \dfrac{2\sqrt{AB}}{A + B}, & \sin (v_2 + \omega) = - \dfrac{2\sqrt{AB}}{A + B} \end{array}\right\} \tag{5}$$

Let Z_1 and Z_2 denote the areas* AaC and bBD (Fig. 10), respectively, and let r_1 and r_2 be the radii vectores for the points C and D.
Then

$$Z_1 = r_1 \sin i \sin (v_1 + \omega)$$
$$Z_2 = r_2 \sin i \sin (v_2 + \omega) = - r_2 \sin i \sin (v_1 + \omega)$$

* These areas represent the distances of the star from the XY-plane at the points in its orbit corresponding to $(v_1 + \omega)$ and $(v_2 + \omega)$.

and therefore

$$-\frac{Z_1}{Z_2} = \frac{r_1}{r_2} = \frac{1 + e \cos v_2}{1 + e \cos v_1} \tag{6}$$

since $r = [a(1 - e^2)]/(1 + e \cos v)$. Write $(v + \omega - \omega)$ for v, in Eq. (6), expand, and reduce, with the aid of the relations in Eqs. (5) and (4), and we have

$$-\frac{Z_1}{Z_2} = \frac{\sin (v_1 + \omega) - e \sin \omega}{\sin (v_1 + \omega) + e \sin \omega}$$

whence

$$e \sin \omega = \frac{Z_2 + Z_1}{Z_2 - Z_1} \sin (v_1 + \omega) = \frac{2\sqrt{AB}}{A + B} \cdot \frac{Z_2 + Z_1}{Z_2 - Z_1} \tag{7}$$

Equation (7) and the last of Eq. (2) determine e and ω. The values of A and B are taken from the curve, and the areas Z_1 and Z_2 are quickly integrated from the curve portions AaC and bBD by means of a planimeter, the latter area being regarded as negative in sign. Since the areas enter as a ratio, the unit of area used is entirely immaterial.

At the time of periastron passage $v = 0°$; hence from Eq. (3) we have

$$\frac{dz}{dt_p} = K(1 + e) \cos \omega \tag{8}$$

which gives the ordinate corresponding to the point of periastron passage. Two points of the curve will have the same ordinate, but since $(v + \omega)$ equals $0°$, $180°$, and $360°$ for the points A, B, and A_1, respectively, there will be no ambiguity as to the position of the periastron point. The abscissa of this point, properly combined with the epoch chosen for the beginning of the curve, defines T, the time of periastron passage. Instead of using Eq. (8) we may find T by determining E for the point C for which the value of v is known, and then employ the formulas

$$\left.\begin{array}{c} \tan \tfrac{1}{2}E = \sqrt{\dfrac{1 - e}{1 + e}} \tan \tfrac{1}{2}v \\[2mm] T = t - \dfrac{E - e \sin E}{\mu} \end{array}\right\} \tag{8a}$$

or, if the eccentricity is less than 0.77, the value of M corresponding to v may be taken directly from the Allegheny Tables, and T found from the relation

$$M = \mu(t - T). \tag{8b}$$

Such procedure is especially advisable when the periastron points fall near point A or B on the curve.

By definition (page 157) we have

$$K = \frac{\mu a \sin i}{\sqrt{1 - e^2}}$$

and hence

$$\mu = \frac{K\sqrt{1 - e^2}}{a \sin i} = \frac{A + B}{2} \cdot \frac{\sqrt{1 - e^2}}{a \sin i}$$

from which we may find the value of the product $a \sin i$. Since the unit of time for A and B is the second, while for μ it is the day, the factor 86,400 must be introduced. Our equation then becomes

$$a \sin i = 86{,}400 \frac{K}{\mu} \sqrt{1 - e^2} = (4.13833)KP \sqrt{1 - e^2} \tag{9}$$

the number in parentheses being the logarithm of the quotient $86400 \div 2\pi$.

Summarizing, the practical procedure is:

1. Find the period as accurately as possible by successive trials and plot the most probable velocity curve on the basis of normal places.

2. Find the position of the V-axis by integration of areas, using the planimeter, if available.

3. Measure the ordinates for points A and B and find the areas of AaC and bBD expressed in any convenient units.

4. From Eqs. (2) and (7) determine K, e, and ω.

5. From Eq. (8), or by calculation from the value of v, for the point C, determine T.

6. From Eq. (9) determine $a \sin i$.

To test the elements by comparison with the observations, we compute the radial velocity for each date by the formulas:

$$\left.\begin{aligned}
M &= \mu(t - T) = E - e \sin E \\
\tan \tfrac{1}{2}v &= \sqrt{\frac{1 + e}{1 - e}} \tan \tfrac{1}{2} E \\
\frac{d\zeta}{dt} &= V + Ke \cos \omega + K \cos (v + \omega)
\end{aligned}\right\} \tag{10}$$

The value of v for each value of M may be taken directly from the Allegheny Tables, if e is less than 0.77.

To illustrate Lehmann-Filhés' method I have chosen the orbit computed for κ *Velorum*, by H. D. Curtis, the velocity curve for which is given in Fig. 10.

The observations used were as follows:

Julian Day, G. M. T.	Velocity	Julian Day, G. M. T.	Velocity
2,416,546.739	+68.5^{km}	2,417,686.591	+33.8^{km}
60.703	+12.9	91.572	+38.2
97.651	+65.7	92.545	+43.2
6,912.601	+53.3	96.480	+46.7
7,587.844	+58.6	7,701.494	+52.7
88.788	+57.9	41.466	+22.1
90.829	+58.5	46.463	+ 0.3
91.824	+64.8	49.470	− 7.6
97.788	+65.8	50.479	− 8.8
7,609.790	+62.0	51.463	−13.3
54.534	−21.0	53.457	−19.2
55.556	−19.2	58.451	−29.0
58.570	−15.2	59.460	−24.6
59.545	−14.5		

The small circles representing the first four observations, which are important in determining the period, owing to their distance in time from the later ones, are barred in the diagram. The period, P, was assumed to be 116.65 days, and the beginning of the curve is at Julian day 2,416,476.0. This is not exactly at a minimum, as may be seen from the diagram.

From measures of the curve we find

$A = 46.3$ $Z_1 = AaC = +0.168$
$B = 46.9$ $Z_2 = bBD = -0.259$
$A + B = 93.2$ $Z_2 + Z_1 = -0.091$
$A - B = -0.6$ $Z_2 - Z_1 = -0.427$
$K = (A + B)/2 = 46.6$

the figures for area being expressed in decimals of the unit of area for the planimeter employed.

The solution of Eqs. (2), (7), and (8) then proceeds as follows:

$$\log 2 \quad 0.3010$$
$$\log \sqrt{AB} \quad 1.6684$$

$$\text{colog } (A + B) \qquad 8.0306$$
$$\log (Z_2 + Z_1) \qquad 8.9560n$$
$$\text{colog } (Z_2 - Z_1) \qquad 0.3696n$$
$$\log e \sin \omega \qquad 9.3286$$
$$\log (A - B) \qquad 9.7782n$$
$$\log \left(\frac{A - B}{A + B} = \right) e \cos \omega \qquad 7.8088n$$
$$\log \tan \omega \qquad 1.5198n$$
$$\omega \qquad 91°73$$
$$\log \sin \omega \qquad 9.9998$$
$$\log e \qquad 9.3288$$
$$e \qquad 0.21$$
$$\log (1 + e) \qquad 0.0828$$
$$\log \cos \omega \qquad 8.4800n$$
$$\log K \qquad 1.6684$$
$$\log \frac{dz}{dt_p} \qquad 0.2312n$$
$$\text{ordinate } p - 1.7 \text{ km}$$
$$\therefore \text{ from curve } t_p = 98.4$$
$$T^* = \text{J. D. } 2{,}416{,}457.75$$
$$\log \text{const.} \quad 4.1383$$
$$\log K \qquad 1.6684$$
$$\log P \qquad 2.0669$$
$$\log \sqrt{1 - e^2} \qquad 9.9902$$
$$\log a \sin i \qquad 7.8638$$
$$a \sin i \qquad 73{,}000{,}000+ \text{ km}$$

The preliminary values thus obtained are next tested by comparing the velocities derived from them by Eqs. (10) with the observed velocities. To illustrate, let us compute the velocity for J. D. 2,416,496.0, twenty days after the origin adopted in our curve. We have

$$t = 2{,}416{,}496.0 \qquad \log \cos (v + \omega) \quad 9.8277n$$
$$t - T = \quad +38.0 \qquad \log K \qquad 1.6684$$
$$\log (t - T) \qquad 1.57978 \qquad\qquad\qquad 1.4961n$$
$$\log \mu \qquad 0.48942 \qquad \frac{A + B}{2} \cos (v + \omega) - 31.3 \text{ km}$$

* T is here taken one revolution earlier than the date for the periastron point marked on the curve. Using Eq. (8a) or (8b) we obtain $T = $ J. D. 2,416,458.0 which is adopted.

$$M \qquad 117°27 \qquad \frac{A-B}{2} \qquad -0.3$$

$$v \qquad 136.01 \qquad V \qquad +20.7$$

$$v+\omega \qquad 227.74 \qquad \frac{d\zeta}{dt} \qquad = -10.9 \text{ km}$$

In this manner we compute as many velocities as necessary to obtain a curve for comparison with the observed velocity curve. In the present instance this was done for every tenth day, and the results plotted as heavy black dots in the figure. By noting the discrepancies, it appears that the branch on the apastron side of the computed curve, if drawn, would be a little too sloping, the other branch too steep, which indicates that the computed value of e is a little too large. Changing this element and making the corresponding slight changes required in T and ω, the test was repeated and after a few trials the following elements were adopted as best representing the observations:

$$V = +21.9 \text{ km}$$
$$P = 116.65 \text{ days}$$
$$e = 0.19$$
$$K = 46.5$$
$$\omega = 96°23$$
$$T = \text{J. D. } 2,416,459.0$$
$$a \sin i = 73,000,000 \text{ km}$$

The correction to the value of V was found last of all from the residuals of the final ephemeris by the simple formula $[v]/n$, where n is the number of observations and v the residual, $(o - c)$. The residuals from the final ephemeris and the final curve may be found in *Lick Observatory Bulletin*, No. 122, 1907.

Lehmann-Filhés' method may be termed the classical one, and it is probably more generally used than any other. The method proposed by Rambaut is considerably longer and more involved than the later ones, and for that reason will not be described here. Wilsing's method, as originally published, was suitable only for orbits of small eccentricity, but Russell later extended it to make it applicable to larger eccentricities as well. This method is purely analytical, consisting in finding a Fourier's series for the velocity in terms of the elements. It should be very useful in special cases, particularly when the period is so nearly a year that one part of the velocity curve is not represented by any observations; but it is considerably longer, in time consumed, than the method of Lehmann-Filhés and other geometrical methods to be described presently and will not be further considered here.

Certain features of the methods proposed by Schwarzschild and Zurhellen are both ingenious and practical. The following account of them is taken in substance from Curtis' article already referred to.

SCHWARZSCHILD'S METHOD

Given the velocity curve and the period, Schwarzschild first determines the time of periastron passage. Let M_1 and M_2 be the observed velocities (*i.e.*, *the velocities measured from the zero-axis*) of maximum and minimum, and draw the line whose ordinate is $(M_1 + M_2)/2$. This line is the mean axis. Mark upon it the points corresponding to $P/2$ and $3P/2$; then lay a piece of semitransparent paper over the plot, copy upon it the curve together with the mean axis and mark also the points 0, $P/2$, P, and $3P/2$. Shift the copy bodily along the mean axis for the distance $P/2$, and then rotate it 180° about this axis, *i.e.*, turn the copy face downward on the original curve keeping the mean axis in coincidence and bring the point 0 or P of the copy over the point $P/2$ of the original. The curves will then cut each other in at least four points, and, in general, in four points only. These will fall into two pairs, the points of each pair separated by an abscissa interval $P/2$. The points of one pair will be on different branches of the velocity curve, and it is easy to see that, if v_1 and v_2 represent their true anomalies, we shall have $v_2 = v_1 + 180°$. Now the only two points in the true orbit which are separated by one-half a revolution and for which at the same time this relation of the true anomalies holds are the points of periastron and apastron passage. Hence, to select these points, choose the two points of intersection of the curve and its copy which are separated by half a revolution and which lie on different branches of the curve. To distinguish periastron from apastron we have the criteria: (1) at periastron the velocity curve is steeper with respect to the axis than at apastron; (2) the curve is for a shorter time on that side of the mean axis on which the point of periastron lies.

This method is exceedingly good except when the eccentricity is small. In this case, ω and T are quite indeterminate and small errors in drawing the velocity curve will be very troublesome. The method of Lehmann-Filhés is then to be preferred.

Having the value of T, the value of ω is next found as follows: From Eqs. (1a) and (3) it is readily seen that the position of the mean axis is

$$\frac{M_1 + M_2}{2} = V + Ke \cos \omega = V_1$$

and that, accordingly, the ordinate z' of any point measured from the mean axis is

$$z' = \frac{d\zeta}{dt} - V_1 = K \cos(v + \omega) \tag{11}$$

Now at periastron $v = 0°$, at apastron $v = 180°$. Hence, if we call the ordinates from the mean axis for these points z_p' and z_a', we shall have

$$\cos \omega = \frac{z_p'}{K} \quad \text{or} \quad \cos \omega = \frac{z_p' - z_a'}{2K} \tag{12}$$

from which to determine ω. This method is at its best when ω is near $90°$.

Zurhellen has simplified Schwarzschild's method of finding e, and we shall give this simpler form in connection with Zurhellen's simple method of finding ω.

ZURHELLEN'S METHODS

Zurhellen's method of determining ω depends upon the relations between the velocities for the two orbit points whose true anomalies are $\pm 90°$. From Eq. (11) we have, when $v = -90°$,

$$z_1 = +K \sin \omega$$

and when $v = +90°$,

$$z_2 = -K \sin \omega$$

Moreover, for these two points we have

$$E_1 = -E_2$$
$$M_1 = -M_2$$
$$(t_1 - T) = -(t_2 - T)$$

Hence the two points are symmetrically placed with respect to the mean axis in the Y-coordinate and with respect to the point of periastron passage in the X-coordinate. They may therefore be determined by rotating the curve copy through 180° about the intersection of the ordinate of periastron with the mean axis, and noting the two points of intersection of the copy with the original curve. If the curve is prolonged through one and one-half revolutions, another point 180° from one of these, say at +270°, can be determined in similar manner and the location of all three can then be checked by drawing the lines connecting the point $v = +270°$ with $v = -90°$, and $v = -90°$ with $v = +90°$. These lines should cut the mean axis at its intersections with the ordinates of periastron and apastron, respectively. From the ordinates of the two points $v = \pm 90°$, measured from the mean axis, we have

$$\sin \omega = \frac{z_1 - z_2}{2K}, \quad \text{or} \quad \tan \omega = \frac{z_1 - z_2}{z_p - z_a} \quad (12a)$$

from which to find ω. The method is at its best when ω is small.

Zurhellen's simplification of Schwarzschild's method of finding e is also based upon the relations between the two points $v = \pm 90°$. Since

$$\tan \tfrac{1}{2}E = \tan \tfrac{1}{2}v \tan (45° - \tfrac{1}{2}\phi)$$

where ϕ is the eccentric angle, we have, when $v = \mp 90°$,

$$E_1 = -(90° - \phi), \qquad E_2 = +(90° - \phi)$$

Similarly,

$$M_1 = -(90° - \phi) + \frac{\sin \phi \sin (90° - \phi)}{\sin 1''}$$

$$M_2 = +(90° - \phi) - \frac{\sin \phi \sin (90° - \phi)}{\sin 1''}$$

and therefore

$$M_2 - M_1 = \frac{360°}{P}(t_2 - t_1) = (180° - 2\phi) - \frac{\sin (180° - 2\phi)}{\sin 1''} \quad (13)$$

The value of $(t_2 - t_1)$ may be read off directly from the diagram, and the value of $(90° - \phi)$ can then be taken from the table for Eq. (13), computed by Schwarzschild, which is given below. Like the above method for finding ω this method is best when ω is small.

SCHWARZSCHILD'S TABLE FOR THE EQUATION

$$2\eta - \sin 2\eta = \frac{360°}{P}(t_2 - t_1)$$

η	$\dfrac{t_2 - t_1}{P}$	η	$\dfrac{t_2 - t_1}{P}$	η	$\dfrac{t_2 - t_1}{P}$
0°	0.0000	30°	0.0290	60°	0.1956
1	0.0000	31	0.0318	61	0.2040
2	0.0000	32	0.0348	62	0.2125
3	0.0000	33	0.0380	63	0.2213
4	0.0001	34	0.0414	64	0.2303
5	0.0001	35	0.0450	65	0.2393
6	0.0002	36	0.0488	66	0.2485
7	0.0004	37	0.0527	67	0.2578
8	0.0006	38	0.0568	68	0.2673
9	0.0008	39	0.0611	69	0.2769
10	0.0011	40	0.0656	70	0.2867
11	0.0015	41	0.0703	71	0.2966
12	0.0020	42	0.0751	72	0.3065
13	0.0025	43	0.0802	73	0.3166
14	0.0031	44	0.0855	74	0.3268
15	0.0038	45	0.0910	75	0.3371
16	0.0046	46	0.0967	76	0.3475
17	0.0055	47	0.1025	77	0.3581
18	0.0065	48	0.1085	78	0.3687
19	0.0077	49	0.1147	79	0.3793
20	0.0089	50	0.1212	80	0.3900
21	0.0103	51	0.1278	81	0.4008
22	0.0117	52	0.1346	82	0.4117
23	0.0133	53	0.1416	83	0.4226
24	0.0151	54	0.1488	84	0.4335
25	0.0170	55	0.1561	85	0.4446
26	0.0191	56	0.1636	86	0.4557
27	0.0213	57	0.1713	87	0.4667
28	0.0237	58	0.1792	88	0.4778
29	0.0262	59	0.1873	89	0.4889
30	0.0290	60	0.1956	90	0.5000

Zurhellen also gives a method for finding the eccentricity by drawing the tangents to the curve at the points of periastron. These can be drawn quite accurately except when the periastron falls near a maximum or a minimum of the curve.

Slight changes in its position will then introduce considerable changes in the inclinations of the tangent lines.

The expression for the slope of a tangent may be written

$$\frac{dx}{dt} = \frac{2\pi}{P} \cdot \frac{dx}{dM} = \frac{2\pi}{P} \cdot \frac{1}{1 - e \cos E} \cdot \frac{dx}{dE}$$

where x ($= dz/dt$) represents the ordinate drawn to the V-axis. Also, by introducing the known values

$$\cos v = \frac{\cos E - \sin \phi}{1 - e \cos E}, \qquad \sin v = \frac{\cos \phi \sin E}{1 - e \cos E}$$

and transforming and simplifying we may write the fundamental Eq. (3) in the form

$$x = \frac{dz}{dt} = K \cos \phi \cdot \frac{\cos \phi \cos \omega \cos E - \sin \omega \sin E}{1 - e \cos E}$$

Differentiating with respect to E, substituting and reducing, we have

$$\frac{dx}{dt} = \frac{2\pi}{P} K \cos \phi \cdot \frac{- \cos \phi \cos \omega \sin E - \sin \omega \cos E + e \sin \omega}{(1 - e \cos E)^3} \quad (14)$$

At periastron $E = 0°$ and at apastron $E = 180°$, whence we have

$$\frac{dx}{dt_p} = \frac{-2\pi K \cos \phi \sin \omega}{P(1 - e)^2}, \qquad \frac{dx}{dt_a} = \frac{+2\pi K \cos \phi \sin \omega}{P(1 + e)^2}$$

and therefore

$$\frac{dx/dt_p}{dx/dt_a} = -\frac{(1 + e)^2}{(1 - e)^2} = -q^2$$

whence

$$e = \frac{q - 1}{q + 1} \quad (15)$$

KING'S METHOD

The methods of orbit computation so far described in this chapter all rest upon the curve drawn to represent as closely as possible the observed velocities and, at the same time, to satisfy the conditions for elliptic motion. Unless the measures are very precise, the first approximation will ordinarily not be satisfactory. As stated on page 157, the only remedy is to compute an ephemeris from the elements and, on the basis of the residuals thus found, to draw a new curve. This process is sometimes repeated three or four times before a curve is found that will yield elements upon which a least squares solution may be based.

The method devised by Dr. King, which is now to be presented, aims to substitute a rapid graphical process for testing

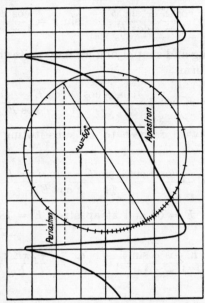

Fig. 11.—King's orbit method. Graph for $e = 0.75$, $\omega = 60°$.

the preliminary curve. Dr. King shows that a circle having its center on the mean axis and a radius equal to K, the semi-amplitude of the velocity curve, "may be used as the equivalent of the hodograph of observed velocities."*

Let the velocity curve and the circle be drawn (see Fig. 11) and the abscissa distance corresponding to one revolution (P being assumed to be known) be divided into any convenient number of parts, say forty.† Now mark consecutive points on the circumference of the circle by drawing lines parallel to

* For the proof of this relation the reader is referred to the original article in *Ap. Jour.* **27**, 125, 1908.

† An even number should be chosen, and it is obviously most convenient to make the drawing upon coordinate paper.

the mean axis at the intersections of the velocity curve with
the ordinates corresponding to successive values of the abscissa
and extending them to the circle. The circumference will
be divided into forty unequal parts, but these inequalities will
be found to vary uniformly. "The points will be close together
in the vicinity of one point of the circle, and will gradually
separate as we proceed in either direction therefrom, until
at the diametrically opposite point they reach their maximum
distance apart." These unequal arcs of the circle correspond
to the increase in the true anomalies in the orbit in the equal
time intervals, and therefore the point of widest separation
of the circle divisions corresponds to periastron, that of least
separation, to apastron. Further, the angle between the
Y-axis and the periastron-half of the diameter between these
two points is equal to ω. To locate the point of periastron
on the velocity curve, find the intersection of the steeper branch
of the curve with a line drawn from the periastron point on the
circle parallel to the mean axis.

It is evident that the division points of the circumference
will be symmetrically disposed with respect to the apsidal
diameter (the diameter joining periastron and apastron points)
only when one of the division points in the line of abscissae
corresponds to an apse. In general, the periastron point will
lie within the longest division of the circumference, the apastron point within the shortest. If desired, the approximate
position of one of these points may be used as a new origin
from which to set off the fortieths of the period along the axis
of abscissae, and two division points on the circle may then be
brought into closer coincidence with the apsidal points.

Since dv/dt varies inversely as the square of the distance from
the focus, by measuring the lengths d_1 and d_2 of the arcs at
points where v equals v_1 and v_2, we have

$$\frac{d_1}{d_2} = \frac{(1 + e \cos v_1)^2}{(1 + e \cos v_2)^2},$$

and hence if the arcs are measured at the points of periastron
and apastron where v equals $0°$ and $180°$, respectively,

$$\frac{d_1}{d_2} = \left(\frac{1 + e}{1 - e}\right)^2, \quad \text{or} \quad e = \frac{\sqrt{d_1} - \sqrt{d_2}}{\sqrt{d_1} + \sqrt{d_2}} \quad (16)$$

which determines e.

It is generally sufficiently accurate to measure the chords instead of the arcs; when the eccentricity is high and the arcs at periastron are inconveniently long, additional points of division may readily be inserted.

It will be observed that this process furnishes a more thorough test of the accuracy of the graph (velocity curve) than the method of equality of areas. If it is imperfect, the points on the circumference of the circle will not be distributed according to the regular order of increase or decrease of the included arcs. If an ordinate of the graph is too long or too short, the corresponding point on the circumference will be too near or too far from the vertical diameter. If the points of maximum and minimum velocity have not been well determined, the diameter of the circle will be too long or too short. In the former case all the points of the circumference will be crowded away from the vertical diameter; in the latter, toward it.*

To test a given set of elements by comparison with the observations proceed as follows:

Construct a circular protractor on some semitransparent material (*e.g.*, celluloid or linen tracing cloth) and divide it into forty parts by radii to points on the circumference representing the true anomalies for the given value of *e* corresponding to every 9° of mean anomaly (*i.e.*, to fortieths of the period). If the eccentricity is less than 0.77 the values of the true anomaly can be taken directly from the Allegheny Tables.

On the plot of the orbit draw a circle of radius K with its center on the mean axis and draw its vertical diameter. Set the protractor upon the circle, making the centers coincide, and turn the apsidal diameter of the protractor until it makes an angle equal to ω with the vertical diameter. Now note the points where the radial lines representing the anomalies intersect the circumference of the circle. The abscissa axis of the plot also having been divided into forty equal parts, erect perpendiculars at the points of division equal to the corresponding ordinates of the circle. A free-hand curve through the extremities of these perpendiculars (*i.e.*, ordinates to the mean axis) gives the computed curve or ephemeris, and the residuals can be read directly from the plot. The advantage of using coordinate paper will be obvious.

From the account just given it will appear that King's method is longer, or at least not shorter, than the others described

---

* King, *loc. cit.*

if only a single orbit is to be computed. But when orbit computation is to be taken up as a part of a regular program of work, the method has very decided advantages. It is then to be used as follows:

Let a set of protractors be constructed on transparent celluloid with radii representing the divisions in true anomaly for every 9° of mean anomaly for the values $e = 0.00$, $e = 0.05$ to $e = 0.95$.

With the aid of these protractors draw curves on tracing linen representing orbits with all values of e from 0.00 to 0.95 and all values of ω from 0° to 360°. The intervals for e should be 0.05, save for the larger values which are seldom used, and for ω, 15°. Practically, values of ω to 90° will suffice, the curves for the values in the remaining quadrants being obtained by inverting the sheet and by looking through the linen from the back in the two positions. Given the protractors, a complete set of curves may be constructed in about 10 hours' time.

Having such a set of curves, plot the normal places for any given binary star *on the same scale as these curves in time and in velocity.** Now place the standard curves upon the plot until one is found that fits the observations. "If two or more curves seem to give about equally good representations, it is quite possible to interpolate elements between the graphs plotted."†

By this process values of e correct to within one- or two-hundredths and of ω correct within a few degrees can generally be obtained at the first trial and with an expenditure of less than 10 minutes' time. The time of periastron passage follows at once, and this set of preliminary elements may then be used as the basis for a least squares adjustment. The procedure has been found very satisfactory at the Dominion Observatory at Ottawa, and at the Dominion Astrophysical Observatory, Victoria, B.C., where very many orbits of spectroscopic binary stars have been computed.

* Since the velocity curve is ordinarily based on from fifteen to twenty normal places the work of multiplying by the appropriate reduction factors will require a very few minutes only. Of course, the amplitude of the curve as well as the period must be known before the reduction factors can be obtained. These are known with sufficient accuracy from the preliminary plots.

† R. K. Young, Orbit of the Spectroscopic Binary 2 *Sagittae, Jour. R.A.S.C.* **11**, 127, 1917.

RUSSELL'S SHORT METHOD

Professor Henry Norris Russell has devised a graphical method which is equally simple in its practical application.*

Write Eq. (1a) in the form

$$\rho = V + \frac{dz}{dt} = V + Ke \cos \omega + K \cos (v + \omega) =$$
$$G + K \cos (v + \omega) \quad (17)$$

where ρ represents the observed radial velocity.

Then $(G + K)$ is the maximum, $(G - K)$ the minimum value of the velocity, so that G and K may be estimated at once from the free-hand curve. The period is also assumed to be known. Equation (17) may then be written in the form

$$\cos (v + \omega) = \frac{\rho - G}{K} \quad (18)$$

and the value of $(v + \omega)$ computed for each observed value of ρ.

If we subtract the corresponding values of $M + M_0$ from each of these, we shall have values of $(v - M) + (\omega - M_0)$. The second part of this expression is constant, while the first is the equation of the center in the elliptic motion. During a revolution this varies between equal positive and negative limits which depend only on the eccentricity, and are nearly proportioned to it, as is shown in the following table.

Eccentricity....	0.10	0.20	0.30	0.40	0.50	0.60	0.70	0.80	0.90
Maximum equation of center.	11°5	23°0	34°8	46°8	59°2	72°3	86°4	102°3	122°2

If the values of $(v - M) + (\omega - M_0)$ are plotted against those of $M + M_0$, we obtain a diagram which, since it represents the relations between the mean and the true anomalies, we may call the anomaly diagram. If on this diagram a curve is drawn to represent the plotted points, half the difference between its maximum and minimum ordinates will be the greatest value of the equation of the center, from which e may be found at once by means of the table. The mean of the maximum and minimum ordinates will be the value of $\omega - M_0$. The instants when $(v - M) + (\omega - M_0)$ has this value are those of periastron and apastron passage, the former corresponding to the ascending branch of the curve, which is always the steeper. The abscissae of the corre-

* *Ap. Jour.* **40**, 282, 1914.

sponding points of the curve are M_0 and $M_0 + 180°$. The values of e, M_0, and ω are now known, and the remaining elements may be found at once from K and G.

.According to Russell, the "principal advantage of this method is that the form of the curves which give $v - M$ as a function of M depends upon e alone." For further details and an illustrative example we refer the reader to the original memoir. Up to the present time the method has not come into general use. This remark applies also to the methods which have been developed by Laves, Henroteau, and more recent writers on the subject. References to the original papers for a number of these methods are given at the end of this chapter.

DIFFERENTIAL CORRECTIONS TO THE ELEMENTS

Whatever method may be used in finding the preliminary orbit it is generally advisable to determine the correction to the elements by the methods of least squares.* The formula derived by Lehmann-Filhés from which the coefficients for the observation equations are to be computed may be written as follows:

$$d\frac{d\zeta}{dt} = dV + [\cos (v + \omega) + e \cos \omega]dK$$

$$+K\left[\cos \omega - \frac{\sin (v + \omega) \sin v}{1 - e^2}(2 + e \cos v)\right]de$$

$$-K[\sin (v + \omega) + e \sin \omega]d\omega$$

* *Publ. Allegheny Obs.* **1**, 33, 1908.

The advantages of applying the method of least squares to the definitive solution of spectroscopic binary stars have been clearly stated by Schlesinger in this paper. "The problem," he says, "involves the evaluation of five quantities (six if the period be included) that are so interwoven as to make their separate determination a matter of some difficulty. Herein lies the chief advantage for this case of the method of least squares; for it enables us to vary all of the unknowns *simultaneously* instead of one or two at a time. . . . Further, the method of least squares not only has the advantage of greater accuracy and of telling us how reliable our results are, but it eliminates from the computations any personal bias or arbitrary step . . . the method should be used in almost every case where the elements are not avowedly provisional." Not all computers are so enthusiastic as to the method. Judgment must of course be exercised in all orbit work as to whether the data at hand warrant anything beyond the computation of purely provisional elements. In spectroscopic binary orbits, for example, such factors, among others, as the number and quality of the plates and their distribution over the velocity curve, the character of the star's spectrum, and the character of the orbit must be considered in making this decision.

$$+ \sin (v + \omega)(1 + e \cos v)^2 \frac{K\mu}{(1 - e^2)^{3/2}} dT$$

$$- \sin (v + \omega)(1 + e \cos v)^2 \frac{K}{(1 - e^2)^{3/2}} (t - T) d\mu \quad (19)$$

In practice the period is almost always assumed to be known with accuracy and the last term of the equation is omitted.

To facilitate the computation, Schlesinger has transformed this equation as follows: Put

$$\alpha = 0.452 \sin v(2 + e \cos v)$$

$$\beta = \frac{(1 + e \cos v)^2}{(1 + e)^2}$$

$$\Gamma = dV + e \cos \omega \, dK + K \cos \omega \, de - Ke \sin \omega \, d\omega$$

$$\kappa = dK$$

$$\pi = -K d\omega$$

$$\epsilon = -K \frac{2.21}{1 - e^2} de$$

$$\tau = K\mu \sqrt{\frac{1 + e}{1 - e}} \cdot \frac{1}{1 - e} dT$$

$$m = -K \sqrt{\frac{1 + e}{1 - e}} \cdot \frac{1}{1 - e} d\mu, \quad \text{and} \quad u = (v + \omega)$$

Then the equations of condition take the form

$$d\frac{d\zeta}{dt} = \Gamma + \cos u \cdot \kappa + \sin u \cdot \pi + \alpha \sin u \cdot \epsilon$$

$$+ \beta \sin u \cdot \tau + \beta \sin u \cdot (t - T)m \quad (20)$$

The quantities α and β can be tabulated once for all and such a tabulation is given by Schlesinger* so arranged "as to render the normal equations homogeneous and to enable all multiplications to be made with Crelle's tables without interpolation." If this notation is used, the computer should have these tables at hand.

When both spectra are visible on the plates, the orbits for the two components with respect to the center of mass may be determined separately. It is obvious that the two sets of values of V, e, T, and P must be identical, the values of ω must differ by 180°, while the two values for K depend upon the relative masses of the components. The preliminary elements

Loc. cit.

for the two components, when independently determined, will, in general, not harmonize perfectly. To obtain the definitive values the best procedure is the one first suggested, I believe, by Dr. King.* It consists in combining all the observations, those for the secondary with those for the primary, into a single set of observation equations (equations of condition) and solving for one complete set of elements. If we write $\omega' = (\omega + 180°)$ and distinguish the values of K for the two components by writing K_1 and K_2, respectively, the equations in the notation of Eq. (19) assume the form

$$d\frac{d\zeta}{dt} = dV + [\cos(v+\omega) + e\cos\omega]dK_1 + [\cos(v+\omega') + e\cos\omega']dK_2$$

$$+ \left\{ \left[\cos\omega - \frac{\sin(v+\omega)\sin v}{1-e^2}(2+e\cos v) \right]K_1 \right.$$

$$\left. + \left[\cos\omega' - \frac{\sin(v+\omega')\sin v}{1-e^2}(2+e\cos v) \right]K_2 \right\}de$$

$$- \{[\sin(v+\omega) + e\sin\omega]K_1 + [\sin(v+\omega') + e\sin\omega']K_2\}d\omega$$

$$+ [\sin(v+\omega)(1+e\cos v)^2 K_1$$

$$+ \sin(v+\omega')(1+e\cos v)^2 K_2]\frac{\mu}{(1-e^2)^{3/2}}dT \quad (21)$$

the value of the period being assumed to require no correction.

Since K_2 does not affect the residuals of the primary component, nor K_1 those of the secondary, the terms containing dK_2 and dK_1 disappear from the equations representing the residuals from the primary and secondary curves, respectively.

SECONDARY OSCILLATIONS

When the orbit of a spectroscopic binary star has been computed and the theoretical velocity curve drawn, it is sometimes found that the observed normal places are so distributed with respect to the curve representing simple elliptic motion as to suggest that a secondary oscillation is superimposed upon it. The question is whether this grouping arises from some source of error in the measurement of the spectrograms, from

---

* See Harper's paper, in *Publ. Dominion Obs.*, 1, 327, 1914. Dr. Paddock independently developed an equivalent equation. *Lick Obs. Bull.* **8**, 156, 1915.

erroneous values of one or more of the orbit elements, or from a real oscillation such as might be produced, for example, by the presence of a third body in the system. This question has been discussed by several investigators, among them Schlesinger, Zurhellen, and Paddock. As early as 1911, Schlesinger, then at the Allegheny Observatory, and his colleagues there, showed that the "blend effect" caused by the overlapping of the absorption lines of the two component spectra "may produce such an apparent oscillation." They have also shown that it may be produced by chance errors in the velocities derived from the different lines of the spectrum, and they are convinced that a critical analysis of the data will dispose of a considerable percentage of cases wherein secondary oscillations have been suspected. Later investigations by others have confirmed these conclusions.

The possibility of a real secondary oscillation must, of course, be recognized, and when a full analysis has shown that such an oscillation is present, additional terms may be introduced into the equations of condition to represent it upon the assumption that it is produced by a third body revolving in a circular orbit about one of the other two components. In the cases that have arisen thus far this simple assumption has yielded a satisfactory representation of the data, though it is apparent that there is no reason for limiting such additional bodies to circular orbits.

Let T' represent the time when the secondary curve crosses the primary from below, K' the semiamplitude of the secondary oscillation, m' the ratio of the principal period to that of the secondary oscillation, assumed to be known (it is generally taken to be an integer), and put $u' = m'\mu(t - T')$, $\tau' = -m'\mu K'dT'$, $\kappa' = dK'$; then the additional terms required in Eq. (20) are

$$+ \sin u' \cdot \kappa' + \cos u' \cdot \tau' \tag{22}$$

For a more complete discussion of secondary oscillations the reader is referred to the articles cited above.

ORBITS WITH SMALL ECCENTRICITY

In a circular orbit the elements T and ω obviously have no significance, and when the eccentricity is very small, they become practically indeterminate by the geometrical or graphical methods which have here been described. Further, if approximate values are assumed, it is impossible to find corrections to both elements from the same least squares solution because the coefficients for the differential corrections will be nearly or quite equal. Some computers have overcome this difficulty by assuming the preliminary value of ω as final, and determining corrections to T, but this is hardly a solution of the problem. In such orbits the analytic method possesses great advantages, as has been shown by several investigators, notably Wilsing, Russell, Zurhellen, and Plummer. Paddock has examined the question in great detail, extending some of the earlier developments and adapting them for computation. A full account of these methods would require more space than is available here, and it has seemed best to refer the reader to the original papers.

References

The following list of papers relating to one phase or another of the computation of orbits of spectroscopic binary stars, while not exhaustive, contains most of the more important ones.

RAMBAUT, A. A.: On the Determination of Double Star Orbits from Spectroscopic Observations of the Velocity in the Line of Sight, *Mon. Not. R.A.S.* **51**, 316, 1891.

WILSING, J.: Über die Bestimmung von Bahnelementen enger Doppelsterne aus spectroskopischen Messungen der Geschwindigkeits-Componenten, *A.N.* **134**, 89, 1893.

LEHMANN-FÍLHÉS, R.: Über die Bestimmung einer Doppelsternbahn aus spectroskopischen Messungen der im Visionsradius liegenden Geschwindigkeits-Componente, *A.N.* **136**, 17, 1894.

SCHWARZSCHILD, K.: Ein Verfahren der Bahnbestimmung bei spectroskopischen Doppelsternen, *A.N.* **152**, 65, 1900.

RUSSELL, H. N.: An Improved Method of Calculating the Orbit of a Spectroscopic Binary, *Ap. Jour.* **15**, 252, 1902.

————: A Short Method for Determining the Orbit of a Spectroscopic Binary, *Ap. Jour.* **40**, 282, 1914.

NIJLAND, A. N.: Zur Bahnbestimmung von spektroskopischen Doppelsternen, *A.N.* **161**, 103, 1903.

LAVES, K.: A Graphic Determination of the Elements of the Orbits of Spectroscopic Binaries, *Ap. Jour.* **26**, 164, 1907.

ZURHELLEN, W.: Der spectroskopische Doppelstern *o Leonis*, *A.N.* **173**, 353, 1907.

————: Bemerkungen zur Bahnbestimmung spectroskopischer Doppelsterne, *A.N.* **175**, 245, 1907.

————: Weitere Bemerkungen zur Bahnbestimmung spectroskopischer Doppelsterne, *u.s.w.*, *A.N.* **177**, 321, 1908.

————: Über sekondäre Wellen in den Geschwindigkeits-Kurven spectroskopischer Doppelsterne, *A.N.* **187**, 433, 1911.

KING, W. F.: Determination of the Orbits of Spectroscopic Binaries, *Ap. Jour.* **27**, 125, 1908.

CURTIS, H. D.: Methods of Determining the Orbits of Spectroscopic Binaries, *Publ. A.S.P.*, **20**, 133, 1908. (This paper has, with the author's permission, been very freely used in preparing my chapter on the subject.)

PLUMMER, H. C.: Notes on the Determination of the Orbits of Spectroscopic Binaries, *Ap. Jour.* **28**, 212, 1908.

SCHLESINGER, F.: The Determination of the Orbit of a Spectroscopic Binary by the Method of Least Squares, *Publ. Allegheny Obs.* **1**, 33, 1908.

———: On the Presence of a Secondary Oscillation in the Orbit of 30 H *Ursae Majoris*, *Publ. Allegheny Obs.* **2**, 139, 1911.

———: A Criterion for Spectroscopic Binaries, etc., *Ap. Jour.* **41**, 162, 1915.

PADDOCK, G. F.: Spectroscopic Orbit Formulae for Single and Double Spectra and Small Eccentricity, *Lick Obs. Bull.* **8**, 153, 1915.

CURTISS, R. H.: Method of Determining Elements of Spectroscopic Binaries, *Publ. Astron. Obs. Univ. of Michigan* **2**, 178, 1916.

HENROTEAU, F.: Two Short Methods for Computing the Orbit of a Spectroscopic Binary Star by Using the Allegheny Tables of Anomalies, *Publ. A.S.P.* **29**, 195, 1917.

KING, E. S.: Standard Velocity Curves for Spectroscopic Binaries, *Harvard Ann.* **81**, 231, 1921.

HALM, J. K. E.: On a Graphical Determination of the Orbital Elements of a Spectroscopic Binary, *Mon. Not. R.A.S.* **87**, 628, 1927.

PICART, L.: Remarques sur le calcul des orbites des étoiles doubles spectroscopiques, *J.O.* **10**, 137, 1927.

POGO, A.: On the Use of the Hodographic Method of Laves for Determining Elements of Spectroscopic Orbits, *Ap. Jour.* **67**, 262, 1928.

MADERNI, A.: La determinazione degli elementi orbitali di una doppia spettroscopica, *Mem. Soc. Astron. Italiana N.S.* **5**, 65, 1930.

ORLOFF, A.: Harmonic Tables for Spectroscopic Binaries, *Odessa Astron. Obs.* 1930.

LUYTEN, W. J.: A Rediscussion of the Orbits of 77 Spectroscopic Binaries (of Small Eccentricities), *Ap. Jour.* **84** (1), 85–103, July 1936.

In his *Third Catalogue of Spectroscopic Binary Stars* (*Lick Obs. Bull.* **11**, 141, 1924) Dr. J. H. Moore lists, in separate tables, all stars for which a variation in radial velocity had been fairly established, before 1924.0. See also his *Fourth Catalogue of Spectroscopic Binary Stars* (*Lick Obs. Bull.* **18**, 1–38, #483, 1936).

CHAPTER VII

ECLIPSING BINARY STARS

We have seen that one of the first binary systems to be discovered with the spectrograph was *Algol* (*β Persei*), long known as a variable star. There are other stars whose light varies in the same peculiar manner as that of *Algol;* that is, while it remains sensibly constant at full brightness the greater part of the time, at regular intervals it fades more or less rapidly to a certain minimum. It may remain constant at this minimum for a short time and then recover full brightness, or the change may be continuous. In either case the entire cycle of change is completed in a small fraction of the time of constant light between the successive minima.

The hypothesis that in every such case the star, as viewed from the Earth, undergoes a total, annular, or partial eclipse, the eclipsing body being a relatively dark star revolving with the other about a common center of gravity, completely accounts for the observed facts and has been proved to be correct not only in the one instance, *Algol*, but also in that of every Algol-type variable which has been investigated with the spectrograph. Undoubtedly it is the correct explanation for all stars of this type; they are all binary systems.

Unless the darker star is absolutely nonluminous, there should be a second minimum when the bright star passes between it and the Earth, the relative depth of the two minima depending upon the relative intensity of the light of the two stars and upon their relative areas. Such a secondary minimum has been observed in *β Lyrae* and in this star the light is not quite constant at any phase, either maximum or minimum. There is now no doubt but that this star and others like it are also binary systems.

It was formerly thought that a distinction could be drawn between variable stars of the type of *Algol* and those of the type of *β Lyrae*, but measures with sensitive modern photometers, such as the selenium cell, the photoelectric cell, and

181

the sliding-prism polarizing photometers, and measures of extrafocal images on photographic plates have attained such a degree of accuracy that a variation considerably less than one-tenth of a magnitude can be detected with certainty; and it now appears that *Algol* itself not only has a slight secondary minimum but that its light is not quite constant at maximum. The distinction, therefore, breaks down and we may regard all the stars of these two types as members of a single class, calling them *eclipsing binaries* or *eclipsing variables*, according to the point of view from which we take up their investigation. In all, nearly 1,000 eclipsing binary stars are known at the present time, a large percentage of them being too faint to photograph with our present spectrographic equipment. It is therefore a matter of great interest to inquire what information, if any, as to the orbits of these systems can be derived from their light curves, the curves, that is, which are constructed by taking the observed stellar magnitudes as ordinates and the corresponding times as abscissae.

Up to the beginning of the present century observations of eclipsing variables were made chiefly to determine the times of minima accurately, with the object of improving the light elements. As data accumulated, variations in the period began to be noted in many instances. Dr. Seth Chandler in particular was greatly interested in these variations and added parabolic or periodic terms to the light elements in his catalogues of variable stars published in the *Astronomical Journal*, but did not find an explanation for them. For the most part, in fact, these variations are so complicated that they are still a puzzle in celestial mechanics, but in the case of Y *Cygni*,* the variation has been definitely traced to a revolution of the line of apsides, produced, apparently, by the ellipsoidal figure of the component stars.

The earlier observations, confined as they were chiefly to estimates of the time of minimum, were unsatisfactory material for the determination of the orbital elements. Among the pioneers in the accurate observation of the entire light curve we may name Roberts and Nijland, using the method of estimates developed by Argelander; Wendell and Dugan, using a polarizing photometer devised by E. C. Pickering; Stebbins, using selenium and photoelectric cells; and Parkhurst, Seares, and Baker, using photographic methods.

* Dugan, *Contr. Princeton Univ. Obs.* 12, 1931.

Professor E. C. Pickering* made an investigation of the orbit of *Algol* on the basis of its light curve as early as 1880, and showed that a solution of such orbits was possible if certain reasonable assumptions—for example, that the two stars are spherical with uniformly illuminated disks and move in circular orbits—were granted. The subject was resumed by him later, and was taken up also by Harting, Tisserand, A. W. Roberts, and others.

In the years 1912 to 1915, Russell and Shapley, at Princeton University,† made a very thorough investigation of the problem, Russell developing a general analytical method, which has formed the basis of nearly all later calculations, and Shapley applying it to the computations of the orbit elements of 90 systems, 31 of the solutions being indicated as of the first grade. Modifications of this method have been proposed by various investigators, and Sitterly has developed a graphical method, but in the present chapter Russell's method will be given.

In the most general case the problem is an extremely complicated one, for the orbits must be regarded as elliptical with planes inclined at a greater or less angle to the line of sight, and the two components as ellipsoids, the longest diameter of each being directed toward the other star. Moreover, the disks may or may not be uniformly illuminated; they may be darker toward the limb, as our own Sun is, the degree of darkening depending upon the depth and the composition of the enveloping atmosphere; and the side of each which receives the radiation from the other may be brighter than the opposite side. The complete specification of an eclipsing binary system therefore requires a knowledge of at least 13 quantities which, in Russell's notation, are as shown in the table on page 184.

The longitude of the node must remain unknown, as there is no hope of telescopic separation of any eclipsing pair.

The value of a in absolute units can be found only from spectroscopic data. In the absence of these, it is desirable to take a as an unknown but definite unit of length, and express all other linear dimensions in terms of it. Similarly, the absolute values of L_1 and L_2 can be determined only if the parallax of the system is known. But in all cases the

---

* Dimensions of the Fixed Stars, with special reference to Binaries and Variables of the Algol Type, *Proc. Amer. Acad. Arts and Sciences* **16**, 1, 1881.

† References to their papers are given, with others, at the end of this chapter.

combined light of the pair, $L_1 + L_2$, can be taken as the unit of light and the apparent brightness at any time expressed in terms of this. This leaves the problem with eleven unknown quantities to be determined from the photometric measures. Of these, the period is invariably known with a degree of accuracy greatly surpassing that attainable for any of the other elements, and the epoch of principal minimum can be determined, almost independently of the other elements, by inspection of the light-curve. Of the remaining elements, the constants expressing ellipticity and reflection may be derived from the observed brightness between eclipses. These effects are often so small as to be detected only by the most refined observations. The question of darkening toward the limb may well be set aside until the problem is solved for the case of stars that appear as uniformly illuminated disks.

Orbital Elements		Eclipse Elements	
Semimajor axis	a	Radius of larger star	r_1
Eccentricity	e	Radius of smaller star	r_2
Longitude of periastron	ω	Light of larger star	L_1
Inclination	i	Light of smaller star	L_2
Period	P	and at least 3 constants defining	
Epoch of principal conjunction	t_0	the amount of elongation, of darkening at the limb, and of brightening of one star by the radiation of the other.	

This leaves us with six unknowns. Fortunately, systems of such short periods as those of the majority of eclipsing variables, usually have nearly circular orbits (as is shown both by spectroscopic data and by the position of the secondary minimum). The assumption of a circular orbit is therefore usually a good approximation to the facts and often requires no subsequent modification.

Russell's papers discuss first the simplified problem:

Two spherical stars, appearing as uniformly illuminated disks, and revolving about their common center of gravity in circular orbits, mutually eclipse one another. It is required to find the relative dimensions and brightness of the two stars, and the inclination of the orbit, from the observed light curve.

The determination of the orbit can be made by simple geometrical methods, but their practical application demands the tabulation and use of rather complicated functions.

We may assume P and t_0 as already known. If the radius of the relative orbit is taken as the unit of length, and the combined light of the two stars as the unit of light, we have to determine four unknown quantities. Of the various possible sets of unknowns, we select the following:

Radius of the larger star...............................r_1
Ratio of radii of the two stars........................k
Light of the larger star...............................L_1
Inclination of the orbit...............................i

The radius of the smaller star is then $r_2 = kr_1$, and its light, $L_2 = 1 - L_1$. It should be noticed that, with the above definitions, k can never exceed unity, but L_2 will exceed L_1 whenever the smaller star is the brighter (which seems to be the fact in the majority of observed cases).

The development of the subject that follows is given, by his courteous permission, largely in Russell's own words, taken partly from his printed memoir but chiefly from a summary sent me recently in manuscript form. The numbers for the equations below are those given in his original paper.

The simplest case is that of a total eclipse which can often be recognized on inspection by a deep, flat-bottomed minimum in which the light is L_1 or λ. Then $L_2 = 1 - \lambda$. If the loss of light at any moment during the partial phase is αL_2 the fraction α of the disk of the smaller star must be obscured. By geometrical similitude α depends only on the ratio k of the radii of the disks and the ratio δ/r_1 of their projected distance of centers to the larger radius, and we may write

$$\alpha = f\left(k, \frac{\delta}{r_1}\right)$$

The function f is transcendental but may be computed with ordinary trigonometric tables. For any given value of k, we may invert this function, and set

$$\frac{\delta}{r_1} = \phi(k, \alpha) \tag{9}$$

If θ is the longitude in the orbit, measured from mideclipse,

$$\delta^2 = \cos^2 i + \sin^2 i \sin^2 \theta = r_1{}^2[\varphi(k, \alpha)]^2 \tag{11}$$

Now let $\alpha_1, \alpha_2, \alpha_3$ be any definite values of α and $\theta_1, \theta_2, \theta_3$ the corresponding values of θ (which may be found from the light curve). Subtracting the corresponding equations of the form (11) in pairs, and dividing one of the resulting equations by the other, we find

$$\frac{\sin^2 \theta_1 - \sin^2 \theta_2}{\sin^2 \theta_2 - \sin^2 \theta_3} = \frac{[\phi(k, \alpha_1)]^2 - [\phi(k, \alpha_2)]^2}{[\phi(k, \alpha_2)]^2 - [\phi(k, \alpha_3)]^2} = \psi(k, \alpha_1, \alpha_2, \alpha_3) \tag{12}$$

The first member of this equation contains only known quantities. The second, if α_1, α_2, and α_3 are predetermined, is a function of k alone. If this function is tabulated, the value of k in any given case can be found by interpolation, or graphically. Equation (11) can then be used to find r_1 and i.

A theoretical light curve may then be found, which passes through any three desired points on each branch of the observed curve (assumed symmetrical). These points may be chosen at will by altering the values of α_1, α_2, and α_3. In practice it is convenient to keep α_2 and α_3 fixed, so that ψ becomes a function of k and α_1 only, and may be tabulated for suitable intervals in these two arguments. This has been done in Table II, in which α_2 is taken as 0.6 and α_3 as 0.9. If $A = \sin^2 \theta_2$, $B = \sin^2 \theta_2 - \sin^2 \theta_3$, (12) may be written

$$\sin^2 \theta_1 = A + B\psi(k, \alpha_1) \tag{13}$$

The points a and b on the light curve corresponding to α_2 and α_3, together with the point corresponding to any one of the tabular values of α_1, then give a determination of k. By taking a suitably weighted mean of these values of k, a theoretical light curve can be obtained which passes through the points a and b, and as close as possible to the others. By slight changes in the assumed positions of a and b (*i.e.*, in the corresponding values of θ, or of $t - t_0$), it is possible with little labor to obtain a theoretical curve which fits the whole course of the observed curve almost as well as one determined by least squares. The criterion of this is that the parts of the observed curve below b (near totality), between a and b, and above a (near the beginning or end of eclipse) shall give the same mean value of k. The individual determinations of k are of very different weight. Between a and b (that is for values of α_1 between 0.6 and 0.9) ψ changes very slowly with k. At the beginning and end of the eclipse the stellar magnitude changes very slowly with the time, and hence, by (13), with ψ. The corresponding parts of the curve are therefore ill adapted to determine k. For the first approximation it is well to give the values of k derived from values of α_1 between 0.95 and 0.99, and between 0.4 and 0.2, double weight (provided the corresponding parts of the curve are well fixed by observation). The time of beginning or end of eclipse cannot be read with even approximate accuracy from the observed curve and should not be used at all in finding k. The beginning or end of totality may sometimes be determined with fair precision, but does not deserve as much weight as the neighboring points on the steep part of the curve. If further refinement is desired, it can most easily be obtained by plotting the light curve for two values of k and comparing with a plot of the observations. This will rarely be necessary.

When once k is given, the determination of the light curve is a very easy matter. For each tabular value of α_1, Eq. (13) gives θ_1, and hence

$(t_1 - t_0)$. The values of the stellar magnitude m corresponding to given values of α_1 are already available, having been used in the previous work. The light curve may thus be plotted by points in a few minutes.

After a satisfactory light curve has been computed, we may proceed to determine the remaining elements. Let θ' and θ'' be the values corresponding to the beginning of eclipse ($\alpha_1 = 0$) and to the beginning of totality ($\alpha_1 = 1$). Then by Eq. (13)

$$\sin^2 \theta' = A + B\psi(k, 0) \text{ and } \sin^2 \theta'' = A + B\psi(k, 1)$$

These computed values are more accurate than those estimated from the free-hand curve drawn to represent the observations. At the first of these epochs $\delta = r_1 + r_2$, and at the second $\delta = r_1 - r_2$. We have then, by Eq. (11)

$$r_1{}^2(1 + k)^2 = \cos^2 i + \sin^2 i \sin^2 \theta'$$
$$r_1{}^2(1 - k)^2 = \cos^2 i + \sin^2 i \sin^2 \theta''$$

whence

$$4k \cot^2 i = (1 - k)^2 \sin^2 \theta' - (1 + k)^2 \sin^2 \theta''$$
$$4kr_1{}^2(1 + \cot^2 i) = \sin^2 \theta' - \sin^2 \theta''$$

Introducing A and B, we have

$$4k \cot^2 i = -4kA + B[(1 - k)^2\psi(k, 0) - (1 + k)^2\psi(k, 1)]$$
$$4kr_1{}^2 \operatorname{cosec}^2 i = B[\psi(k, 0) - \psi(k, 1)]$$

The coefficients are functions of k alone, and may be tabulated. It is most convenient for this purpose to put the equations in the form

$$\left. \begin{aligned} r_1{}^2 \operatorname{cosec}^2 i &= \frac{B}{\phi_1(k)} \\ \cot^2 i &= \frac{B}{\phi_2(k)} - A \end{aligned} \right\} \tag{14}$$

as in this way we obtain functions whose tabular differences are comparatively smooth (which is not true of their reciprocals). With the aid of these functions the elements may be found as soon as A and B are known.

Occasionally $\cot^2 i$ comes out negative. The curve must then be fitted as well as possible on the assumption of central transit ($\cot i = 0$).

The secondary eclipse will then be annular, with maximum depth $1 - \lambda = k^2 L_1$. When observed, it may be used to test the applicability of the simplified theory. In a few cases the

eclipse at principal minimum may be annular. The process of
solution is identical, but the computed depth of secondary is
greater. If $(1 - \lambda) > k^2$ only the total solution is possible,
since L_1 cannot exceed 1. Otherwise the secondary minimum
must be observed to settle the question. When the eclipses
are partial (round-bottomed curves) an additional unknown
has to be found, α_0, the maximum fraction of the area of the
smaller star which is eclipsed. The detailed analysis shows that
if only the primary minimum has been observed, a variety of
solutions, with different values of k and α_0, can be found, which
will give light curves practically indistinguishable even by the
best observations. The computed depth of secondary minimum,
however, differs from one solution to another; and if this has been
observed, a definite determination is possible so long as the
primary is deep—or both eclipses fairly deep. When both
are shallow there is a considerable range of admissible solutions,
and a definite answer can be obtained only from additional
data, such as a spectrographic estimate of the relative brightness
of the components.

Russell's paper contains a number of tables, of which the
four directly applicable to the cases of total or annular eclipses
which have been discussed are reprinted here. His Table I,
tabulating the function given in Eq. (9), is omitted, though it is
fundamental, because it is used, so far as we are at present
concerned, only in constructing the subsequent tables.

His Table II contains the function $\psi(k, \alpha_1)$ defined by the equation

$$\psi(k, \alpha_1) = \frac{[1 + kp(k, \alpha_1)]^2 - [1 + kp(k, \alpha_2)]^2}{[1 + kp(k, \alpha_2)]^2 - [1 + kp(k, \alpha_3)]^2}$$

(where $\alpha_2 = 0.6$ and $\alpha_3 = 0.9$), which is used in determining k
in the case of total eclipse. The uncertainty of the tabular quantities does not exceed one or two units of the last decimal place,
except for the larger values of ψ, corresponding to values of α_1
less than 0.3, for which the actual errors may be greater, but
are not more serious in proportion to the whole quantity
tabulated.

Table II*a* contains the functions

$$\phi_1(k) = \frac{4k}{\psi(k, 0) - \psi(k, 1)}$$

TABLE II.—For Use in Case of Total Eclipse. Values of ψ (k, α_1)

α_1	$k = 1.00$	0.90	0.80	0.70	0.60	0.50	0.40	0.30	0.20	0.10	0.00
0.00	+9.464	+7.478	+6.200	+5.279	+4.556	+3.984	+3.503	+3.104	+2.755	+2.454	+2.199
0.02	8.095	6.457	5.373	4.606	4.000	3.504	3.106	2.768	2.478	2.216	2.000
0.05	7.042	5.616	4.704	4.047	3.534	3.118	2.777	2.488	2.241	2.017	1.829
0.10	+5.759	+4.625	+3.895	+3.364	+2.960	+2.627	+2.358	+2.131	+1.934	+1.754	+1.603
0.15	4.755	3.839	3.248	2.826	2.504	2.240	2.024	1.841	1.682	1.537	1.412
0.20	3.906	3.184	2.712	2.374	2.110	1.898	1.726	1.581	1.453	1.336	1.235
0.25	+3.158	+2.600	+2.232	+1.969	+1.760	+1.591	+1.453	+1.344	+1.242	+1.146	+1.070
0.30	2.522	2.088	1.803	1.603	1.443	1.314	1.205	1.115	1.039	0.968	0.911
0.35	1.979	1.641	1.425	1.276	1.157	1.061	0.982	0.911	0.854	0.797	0.756
0.40	+1.490	+1.245	+1.087	+0.978	+0.894	+0.825	+0.770	+0.721	+0.675	+0.633	+0.604
0.45	1.040	0.881	0.777	0.705	0.649	0.603	0.566	0.530	0.501	0.473	0.453
0.50	0.648	0.555	0.491	0.451	0.418	0.392	0.370	0.348	0.331	0.314	0.302
0.55	+0.300	+0.258	+0.233	+0.217	+0.202	+0.191	+0.181	+0.171	+0.164	+0.156	+0.151
0.60	0.000	0.000	0.000	0.000	0.000	0.000	0.000	0.000	0.000	0.000	0.000
0.65	−0.258	−0.231	−0.214	−0.202	−0.191	−0.181	−0.174	−0.167	−0.160	−0.156	−0.152
0.70	−0.480	−0.435	−0.408	−0.387	−0.369	−0.354	−0.344	−0.331	−0.320	−0.314	−0.306
0.75	−0.660	−0.613	−0.584	−0.558	−0.539	−0.522	−0.508	−0.494	−0.483	−0.475	−0.465
0.80	−0.805	−0.765	−0.738	−0.717	−0.700	−0.684	−0.670	−0.659	−0.647	−0.639	−0.632
0.85	−0.922	−0.893	−0.877	−0.863	−0.854	−0.843	−0.833	−0.825	−0.818	−0.812	−0.808
0.90	−1.000	−1.000	−1.000	−1.000	−1.000	−1.000	−1.000	−1.000	−1.000	−1.000	−1.000
0.95	−1.045	−1.085	−1.112	−1.134	−1.152	−1.166	−1.179	−1.190	−1.203	−1.214	−1.226
0.98	−1.0625	−1.126	−1.176	−1.220	−1.256	−1.284	−1.308	−1.329	−1.350	−1.369	−1.391
0.99	−1.0643	−1.139	−1.199	−1.250	−1.293	−1.328	−1.362	−1.390	−1.419	−1.444	−1.471
1.00	−1.0650	−1.155	−1.231	−1.297	−1.354	−1.402	−1.445	−1.484	−1.525	−1.556	−1.596

and

$$\phi_2(k) = \frac{4k}{(1 - k)^2\psi(k, 0) - (1 + k)^2\psi(k, 1)}$$

which are useful in determining the elements in the case of total eclipse.

TABLE IIa.—FOR COMPUTING THE ELEMENTS IN THE CASE OF TOTAL ECLIPSE

k	$\phi_1(k)$	$\phi_2(k)$
1.00	0.380	0.939
0.95	0.401	0.894
0.90	0.417	0.848
0.85	0.427	0.802
0.80	0.431	0.755
0.75	0.431	0.709
0.70	0.427	0.663
0.65	0.419	0.617
0.60	0.406	0.572
0.55	0.390	0.527
0.50	0.371	0.482
0.45	0.349	0.436
0.40	0.323	0.390
0.35	0.294	0.345
0.30	0.262	0.298
0.25	0.226	0.250
0.20	0.187	0.202
0.15	0.145	0.153
0.10	0.100	0.103
0.05	0.052	0.052
0.00	0.000	0.000

Table A gives the *loss* of light $(1 - \lambda)$, corresponding to a given change Δm in stellar magnitude. For a difference of magnitude greater than 2.5, the loss of light is $0.9000 +$ one-tenth of the tabular value for $\Delta m - 2^m.5$. Table B gives the values of $(\theta - \sin \theta)$ for every 0.01 of θ (expressed in circular measure), and saves much labor in computing the values of $\sin \theta$ corresponding to a given interval for minimum.

TABLE A.—LOSS OF LIGHT CORRESPONDING TO AN INCREASE Δm IN STELLAR MAGNITUDE

Δm	0	1	2	3	4	5	6	7	8	9
0.0	0.0000	0.0092	0.0183	0.0273	0.0362	0.0450	0.0538	0.0624	0.0710	0.0795
0.1	0.0880	0.0964	0.1046	0.1128	0.1210	0.1290	0.1370	0.1449	0.1528	0.1605
0.2	0.1682	0.1759	0.1834	0.1909	0.1983	0.2057	0.2130	0.2202	0.2273	0.2344
0.3	0.2414	0.2484	0.2553	0.2621	0.2689	0.2756	0.2822	0.2888	0.2953	0.3018
0.4	0.3082	0.3145	0.3208	0.3270	0.3332	0.3393	0.3454	0.3514	0.3573	0.3632
0.5	0.3690	0.3748	0.3806	0.3862	0.3919	0.3974	0.4030	0.4084	0.4139	0.4192
0.6	0.4246	0.4298	0.4351	0.4402	0.4454	0.4505	0.4555	0.4605	0.4654	0.4703
0.7	0.4752	0.4800	0.4848	0.4895	0.4942	0.4988	0.5034	0.5080	0.5125	0.5169
0.8	0.5214	0.5258	0.5301	0.5344	0.5387	0.5429	0.5471	0.5513	0.5554	0.5594
0.9	0.5635	0.5675	0.5715	0.5754	0.5793	0.5831	0.5870	0.5907	0.5945	0.5982
1.0	0.6019	0.6055	0.6092	0.6127	0.6163	0.6198	0.6233	0.6267	0.6302	0.6336
1.1	0.6369	0.6403	0.6435	0.6468	0.6501	0.6533	0.6564	0.6596	0.6627	0.6658
1.2	0.6689	0.6719	0.6749	0.6779	0.6808	0.6838	0.6867	0.6895	0.6924	0.6952
1.3	0.6980	0.7008	0.7035	0.7062	0.7089	0.7116	0.7142	0.7169	0.7195	0.7220
1.4	0.7246	0.7271	0.7296	0.7321	0.7345	0.7370	0.7394	0.7418	0.7441	0.7465
1.5	0.7488	0.7511	0.7534	0.7557	0.7579	0.7601	0.7623	0.7645	0.7667	0.7688
1.6	0.7709	0.7730	0.7751	0.7772	0.7792	0.7812	0.7832	0.7852	0.7872	0.7891
1.7	0.7911	0.7930	0.7949	0.7968	0.7986	0.8005	0.8023	0.8041	0.8059	0.8077
1.8	0.8095	0.8112	0.8129	0.8146	0.8163	0.8180	0.8197	0.8214	0.8230	0.8246
1.9	0.8262	0.8278	0.8294	0.8310	0.8325	0.8340	0.8356	0.8371	0.8386	0.8400
2.0	0.8415	0.8430	0.8444	0.8458	0.8472	0.8486	0.8500	0.8514	0.8528	0.8541
2.1	0.8555	0.8568	0.8581	0.8594	0.8607	0.8620	0.8632	0.8645	0.8657	0.8670
2.2	0.8682	0.8694	0.8706	0.8718	0.8729	0.8741	0.8753	0.8764	0.8775	0.8787
2.3	0.8798	0.8809	0.8820	0.8831	0.8841	0.8852	0.8862	0.8873	0.8883	0.8893
2.4	0.8904	0.8914	0.8924	0.8933	0.8943	0.8953	0.8962	0.8972	0.8981	0.8991
2.5	0.9000	0.9009	0.9018	0.9027	0.9036	0.9045	0.9054	0.9062	0.9071	0.9080

For values of Δm greater than 2.5, the loss of light is 0.9000 plus $\frac{1}{10}$ of the loss of light corresponding to $\Delta m - 2.5$.

TABLE B.—VALUES OF $\theta - \sin \theta$

	0.0	0.1	0.2	0.3	0.4	0.5	0.6	0.7	0.8	0.9
0.00	0.0000	0.0002	0.0013	0.0045	0.0105	0.0206	0.0354	0.0558	0.0826	0.1167
0.01	0.0000	0.0002	0.0015	0.0049	0.0114	0.0218	0.0372	0.0582	0.0857	0.1205
0.02	0.0000	0.0003	0.0018	0.0055	0.0122	0.0231	0.0390	0.0607	0.0889	0.1243
0.03	0.0000	0.0004	0.0020	0.0060	0.0131	0.0244	0.0409	0.0632	0.0920	0.1283
0.04	0.0000	0.0005	0.0023	0.0066	0.0141	0.0258	0.0428	0.0658	0.0953	0.1324
0.05	0.0000	0.0006	0.0026	0.0071	0.0151	0.0273	0.0448	0.0684	0.0987	0.1365
0.06	0.0000	0.0007	0.0029	0.0078	0.0161	0.0288	0.0469	0.0711	0.1022	0.1407
0.07	0.0001	0.0008	0.0033	0.0084	0.0171	0.0304	0.0490	0.0739	0.1057	0.1450
0.08	0.0001	0.0010	0.0037	0.0091	0.0183	0.0320	0.0512	0.0767	0.1093	0.1494
0.09	0.0001	0.0011	0.0041	0.0098	0.0194	0.0337	0.0535	0.0796	0.1130	0.1539

To illustrate Russell's method I have chosen his orbit of W *Delphini,* which is a "typical *Algol* variable with a deep primary minimum, showing a constant phase, and little or no secondary minimum." Its light curve, "defined by the 500 observations by Professor Wendell, with a polarizing photometer, which are published in the *Harvard Annals,* 69, Part 1,"

TABLE *a.*—OBSERVED MAGNITUDES

Phase	Mag.	No. obs.	O − C	Phase	Mag.	No. obs.	O − C
−0^{d}2894	9.41	6	+0^{m}01	+0^{d}0560	11.76	7	+0^{m}01
0.2637	9.49	5	+0.02	0.0659	11.58	8	+0.01
0.2458	9.58	5	+0.04	0.0753	11.33	7	−0.04
0.2306	9.59	4	−0.01	0.0859	11.14	5	−0.02
0.2200	9.67	5	0.00	0.0937	10.97	5	−0.05
0.2106	9.73	8	+0.01	0.1036	10.88	8	+0.02
0.2007	9.79	10	0.00	0.1147	10.73	8	+0.05
0.1911	9.88	12	+0.02	0.1246	10.56	12	+0.03
0.1817	9.95	10	+0.01	0.1351	10.39	14	0.00
0.1718	10.02	8	0.00	0.1445	10.31	11	+0.04
0.1615	10.16	17	+0.04	0.1546	10.13	10	−0.02
0.1506	10.23	14	0.00	0.1641	10.10	11	+0.04
0.1396	10.37	14	+0.01	0.1744	9.97	10	0.00
0.1311	10.44	16	−0.03	0.1847	9.90	9	+0.02
0.1212	10.59	17	−0.03	0.1941	9.79	9	−0.02
0.1121	10.78	14	+0.01	0.2050	9.71	8	−0.02
0.1013	10.91	17	−0.04	0.2157	9.71	6	+0.04
0.0906	11.12	14	−0.01	0.2242	9.63	8	+0.01
0.0809	11.30	10	−0.02	0.2345	9.57	7	0.00
0.0715	11.51	12	0.00	0.2507	9.50	7	0.00
0.0617	11.69	10	0.00	0.2708	9.48	7	+0.03
0.0509	11.88	7	0.00	0.2811	9.43	4	+0.02
0.0313	12.05	5	−0.04	0.94	9.42	5	+0.02
0.0169	12.08	4	−0.02	1.90	9.35	5	−0.05
−0.0082	12.07	7	−0.03	2.04	9.41	7	+0.01
+0.0060	12.16	5	+0.06	2.67	9.38	5	−0.02
0.0139	12.09	4	−0.01	3.04	9.42	3	+0.02
0.0261	12.03	5	−0.07	4.04	9.44	6	+0.04
0.0356	12.02	6	−0.03	4.48	9.36	7	−0.04
+0.0460	11.87	6	−0.04				

is shown in Fig. 12. The observations have been combined into the normal places given in Table *a,* on the basis of a period of 4.8061 days, which was found to require no correction.

From the 38 observations outside minimum we find the magnitude during constant light to be $9^{m}.395 \pm 0.009$. There is no evidence of any change during this time. With a circular orbit, the secondary minimum should occur at phase $2^{d}.40$. As none of the observations fall within $0^{d}.27$ of this, they give us no information whether such a minimum exists. The light curve of the principal minimum is very well determined. The eclipse lasts from about $-0^{d}.28$ to $+0^{d}.28$, and there is a short constant period at the middle, of apparently a little less than one-tenth the total duration of the eclipse. The mean of the 20 observations lying within $0^{d}.02$ of the middle of eclipse gives for the magnitude at this phase $12^{m}.10 \pm 0.014$. The range of variation is therefore $2^{m}.70$,

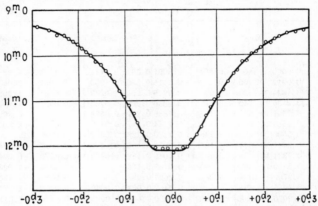

FIG. 12.—Light curve of the principal minimum of W *Delphini.*

and the light intensity at minimum 0.0832 times that at maximum. This shows at once that the eclipse is total, for if it was annular, the companion (even if perfectly dark) must cut off at least 0.917 of the light of the primary, and hence its radius cannot be less than 0.956 times that of the latter. In such a system the duration of the annular phase could not exceed 0.044/1.956, or 0.022 of the whole duration of eclipse. The observed constant phase is almost five times as long as this.

The brighter star, therefore, gives 0.9168 of the whole light of the system, and if isolated would appear of magnitude 9.49; while the fainter but larger star which eclipses it gives out only one-eleventh as much light, and when seen alone at minimum is of magnitude 12.10.

The loss of light $(1 - l)$ at any given time, t, will be $0.9168\alpha_1$, since α_1 is the percentage of obscuration. For a series of values of α_1 we tabulate the values of $(1 - l)$ and then take from Table A the corresponding changes of magnitude and apply them to magnitude 9.4. Next, from the free-hand curve drawn to represent the data of observation, we read off the epochs t_1 and t_2 at which the magnitudes so computed are reached before and after the middle of eclipse. Half the difference of t_1 and t_2 may be taken as the interval t from the middle of eclipse to each phase and the corresponding value of θ formed from

$$\theta = \frac{2\pi}{P}t = 1.3065t,$$ where θ is expressed in radians and t in days.

With the aid of Table B sin θ is found and then $\sin^2 \theta$. These quantities are all entered in Table b.

TABLE b

α_1	$1 - l$	Mag.	t_1	t_2	θ	$\sin^2 \theta$	$\sin^2 \theta - A$	$\psi(k, \alpha_1)$	k
0.0	0.0000	$9^m.400$	$-0^d.304$:	$+0^d.300$:	0.394:	0.1474:	0.1105:	+4.28:	0.56:
0.1	0.0917	9 .505	0.2540	0.2515	0.3304	0.1050	0.0681	2.64	0.504
0.2	0.1834	9 .620	0.2285	0.2258	0.2968	0.0860	0.0491	1.908	0.505
0.3	0.2750	9 .749	0.2075	0.2030	0.2681	0.0702	0.0333	1.290	0.480
0.4	0.3667	9 .896	0.1884	0.1830	0.2426	0.0576	0.0207	0.802	0.462
0.5	0.4584	10 .066	0.1682	0.1644	0.2173	0.0462	0.0093	+0.361	0.36:
0.6	0.5500	10 .266	0.1486	0.1470	0.1931	0.0369	0.0000	....	....
0.7	0.6417	10 .514	0.1270	0.1274	0.1661	0.0272	−0.0097	−0.376	0.64:
0.8	0.7334	10 .835	0.1070	0.1048	0.1381	0.0190	−0.0179	−0.694	0.56:
0.9	0.8250	11 .292	0.0824	0.0788	0.1054	0.0111	−0.0258	−1.000	....
0.95	0.8709	11 .624	0.0655	0.0624	0.0886	0.0071	−0.0298	−1.155	0.58:
0.98	0.8985	11 .884	0.0505	0.0462	0.0632	0.0040	−0.0329	−1.277	0.525
0.99	0.9076	11 .985	0.0430	0.0390	0.0536	0.0029	−0.0340	−1.318	0.528
1.00	0.9168	12 .100	−0.021:	+0.019:	0.026:	0.0007:	−0.0362:	−1.404:	0.50:

[1] Russell's computations were made with a slide rule. Repeating them with five-place logarithms, I obtain figures, which sometimes differ slightly from those tabulated. These differences, however, are unimportant for they produce no appreciable changes in the final elements.

From the values of t_1 and t_2 it appears that the observed curve is remarkably symmetrical, and that the actual epoch of mideclipse is 0.0015 days earlier than that assumed by Wendell. The times of beginning and ending of the eclipse cannot be read accurately from the curve and are marked with colons to denote uncertainty.

From the values of $\sin^2 \theta$ we have now to find k with the aid of Table II. From Eq. (13) we have

$$\psi(k, \alpha_1) = \frac{\sin^2 \theta_1 - A}{B},$$

hence, if we let A be the value of $\sin^2 \theta$ when $\alpha_1 = 0.6$ and $A - B$ its value when $\alpha_1 = 0.9$, we may find a value of k for every tabulated value of α_1 by inverse interpolation in Table II. Thus, taking $A = 0.0369$ and $B(= \sin^2 \theta_2 - \sin^2 \theta_3) = 0.0258$, as given by our curve, we find for $\alpha_1 = 0.0$ that

$$\psi(k, \alpha_1) = +4.28:$$

and hence, from the first line of Table II, $k = 0.56$:. Colons are here used because the values of k are less accurate when the tabular differences of $\psi(k, \alpha_1)$ are small.

The values of k are seen to be fairly accordant except for those corresponding to values α_1 near 0.6. Inspection of Table II "shows that this discrepancy may be almost removed by increasing all the values of ψ by 0.024 — which may be done by diminishing A by 0.024B. Our new value of A is therefore 0.0363." The new set of k's are found to be discordant for values of α_1 near 0.9; "but by diminishing B by 2.5 per cent [giving $B = 0.0252$] and hence increasing all the computed values of ψ in the corresponding ratio, we obtain a third approximation of a very satisfactory character." The general mean is now $k = 0.528$.

With these final constants, $A = 0.0363$, $B = 0.0252$, $k = 0.528$, we may compute a theoretical light curve and also the elements of the system from Eq. (14). Table c gives the second and third approximations to the value of k and the data for the final light curve.

TABLE c

	2d Approx.		3d Approx.		Final light curve				
α_1	ψ	k	ψ	k	$\psi(0.528, \alpha_1)$	$B\psi$	$\sin^2 \theta$	$\sin \theta$	t
0.0	+4.30:	0.56:	+4.40:	0.58:	+4.100	0.1032	0.1395	0.373	0.292
0.1	2.665	0.512	2.73	0.534	2.713	0.0683	0.1046	0.324	0.252
0.2	1.932	0.517	1.974	0.538	1.949	0.0491	0.0854	0.292	0.227
0.3	1.314	0.500	1.344	0.527	1.348	0.0338	0.0701	0.265	0.205
0.4	0.826	0.503	0.845	0.532	0.843	0.0212	0.0575	0.240	0.185
0.5	0.385	0.47:	0.394	0.51:	+0.400	0.0101	0.0464	0.215	0.166
0.6	+0.024	.....	+0.025	.....	0.000	0.0000	0.0363	0.191	0.146
0.7	−0.352	0.48:	−0.360	0.54:	−0.358	−0.0090	0.0273	0.165	0.127
0.8	−0.670	0.40:	−0.685	0.51:	−0.689	−0.0173	0.0190	0.138	0.106
0.9	−0.976	.....	−1.000	.....	−1.000	−0.0252	0.0111	0.105	0.081
0.95	−1.131	0.714	−1.157	0.564	−1.162	−0.0293	0.0070	0.084	0.064
0.98	−1.253	0.610	−1.282	0.507	−1.276	−0.0322	0.0041	0.064	0.049
0.99	−1.294	0.597	−1.324	0.512	−1.318	−0.0332	0.0031	0.056	0.043
1.00	−1.38:	0.55:	−1.412:	0.48:	−1.389	−0.0350	0.0013	0.026	0.028

Plotting the magnitudes computed in Table *a* against the epochs $-0\overset{d}{.}0015 \pm t$, we obtain the computed light curve. The residuals $(O-C)$ are given in the last column of Table *a*. Their average value, regardless of sign, is $0\overset{m}{.}020$.

From Table II*a* we find for $k = 0.528$, $\phi_1(k) = 0.382$,

$$\phi_2(k) = 0.507;$$

whence

$$\cot^2 i = \frac{B}{\phi_2(k)} - A = 0.0133, \qquad \cot i = 0.115, \qquad i = 83° \ 25'$$

$$r_1{}^2 \cosec^2 i = \frac{B}{\phi_1(k)} = 0.0660, \qquad r_1{}^2 = 0.0652, \qquad r_1 = 0.256$$

and finally

$$r_2 = kr_1 = 0.135.$$

In other words, we have, taking the radius of the orbit as unity,

Radius of larger star.........................	0.256
Radius of smaller star.......................	0.135
Inclination of orbit plane...................	83° 25'
Least apparent distance of centers...........	0.114
Light of larger star.........................	0.0832
Light of smaller star........................	0.9168
Period of revolution.........................	4.8061 days

At the middle of eclipse, the larger star overlaps the other by only 0.007 of the radius of the orbit, or about one-twentieth of the radius of the smaller body, so that the eclipse is very nearly grazing. The smaller star gives off eleven times as much light as the other, and exceeds it fortyfold in surface brightness.

The loss of light at secondary minimum should be k times the light of the fainter star, or 0.023 of that of the system. The corresponding change in stellar magnitude is 0.027, which could only be detected by refined observations.

For disks darkened toward the limb the solution proceeds along essentially similar lines. The function f must be determined by numerical integration. The principal difference is that an annular eclipse is not flat-bottomed, since more light is cut off when the companion obscures the bright center than when it obscures a region near the limb. (An actual case of this sort has been reported by McDiarmid, TX *Cassiopeiae*.*)

* *Contr. Princeton Univ. Obs.* No. 7, 1924.

The changes of light at the beginning and end of eclipse are slower, so that the times of first and last contact, calculated from the deeper parts of the eclipse tend to be farther apart, and the computed diameter of the brighter star, at least, larger than for the "uniform" solution.

Tables for disks in which the brightness falls off to zero at the limb have been computed by Russell and Shapley.*

Orbital eccentricity produces no perceptible asymmetry in the form of the light curve for a single minimum but displaces the secondary minimum from the half-way point between the

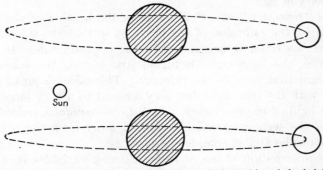

Fig. 13.—The system of W *Delphini.* Two relative orbits of the bright star are shown, the upper one representing the elements as given in the accompanying solution, the lower, Shapley's, on the assumption that the stars are darkened to zero at the limb. The diameters of the disks of stars and Sun are drawn on the same scale. The three bodies are of equal mass, but the stars are less dense than the Sun. (*From Shapley's article in Popular Astronomy,* **20**, 572, 1912.)

primary minima, and may change the durations and depths of both. It is even theoretically possible for the eclipse to fail altogether near apastron. The component $e \cos \omega$ which displaces the epoch of secondary, can often be very accurately determined from the observations; the component $e \sin \omega$, which alters the length of minimum, is very hard to find with accuracy. In one noteworthy case, Y *Cygni,* to which reference has been made on an earlier page† a rotation of the line of apsides detected photometrically has been confirmed by spectrographic observations.

Ellipticity of the components, caused by their mutual attraction, has been found in practically all cases where pairs of small separation have been well observed. It causes the light curve

* *Ap. Jour.* **36**, 239, 385, 1912.
† See p. 182.

to be bowed up between the minima, with maxima halfway between them. Its amount increases as the relative distance separating the two stars diminishes, in close agreement with Darwin's theoretical calculation for masses of homogeneous fluid. The computed ellipticity of figure corresponding to a given light curve depends, however, on the assumed degree of darkening at the limb, so that it is the relative, rather than the absolute, values which are of importance.

For certain systems whose components are almost in contact (VW *Cephei*, etc.) the greater part of the variation is due to ellipticity of figure.

The "reflection" effect* arises from the heating of the companion by the radiation of the primary, so that the side turned toward the latter is brighter than the opposite side. In consequence, the light curve is higher just outside the secondary minimum than outside the primary. This effect is small compared with the total light but may amount to a very large part of the light of the secondary. In Y *Camelopardalis*, indeed, the side of the secondary which is turned away from the primary appears to be almost completely dark.

The information obtained from eclipsing variables is of far-reaching value. When supported by spectrographic observations, it provides the most complete knowledge of a stellar system that we can hope for at present—masses, linear diameters, densities, surface brightness (when the parallax is known, as for the distant companion of *Castor*), and even something regarding the law of internal density from the motion of periastron (Y *Cygni*). Even without this potent aid we may obtain data otherwise inaccessible regarding the relation of surface brightness to spectral type and color, and especially concerning stellar densities.

The equations for computing the latter are simple. Let the total mass of the system be m, that of the larger star my, and that of the smaller $m(1 - y)$. If a is the semimajor axis of the orbit, we shall have $a = Km^{1/3} \cdot P^{2/3}$, where K is a constant depending on the units of measurement. If we choose the Sun's mass, the Sun's radius, and the day as units, then, for the Earth's orbital motion, $a = 214.9$, $P = 365.24$, whence $K = 4.206$.

* First detected by Dugan in the light curve of RT *Persei* and by Stebbins in that of *Algol*.

In determining the elements of the system we have taken a as our unit of length. The actual radius of the larger star is therefore ar_1, and its volume, in terms of the volume of the Sun, $K^3mP^2r_1^3$, or $74.4mP^2r_1^3$. Hence its density is

$$\rho_1 = \frac{0.01344y}{P^2r_1^3}$$

and similarly that of the smaller star,

$$\rho_2 = 0.01344\frac{(1-y)}{P^2r_2^3}.$$

If the magnitudes and spectral classes are known, the ratio $y/(1-y)$ can be estimated closely with the aid of the mass-luminosity law. This procedure will give close approximations to the true densities, particularly for the brighter and more massive components.

Russell summarizes the conclusions he has drawn from his extensive statistical investigations as follows:

The great majority of them (the brighter components) belong to the main sequence, and are of classes B8 to A5. These are strikingly similar in density, clustering closely about a mean value 0.32 times that of the Sun. (This is the geometric mean which in a case like this is more representative than the arithmetic.) Every spectral type is, however, represented, the whole main sequence, from the M-dwarf YY *Geminorum* to the supergiant O-type stars Y *Cygni*[*] and H.D. 1337,[†] Giants are fewer, but cover a wide range of spectral type and density. Only the white dwarfs are absent. (It is worth notice in passing that a pair of white dwarfs revolving nearly in contact might have a period of only two or three minutes!)

The faint components of eclipsing systems are usually larger than their primaries. This is a conspicuous example of observational selection—small companions producing only shallow eclipses which are unlikely to be discovered. The stars thus selected appear to belong to a rather unusual type, intermediate between ordinary giants and dwarfs, about which we would otherwise know next to nothing.

In Table 1, I have listed the dimensions, masses and densities of 22 systems for which complete spectrographic and photometric

[*] *Princeton Contrib.* No. 12, 1931.
[†] *Publ. Dom. Ap. Obs.* **3**, 275, 1926.

TABLE 1.—DIMENSIONS, MASSES, AND DENSITIES OF 22 ECLIPSING BINARY SYSTEMS*

	Star	P_1	SP	rb	rf	mb	mf	pb	pf	Dist. bet. centers	Authority
		d.		$\odot = 1$	$= 1$	$\odot = 1$	$= 1$	$\odot = 0.0027$	$= 1$	$10^6\ km \times$	
1	Boss 46	3.52	B0	23.8	15.5	36.3	33.8	0.0027	0.0091	27.92	Pearce, *Publ. D.A.O.* **3**, 275, 1926
2	V Puppis	1.45	B1	8.45	7.70	19.4	19.4	0.042	0.055	8.83	Shapley, *Ap. J.* **38**, 169, 1913
3	Y Cygni	3.00	B2	4.7	4.7	17.4	17.6	0.16	0.16	19.90	Redman, *Publ. D.A.O.* **4**, 341, 1930
4	AG Persei	2.03	B3	3.75	2.62	5.18	4.57	0.10	0.25	9.92	Huffer, *Publ.* Washburn 0, 15, 192, 1931
5	U Cor. Bor.	3.45	B3	2.90	4.74	4.27	1.63	0.175	0.015	12.08	Plaskett, *Publ. D.A.O.* **1**, 187, 1921
6	u Herculis	2.05	B3	4.56	5.35	7.66	2.93	0.095	0.022	10.29	Shapley, *Ap. J.* **38**, 169, 1913
7	Z Vulp.	2.45	B3	4.23	4.46	5.24	2.36	0.085	0.033	10.47	Plaskett, *Publ. D.A.O.* **1**, 251, 1920
8	σ Aquilae	1.95	B3	3.56	3.56	6.19	5.14	0.15	0.12	10.22	Wylie, *Ap. J.* **56**, 232, 1922
9	TT Aurigae	1.33	B5	4.5	4.0	6.7	5.3	0.11	0.12	8.10	Joy and Sitterly, *Ap. J.* **73**, 77, 1931
10	U Ophiuchi	1.68	B8	3.23	3.23	5.36	4.71	0.18	0.16	8.92	Plaskett, *Publ. D.A.O.* **1**, 138, 1919
11	RS Vulp.	4.48	B8	2.05	10.25	5.40	1.69	0.63	0.0016	15.30	Plaskett, *Publ. D.A.O.* **1**, 141, 1919
12	TV Cass.	1.81	B9	2.50	2.83	1.83	1.01	0.118	0.044	6.16	Plaskett, *Publ. D.A.O.* **2**, 141, 1922
13	U Sagittae	3.38	B9	3.4	5.7	6.7	2.0	0.171	0.011	13.63	Joy, *Ap. J.* **71**, 336, 1929
14	β Aurigae	3.96	A0p	2.81	2.81	2.40	2.36	0.11	0.11	12.31	Shapley, *Ap. J.* **38**, 169, 1913
15	RX Herculis	1.78	A0	1.54	1.38	0.89	0.89	0.25	0.34	5.20	Shapley, *Ap. J.* **40**, 399, 1914
16	TX Herculis	2.06	A5	1.33	1.33	2.04	1.77	0.87	0.75	7.41	Plaskett, *Publ. D.A.O.* **1**, 207, 1920
17	S Antliae	0.648	F0	1.67	1.29	0.75	0.42	0.31	0.38	2.30	Joy, *Ap. J.* **64**, 287, 1926
18	Z Herculis	3.99	F5p	1.77	3.29	1.6	1.3	0.3	0.04	10.52	Adams & Joy, *Ap. J.* **49**, 192, 1919
19	RS Can. Ven.	4.80	F8	1.6	5.3	1.85	1.71	0.45	0.012	12.78	Joy, *Ap. J.* **72**, 41, 1930
20	W Urs. Maj.	0.334	G	0.78	0.78	0.69	0.49	2.8	1.9	1.50	Adams & Joy, *Ap. J.* **49**, 189, 1919
21	RT Lacertae	5.07	G5	5.0	5.0	1.0	1.9	0.01	0.02	12.45	Joy, *Ap. J.* **74**, 101, 1931
22	α Gem. c	0.814	M1e	0.76	0.68	0.63	0.571	1.4	1.8	2.70	Joy and Sanford, *Ap. J.* **64**, 250, 1926

* [See *Lick Obs. Bull.* #483, Table Ia, 1936; and Gaposchkin and Gaposchkin, *Variable Stars*, Tables II, vii and II, xi.—J.T.K.]

data are available, taking the figures from the authorities cited. The stars are arranged in the order of spectral class of the primary, and the various columns give, in addition to the star's name, spectral class and approximate revolution period, the radii of the two components (*b*, bright, *f*, faint), their masses, and their densities, all in terms of the Sun as unit, and the distance between their centers in millions of kilometers.

There are many additional systems for which similar data have been or might be computed with the aid of the mass luminosity relation, on the basis of the light curves supplemented, in some instances, by spectrographic orbits of the brighter component. In fact, in his recent memoir *Die Bedeckungsveränderlichen,*" Gaposchkin gives such data for 218 of the 349 eclipsing variables (many of them as faint as the tenth magnitude) he catalogues. In many cases his figures are but rough approximations, computed, without even the aid of a light curve, from the observed depths of the minima at the two eclipses, and the observed durations of the eclipses. For 54 systems he gives more precise values for some or all of these quantities.

Utilizing all of the available data, Gaposchkin discusses not only the complicated relations between mass, density, luminosity, and spectral type in the eclipsing variables but also the general characteristics of their orbits and the question of their galactic concentration. He finds, among other results, that there is a definite concentration toward the plane of the Milky Way, most markedly in the case of the pairs of spectral classes O and B, and that the eccentricity of the orbit increases both with increasing period and with the spectral class as we pass from A toward M.

References

PICKERING, E. C.: Dimensions of the Fixed Stars with Special Reference to Binaries and Variables of the *Algol* Type, *Proc. Amer. Acad. Arts and Sciences* **16,** 1, 1881.

ROBERTS, A. W.: On the Relation Existing between the Light Changes and the Orbital Elements of a Close Binary System, *Mon. Not. R.A.S.* **63,** 527, 1903.

————: On a Method of Determining the Absolute Dimensions of an Algol Variable Star, *Mon. Not. R.A.S.* **66,** 123, 1906.

RUSSELL, H. N.: On the Determination of the Orbital Elements of Eclipsing Variable Stars, *Ap. Jour.* **35,** 315, 1911; **36,** 54, 1912.

RUSSELL, H. N., and H. SHAPLEY: On Darkening at the Limb in Eclipsing Variables, *Ap. Jour.* **36,** 239, 385, 1912.

SHAPLEY, H.: The Orbits of Eighty-seven Eclipsing Binaries—A Summary, *Ap. Jour.* **38**, 158, 1913.

————: A Study of Eclipsing Binaries, *Contrib. Princeton Univ. Obs.* 3, 1915.

VOGT, H.: Zur Theorie der Algolveränderlichen, *Veröff. Sternwarte Heidelberg* **7**, 183, 1919.

FETLAAR, J.: A Contribution to the Theory of Eclipsing Binaries. *Recherches Astron. de l'Obs. d'Utrecht* **9**, Pt. 1, 1923.

SITTERLY, B. W.: A Graphical Method for Obtaining the Elements of Eclipsing Variables, *Pop. Astron.* **32**, 231, 1924; *Contrib. Princeton Univ. Obs.*, #11, Pt. I, 1930.

SCHARBE, S.: Bestimmung der Kreisbahnen der Veränderlichen vom Algoltypus nach der Helligkeitskurve, *Bull. Obs. Central de Russie* **10**, No. 94, 1925.

GAPOSCHKIN, S.: Die Bedeckungsveränderlichen, *Veröff. Univ. Sternwartezn Berlin-Babelsberg* **9**, No. 5, 1932.

W. KRAT: Some Remarks on the Determination of the Orbital Elements of Eclipsing Variable Stars, Veränderliche Sterne, *Forschungs- und Informations Bulletin* **4**, 97, 1933. Nishni-Novgorod. The note presents a generalization of Russell's method extending it to apply also to systems of great eccentricity. The formulas for finding e and ω from the light curve are free from the assumption that $i = 90°$.

WALTER, KURT: Die Bewegungsverhältnisse in sehr engen Doppelsternsystemen, *Schriften der Königsberger Gelehrten Gesellschaft* **10**, Heft 4, 1933; or *Veröff. Univ. Sternwarte Königsberg* Heft 3.

Many papers dealing with the orbits of particular systems will be found in Bulletins of the Laws Observatory, the Publications of the Dominion Astrophysical Observatory, the Contributions from the Princeton University Observatory, the *Astrophysical Journal*, the *Astronomische Nachrichten*, the *Monthly Notices of the Royal Astronomical Society*, and other journals and observatory publications.

The sections on the *Algol* variables in such works as Die veränderlichen Sterne, by J. G. Hagen, S. J., and J. Stein, (1913–1924) and Geschichte und Literatur der veränderlichen Sterne, by G. Müller and E. Hartwig (1918) may also be consulted.

R. Prager publishes annually (*Kleine Veröff. der Univ. Sternwarte zu Berlin-Babelsberg*) a *Katalog und Ephemeriden Veränderlicher Sterne*, which includes *Algol* variables, and T. Banachiewicz, in the *Supplements Internationale* of the Krakow Observatory Publications, a list of the eclipsing variables with ephemerides for those of established orbits. In the issues for 1933, Prager gives elements for 582 eclipsing variables, and Banachiewicz, light elements and ephemerides for 300, and a list of 722 others, some which may prove not to be of the *Algol* type.

CHAPTER VIII

THE KNOWN ORBITS OF THE BINARY STARS

Several hundred orbits of visual binary stars and of stars with periodic variable radial velocity have been computed by the methods presented in the preceding chapters. Every computation was undertaken with the immediate object in view of representing the observed motion and of predicting the future motion in the particular system on the assumption that the bodies are moving in obedience to the law of gravitation. It is satisfactory to find that while the computed orbits exhibit the utmost diversity in form and in dimensions, we have found no reason to question the validity of that assumption.

Back of this immediate objective, long since attained, lay the broader motive of providing additional data for the study of the greater questions of the origin and evolution of the binary star systems and of their relation to single star systems. In the present chapter we shall examine the computed orbit elements, first with respect to correlations that may exist between them and then more particularly for the information we may derive from them as to stellar masses and densities.

Not all the orbits which have been computed can be used in such studies. The observed arcs upon which many of the orbits of the visual binary stars rest are so short that a great variety of apparent ellipses may be drawn that will represent the data within the error of measure. The well-known binary *σ Coronae Borealis* offers a striking example: using practically the same data, Lewis found the period to be 340 years, while Doberck gave 1,679 years. Even with longer arcs we have, in a number of cases, two or more radically different orbits. Rejecting all of these, as well as a few that rest upon assumptions which seemed plausible but which have not been supported by later observations, we still find in those retained a wide range in reliability. The majority are fairly good, some, for all practical purposes, are definitive, a few others only slightly better than some of those that have been rejected.

In Table I in the Appendix, I have listed the 116 pairs retained (including Cc** of ζ *Cancri* and Aa of ξ *Ursae Majoris*) giving in general the latest* set of elements when two or more have been computed for the same pair.   The columns of the table give, in order, the name of the pair, its position for 1900.0, and the magnitudes and spectral class† (or classes), the orbit elements, and the authority.

Similar tables of the best available orbits have been published from time to time, the most recent one being the one by W. H. van den Bos‡).   Luplau-Janssen and his colleagues at the Urania Sternwarte, Copenhagen, have also published a catalogue§ containing every orbit published up to 1926.   For 21 systems, 10 or more orbits are listed by them, 70 *Ophiuchi* leading, with 33 different sets of elements.

The orbits of spectroscopic binary stars, based upon measures of radial velocity, which in every case cover at least one complete revolution period and as a rule a considerable number of revolutions, are, with few exceptions, more accurate than the orbits of visual binaries.   *But not every star whose observed radial velocity varies periodically is a binary system.*   The observed variation may be the result of motion of a periodic character in the atmosphere of a single star.   This is apparently true of all those which also show variation in brightness of the *Cepheid* type, and also in general, of those in which the period of variation is but a fraction of a day, unless they are eclipsing variables like W *Ursae Majoris.*

Otto Struve¶ has given special attention to stars of this class and has developed a criterion based upon the relation between K, the semiamplitude of the velocity variation, and P, the period.

When mean values are used for the quantities involved, including the masses, this relation‖ may be written

$$K = CP^{-\frac{1}{3}} \qquad (1)$$

It is simply Kepler's harmonic law in different form, and shows

** = τ bnc Cc, the Spectroscopic Binary.

* The tabulation, however, does not include orbits published after September, 1934, unless they were available to me in advance of publication.

† From the *Henry Draper Catalogue*, if the star is listed there.

‡ *B.A.N.* **3**, 149, 1926.

§ *Ergänzungshefte zu den A.N.* **5**, Nr. 5, 1926.

¶ *Ap. Jour.* **60**, 167, 1924.

‖ The equation from which Struve derives this relationship is given in the section on the Masses of the Binary Stars, on p. 218(4).

that the semiamplitude should vary inversely as the cube of the period. Struve finds a very satisfactory agreement between the observed and the computed values for K for stars of all periods with the exception of those of two classes: the Cepheid variables and the stars, *not eclipsing binaries*, which show variable radial velocity with periods of but a small fraction of a day. The mean value of K for 10 stars of this latter class is very nearly the same as the mean for 15 Cepheid variables which he investigated, and in neither class do the values vary in accordance with Kepler's law. Excluding the Cepheid variables and these short period pseudo-Cepheids, and also a few stars of doubtful character, like α *Orionis*, for which rather uncertain orbits of long period have been computed, there remain 326 stars which are undoubtedly spectroscopic binary systems. These are listed in Table II in the Appendix, which is similar to Table I in its arrangement. One orbit only is given for each system, but when the spectra of both components are visible on the plates, the significant elements for the secondary, if they have been computed, are also entered. Eclipsing binaries, in this table, are indicated by an asterisk.

RELATIONS BETWEEN PERIOD AND ECCENTRICITY

Certain striking characteristics of the orbits in the two tables are recognized on the most casual inspection; for example the eccentricity of the visual orbits is generally large, that of spectroscopic orbits generally small; the periods of the former are long—the shortest known so far (if we exclude *Capella*, measured with the interferometer, and pairs like Aa of ξ *Ursae Majoris*, in which one component is invisible) being 4.56 years ($\delta 31 = \beta 1000 AB$);* those of the latter generally short, ranging, with few exceptions, from a few hours to about 150 days.

See, Doberck, and others have called attention to the high average eccentricity of the visual binary star orbits and to the contrast, in this respect, between these orbits and those of the planets in the solar system. This appears again in Table I. The average value of e for the 116 systems listed is 0.517 and no

---

* Kuiper, in his examination of stars of large parallax, has recently found that the 9.2 star *Wolf* 390 (= B.D. $-8°$ 4352, 16^h 50^m1, $-8°$ 09', class M3e) is a close pair with components of nearly equal magnitude, and maximum separation $0''2$. His measures indicate that its period of revolution is less than two years.

less than seven of the individual values exceed 0.90. The average value for the planets, including *Pluto* ($e = 0.249$), is only 0.08.

On the other hand, the average eccentricity for the 326 orbits* of spectroscopic binaries in Table II is but 0.174. Recalling the fact that the periods of the visual binaries are, on the average, much longer than those of the spectroscopic, it is natural to try to establish a relation between the two elements. Doberck long ago presented evidence tending to show that the eccentricity of the visual binaries increased with the length of the period; Campbell, Schlesinger, Ludendorff, and others have shown that a similar relationship exists among the spectroscopic binaries.

If we order the 116 systems in Table I in the Appendix according to period and eccentricity, we have Table 1.

TABLE 1.—PERIODS AND ECCENTRICITIES OF VISUAL BINARY ORBITS

P, years / e	0–50	50–100	100–150	150+	Sums
0– 10	0	0	0	0	0
10– 20	7	1	2	1	11
20– 30	7	0	2	0	9
30– 40	7	4	2	1	14
40– 50	9	5	4	6	24
50– 60	8	7	5	5	25
60– 70	2	1	0	3	6
70– 80	4	2	5	2	13
80– 90	2	2	0	3	7
90–100	1	1	2	3	7
Sums.........	47	23	22	24	116

Table 2 gives a similar grouping for 324 of the spectroscopic binary star orbits listed in Table II, omitting μ *Orionis* and ϵ *Hydrae* because they have been counted among the visual binaries.

The data utilized in these two tables may be summarized as in Table 3.

These three tables, containing 440 pairs, show practically the same relations between period and eccentricity as those brought out by the corresponding tables in the first edition (drawn up in 1917) when only 187 systems were available for

* Omitting μ *Orionis* and ϵ *Hydrae*, which are also visual binaries, the mean value is 0.173.

study. There is an increase of eccentricity with increasing period, *on the average*, in the orbits of the spectroscopic binaries and also in those of the visual pairs, and the average eccentricity is decidedly larger in the visual than in the spectroscopic binary orbits. Half the values of *e*, in Table 1, exceed 0.50, and less

TABLE 2

P, days $\diagdown$ e	0–5	5–10	10–20	20–50	50–100	100–500	500+	Sums
0– 10	100	26	19	8	4	10	4	171
10– 20	14	10	5	0	2	10	6	47
20– 30	2	9	10	4	3	2	5	35
30– 40	1	3	7	3	2	2	5	23
40– 50	1	2	1	6	1	3	3	17
50– 60	1	2	4	3	1	5	1	17
60– 70	0	1	2	2	0	2	2	9
70– 80	0	0	0	3	0	1	0	4
80– 90	0	0	0	0	0	1	0	1
90–100	0	0	0	0	0	0	0	0
Sums.......	119	53	48	29	13	36	26	324

TABLE 3.—THE RELATION BETWEEN PERIOD AND ECCENTRICITY IN BINARY SYSTEMS

P	n	Av.P	Av.e
0– 5^d	119	2^d.736	0.053
5– 10^d	53	7.424	0.155
10– 20^d	48	13.551	0.222
20– 50^d	29*	29.779	0.358
50–100^d	13	69.829	0.234
100–500^d	36	229.390	0.279
500^d+	26	5^y.81	0.286
0– 50^y	47	27.90	0.444
50–100^y	23	72.44	0.546
100–150^y	22	119.75	0.530
150^y+	24	249.02	0.615

* Eight of these 29 pairs have computed values of *e* in excess of 0.53; the remaining 21 values range from 0.0 to 0.49, with a mean of 0.249.

than one-tenth of all are as low as 0.20; in Table 2, on the other hand, two-thirds of the values of *e* range from 0.0 to 0.20, and only 31 of the 324 exceed 0.50.

To bring out more clearly the "scatter" in the values of *e* in orbits having approximately the same period, and, simultaneously, to show that the curve of relationship between *P* and *e* has no break in its continuity from the short-period spectroscopic binaries to the longest period visual binaries for which orbits are available, we may arrange the data as in Table 4. Here the spectroscopic binaries are gathered into 11 groups according to period, and the visual binaries into 9 groups, the successive columns giving the number of pairs in each group, the mean period and the mean eccentricity. If the values of *e* are plotted against the logarithms of *P*, and the points are connected we shall have an irregular broken line, illustrating the scatter in the values of *e*; but there is no indication whatever that we are dealing with more than one relationship curve.

TABLE 4

N	P	e
30	1^d260	0.051
30	2.236	0.038
30	3.248	0.072
30	4.276	0.060
30	6.830	0.125
30	9.528	0.238
30	13.376	0.181
30	23.457	0.356
30	76.090	0.242
30	299.701	0.268
24	2457.36	0.312
13	11^y69	0.455
13	24.11	0.489
13	36.89	0.383
13	49.33	0.529
13	77.43	0.519
13	98.44	0.468
13	126.91	0.601
13	186.18	0.579
12	308.82	0.627

The results of Russell's statistical investigations of the wider visual binaries for which no orbits are likely to be available for many years or even centuries, are of interest in this connection.

He finds the average eccentricity for 500 pairs, of average period roughly estimated at 2,000 years, to be 0.61, and "of nearly 800 more with average period of perhaps 5,000 years" to be 0.76.

We may summarize the data most effectively as follows:

P	n	Av.P	Av.e
0 to 100^d	262	13^d5	0.147
$100^d +$	62	$1,023.0(= 2^y8)$	0.282
0 to 100^y	70	42^y5	0.478
$100^y +$	46	187.2	0.574
	500	$2,000 \pm$	0.61
	$800 \pm$	$5,000 \pm$	0.76

But if there is a correlation between the two elements, it is not a simple one; disturbing factors evidently enter. We note, for example, the outstanding high average eccentricity for the 29 orbits of spectroscopic binaries with periods ranging from 20 to 50 days.* The value of e exceeds 0.60 in five of these orbits, as well as in three of shorter period. Again, we note that the eccentricity of the visual binary $O\Sigma 341$,† with a period of only 19.75 years is 0.96, and that in six other visual orbits of period under 50 years‡ the value of e exceeds 0.70. Orbits of long period and small eccentricity are also found both among the visual and among the spectroscopic binaries. We have, moreover, to reckon with the fact that the tabulated orbits may to a certain degree be affected by observational and computational selection and to that extent fail to be truly representative of binary star orbits in general. In the case of the spectroscopic binaries this selection factor may not be very important, although it is easy to see that systems of long period, and consequently small values of K, are more easily overlooked than those of short period, and that of the systems actually discovered, the short-period ones are more likely to be selected for orbit computation.

The situation with respect to the visual binaries may be more serious, though here it is not so much a matter of discovery as of observation. If the eccentricity of the orbit is high, the com-

* A similar high appeared in the 1917 tabulation which had 13 systems with periods between 20 and 50 days.

† ADS 11060; cf. τ Boo, $\Sigma 186$, ADS 9343.

‡ In a letter received after this passage was written, Dr. van den Bos gives reasons for believing that the visual binary $O\Sigma 536$ may have a period of only 27 years and an eccentricity of 0.98!

panion will spend most of its time at or near the apastron end of the ellipse and the chances are that the pair will be discovered when the apparent angular separation is at or near its maximum. It may then show little orbital motion for a number of years, particularly if the orbit has a high inclination, and be regarded by observers as "practically fixed," and therefore be neglected.

Again, a high percentage of the known closer visual binaries have components that are sensibly equal in magnitude. If such a pair has an orbit of great eccentricity, it may readily happen that observers will miss the times of minimum separation and that the computed orbit will be one of low eccentricity and of approximately twice the true period. Two systems, δ *Equulei* and ξ *Scorpii*, in which this mistake was actually made, are listed in Table 1.

Making due allowance, however, for all these and other possible selective effects, for the actual "spread" in the values of *e* in the various period categories, and for the irregularities in the tabulated progression, it still remains true that there is a general tendency toward greater values of the eccentricity as the period increases. This is a fact to be taken into account in theories of the origin of the binary stars, particularly if we assume that the spectroscopic and the visual binaries are objects of the same class.

RELATIONS BETWEEN PERIOD AND SPECTRAL CLASS

Campbell, in his study of the spectroscopic binary stars, found evidence of a relationship between the period and the spectral class; taking the spectra in the order B, A, F, G, K, and M, the period increases as we pass from B toward M. Before analyzing the present data to see whether they support this conclusion, it should be said that in combining the various subclasses, I have taken Class B to include subclasses O to B5; Class A, subclasses B8 to A3; Class F, subclasses A5 to F4; Class G, subclasses F5 to G0; Class K, subclasses G5 to K2; and Class M, subclasses K5 to M6. This agrees with the Harvard system, except in the inclusion of subclass B8 under Class A, but differs somewhat from the grouping adopted by Campbell.*

* Campbell also included a number of systems whose periods were known to be "long" or "short," though their orbits had not then been computed.

Table 5 shows the distribution with respect to period and spectral class of 439 pairs* entered in the preceding tables.

TABLE 5.—THE RELATION BETWEEN SPECTRAL CLASS AND PERIOD

Spectrum P	B	A	F	G	K	M	Sum
0– 5^d	41	42	16	18	1	1	119
5– 10^d	13	23	1	11	5	0	53
10– 20^d	10	18	3	11	6	0	48
20– 50^d	6	8	6	4	5	0	29
50–100^d	3	4	0	5	1	0	13
100–500^d	7	3	3	6	14	3	36
500^d +	4	2	0	5	14	1	26
0– 50^y	0	8	4	25	8	2	47
50–100^y	0	4	1	13	5	0	23
100–150^y	1	4	3	9	4	1	22
150^y +	0	6	5	7	5	1	2
Totals.........	85	122	42	114	68	9	440

It will be noted that, while there is a wide range in period in pairs of every one of the spectral classes, more than two-thirds of the spectroscopic binaries with periods of ten days or less belong to spectral classes B or A, that pairs with periods in excess of 100 days are most numerous in Class K, whereas Class M has, in all, but five representatives. In the visual orbits, on the other hand, Class G is best represented, especially in pairs with periods not exceeding 100 years. Class M, again, has few representatives and but one Class B pair appears.

To investigate the question of progression in period with advancing spectral class, I have computed the average periods of pairs of each spectral class, but in doing so have omitted four spectroscopic binaries of Class B, two of Class A, and one of Class G, because of their abnormally long periods. The results are given in Table 6, which records also the average eccentricity for each group. If the pairs just referred to were retained, the average period for Class B (84 stars) would become 149^{d}9, for Class A (100 stars), 36^{d}82, and for Class G (60 stars), 274^{d}20. The average eccentricities would be but slightly changed.

* The spectral class of the primary star, in visual binaries, is the one tabulated. The system ξ *Urs. Maj.* Aa is therefore omitted, since the primary has already been counted.

TABLE 6.—THE RELATION BETWEEN SPECTRAL CLASS AND AVERAGE
PERIOD AND ECCENTRICITY

Class	Av. P	Av. e	N
B	24^{d}61	0.153	80
A	15.08	0.162	98
F	25.80	0.225	29
G	101.20	0.152	59
K	681.12	0.212	46
M	336.07	0.096	5
B	104^{y}3	0.314	1
A	120.3	0.565	22
F	133.4	0.566	13
G	84.0	0.518	54
K	97.5	0.478	22
K5	167.45	0.556	2
Ma, b,	43.7	0.296	2

It again appears that the spectroscopic binaries of the "early" spectral classes have, on the average, short periods, those of the "late" classes, long periods; but the progression is irregular, the pairs of Class A having the shortest periods, those of Class K, the longest. Except for the fact that pairs of Classes G and K have, on the average, the shortest periods,* the visual binaries give little evidence of correlation between period and spectral class.

It has already been pointed out that spectroscopic systems of short period are more readily discovered than those of long period, for not only is the amplitude of the velocity curve greater, in general, in the former, but the variation in the velocity becomes apparent in a much shorter time. We may expect relatively more long-period systems in future discoveries among stars of all classes of spectra and hence an increase in the average values of the periods. It should also be noted that the spectra of stars of the later types, in general, show more lines, and these more sharply defined, than the spectra of the early-type stars. The probable error of measure is therefore less and hence a variable radial velocity of small amplitude may be unmistakable in, say, a Class G or K star, whereas one of equal amplitude may escape recognition in a star of Class B. This may account, in part, for the distribution in spectral class shown by the longer

* Unless we count the two M type stars μ *Herculis* BC, and Krueger 60.

period spectroscopic binaries in Table 5, but it obviously does not explain the large number of short-period binaries of classes B and A.

The decrease in the average eccentricity of the visual binaries with the advance in spectral class from A,F to G,K, is a curious feature of Table 6. It is apparently a selective effect, for the percentage decrease is definitely smaller than in the corresponding table in the first edition which listed 68 pairs. The spectroscopic binaries show no such progression.

Absolute trigonometric parallaxes are available for 89 of the visual pairs listed in Table I. I have computed the absolute magnitudes for the primary components in these systems, and have divided them into two groups at $M = 3.0$, which is ordinarily taken as the point of division between giant and dwarf stars. Omitting the exceptional white dwarf star, 40 *Eridani* BC ($M = 10.7$), we have the following table:

TABLE 7.—THE RELATIONS BETWEEN ABSOLUTE MAGNITUDE, SPECTRAL CLASS, PERIOD, AND ECCENTRICITY

	$M \lessgtr 3.0$				$M > 3.0$			
Sp	*N*	*M*	*P*	*e*	*n*	*M*	*P*	*e*
B	1	−0.4	104.ʸ3	0.31	0	......	.....	....
A	19	+1.53	111.1	0.58	1	+3.2	139.ʸ3	0.59
F	8	2.28	134.3	0.58	3	3.33	156.3	0.46
G	9	2.26	55.3	0.51	29	4.42	84.6	0.46
K	0	......	.....	....	16	5.71	111.8	0.46
Ma, b	0	......	.....	....	2	11.00	83.2	0.30

The distribution of stars of the different spectral classes in the two groups occasions no surprise, but it is of interest to note that fully two-fifths of the pairs fall into the group with $M \lessgtr 3.0$. In classes F and G, the average P for pairs in this group is smaller and the average e larger than for pairs in the group $M > 3.0$; but these facts, especially in view of the small numbers of pairs involved, are probably without significance.

THE DISTRIBUTION OF THE LONGITUDES OF PERIASTRON

In 1908 Mr. J. Miller Barr called attention to a singular distribution of the values of ω, the longitude of periastron, in those spectroscopic binaries whose orbits are elliptic. In the

30 orbits available to him in which e was greater than 0.0, 26 had values of ω falling between 0° and 180° and only four between 180° and 360°. He concluded that the effect was due to "some neglected source of systematic error" in the observed radial velocities, but both Ludendorff and Schlesinger, examining the data, were of opinion that it "was nothing more than a somewhat extraordinary coincidence," for it became less marked as additional orbits were computed.

In more recent years this question has been discussed by a number of investigators, some offering theoretical explanations for the unequal distribution which they regard as real, others refuting the explanations advanced. The history of these discussions, with full references, is given by O. Struve and A. Pogo* in a paper they published in 1929. Their own investigation leads them to the conclusion that the observed distribution may be real and may arise from conditions in the stellar systems that would produce a tendency toward a particular orientation of the periastra with respect to the direction to the center of the galactic system, but they admit that the evidence is not conclusive.

I have examined the data in Table II with respect to the distribution of the values of ω, with the result given in Table 8.

TABLE 8

e \ ω	0°–90°.0	90°–180°.0	180°–270°.0	270°–360°.0
0–0.10	47	27	22	24
0.10–0.20	8	13	10	15
0.20–0.50	28	14	21	13
0.50–0.88	10	6	7	10
Totals.........	93	60	60	62

All orbits in Table II, except those definitely noted as circular and two in which ω was set down as variable, are included. It appears that the number of values for ω in the first quadrant exceeds by 50 per cent the number in any of the other three quadrants, but that the excess is most marked in the orbits for which the value of the eccentricity is not greater than 0.10;

* Über die Ursache der ungleichen Verteilung der Periastronlängen bei spektroskopischen Doppelsternen, *A.N.* **234**, 297, 1929.

that is, in those orbits for which the value of ω is least determinate. For the orbits with $e > .10$, the sums, in the four quadrants, are, respectively, 46, 33, 38, 38, and the excess in the first quadrant is but 28 per cent. Even this is rather larger than would be expected in a purely random distribution of values, but it will be well to wait until a much larger number of accurate orbits becomes available before accepting it as proof of a real inequality in the distribution of the periastra.

THE ORIENTATION OF THE ORBIT PLANES OF THE VISUAL BINARY STARS

A related problem is that of the orientation of the orbit planes of the visual binary stars. A number of investigations have been made to ascertain whether these orbit planes exhibit a random distribution or whether there is a tendency to parallelism to a particular plane as, for example, the central plane of the Milky Way.

Practically, the problem is to determine the distribution of the poles of the orbits, and in its solution we encounter the serious difficulty that the orbit elements of a binary star do not define its plane uniquely unless the inclination is 0° or 90°. It is only when the indetermination in the sign of the inclination has been removed by spectrographic observations that we can discriminate between the true and the "spurious" pole. For this reason, the conclusions reached by the earlier investigators are all open to question, and it is not surprising that they differ widely. Miss Everett,* See,† and Doberck‡ found the distribution to be a random one: Lewis and Turner§ concluded that the evidence indicated, somewhat doubtfully, a tendency of the poles to group themselves along the Milky Way; Bohlin¶ noted a division into two groups, one with a concentration of the poles near the pole of the ecliptic and the solar apex, the other with a concentration near the pole of the Galaxy. The more recent investigations by Kreiken‖ and Shajn** also indicate a concentration near the pole of the Galaxy.

* Alice Everett, *Mon. Not. R.A.S.* **56**, 462, 1896.
† T. J. J. See, *Evolution of the Stellar Systems*, **1**, 247, 1896.
‡ W. Doberck, *A.N.* **147**, 251, 1898; *A.N.* **179**, 299, 1908.
§ T. Lewis and H. H. Turner, *Mon. Not. R.A.S.* **67**, 498, 1907.
¶ K. Bohlin, *A.N.* **176**, 197, 1907.
‖ E. A. Kreiken, *Mon. Not. R.A.S.* **88**, 101, 1927.
** G. Shajn, *Mon. Not. R.A.S.* **86**, 543, 1925.

All of these studies rest upon the known orbits of visual binary stars.   Professor J. M. Poor,[*] on the assumption that parallelism of the orbit planes would reveal itself as a variation in correlation between position angle and distance of double stars in different parts of the sky, based a statistical study on all the data available in 1913 and concluded that there is a concentration of poles near the vertex of the preferential motion of the stars.

Quite recently Y. C. Chang[†] and W. S. Finsen[‡] have investigated the question using as data only those orbits for which the true pole is known.   Chang, in 1928, based his study upon 16 pairs, including *Capella*, and the two systems 42 *Comae Berenices* and *ζ Cancri*,[§] whose orbit planes are, respectively, approximately parallel and perpendicular to the line of sight. Finsen, in 1933, found 28 pairs available, including five for which the values of cos i lay between 0.95 and 1.00 or between 0.00 and 0.05.   Neither investigator found any striking concentration of the poles, and both conclude that the distribution is probably a random one.   We may accept that as the best answer to the question on the basis of existing data.

THE MASSES OF THE BINARY STARS

The only direct method we have of determining the mass of a celestial body is to measure its effect upon the motion of another body.   It follows that the binary stars are the only ones whose masses we can determine directly.   Since a knowledge of stellar masses is fundamental in all studies of the dynamics of the stellar system, the methods by which we calculate the absolute and the relative masses of the components in the visual and spectroscopic binaries merit careful attention.

Unfortunately, the orbit elements alone do not afford all the data necessary for the determination of either mass or density.   The well-known harmonic law

$$D^3 : d^3 = P^2(M + M_1) : p^2(m + m_1),$$

will give the mass of any system in terms of the Sun's mass when the linear dimensions of the system as well as the orbit elements are known.   But the semimajor axis of the visual

---

[*] J. M. Poor, *A.J.* **28**, 145, 1914.

[†] Y. C. Chang, *A.J.* **40**, 11, 1929.

[‡] W. S. Finsen, Communicated in manuscript form in August, 1933.

[§] Schnauder's orbit.

binary stars is known only in terms of seconds of arc, and its value, so expressed, must be divided by its parallax to reduce it to linear measure;* and we do not know the true semimajor axis of the spectroscopic binary orbits at all, but only the function $a \sin i$. This, however, is expressed in kilometers.

The parallax of a number of visual binaries is known with a greater or less degree of certainty, and mass values for those systems may be computed, using the harmonic law in the form

$$(m + m_1) = \frac{a^3}{\pi^3 P^2} \tag{1}$$

in which π is the parallax of the system, P the period and a the semimajor axis of its orbit, and the units of mass, length, and time are, respectively, the Sun's mass, the astronomical unit, and the year.

While we are unable to derive the mass of any given spectroscopic binary until we have a knowledge of the value of i, the inclination, we may nevertheless estimate the *average* mass of a number of systems with approximate accuracy, by determining the probable average value of i and hence of $\sin i$. The formulas required differ for the two cases (1) when both spectra have been observed, and (2) when only one spectrum is visible. They may be derived from the well-known relation

$$(m + m_1) = \frac{4\pi^2}{k^2} \cdot \frac{(a + a_1)^3}{P^2} \tag{2}$$

in which π denotes, not the parallax, but the circumference of radius unity, k the Gaussian constant (log 8.23558), a and a_1, the major semiaxes of the orbits of the primary and secondary, respectively, and P their revolution period expressed in mean solar days. Since we do not know a but only the function $a \sin i$, we must multiply both members of (2) by $\sin^3 i$, and since $a \sin i$ is expressed in kilometers, we must divide its value by that of the astronomical unit expressed in kilometers. The numerical value of $4\pi^2/k^2 A^3$ is approximately† $4/10^{20}$ and we therefore have

$$(m + m_1)\sin^3 i = \frac{4}{10^{20}} \cdot \frac{(a \sin i + a_1 \sin i)^3}{P^2} \tag{3}$$

* This gives the length in astronomical units. The astronomical unit or the Earth's mean distance from the Sun is, in round numbers, 149,500,000 km.

† The more precise value $3.99455/10^{20}$ is used in obtaining the logarithm in Eq. (4).

From Eq. (9) of Chap. VI,

$$a \sin i = [4.13833]KP\sqrt{1 - e^2}$$

hence

$$(m + m_1) \sin^3 i = [3.01642 - 10](K + K_1)^3 P(1 - e^2)^{3/2} \quad (4)$$

the numbers in square brackets being logarithms. This equation is independent of the parallax, or distance of the system.

When both spectra have been measured and the corresponding velocity curves drawn we obtain at once the *relative masses* of the two components, from the relation $m : m_1 = K_1 : K$; and we also have the equations

$$\left.\begin{array}{l} m \ \sin^3 i = [3.01642 - 10](K + K_1)^2 K_1 P(1 - e^2)^{3/2} \\ m_1 \sin^3 i = [3.01642 - 10](K + K_1)^2 K P(1 - e^2)^{3/2} \end{array}\right\} \quad (5)$$

from which to compute the masses of the components separately.*

When only one spectrum is visible we must apply a somewhat different formula, *viz.*,

$$\frac{m_1^3}{(m + m_1)^2} \sin^3 i = \frac{4}{10^{20}} \frac{(a \sin i)^3}{P^2} \quad (6)$$

in which $a \sin i$ and m refer to the component whose spectrum is given. We may write this in a form similar to Eq. (4) thus:

$$\frac{m_1^3 \sin^3 i}{(m + m_1)^2} = [3.01642 - 10]K^3 P(1 - e^2)^{3/2} \quad (7)$$

In applying Eqs. (4) and (7) it is necessary to assume a value for $\sin^3 i$ and the question of obtaining such a value has next to be considered. "It can be shown for an indefinitely great number of binary systems whose orbital planes are distributed

---

* It is possible, in the case of certain eclipsing binaries, to determine the value of the velocity range (K_2) of the fainter star even when the direct measures of its velocity do not in themselves suffice to define the velocity curve. It is only necessary to have enough observations to define the slope of velocity curve of the secondary relatively to that of the primary. From this relation slope and the orbital elements of the primary, the value of K_2 can be computed, and thus the mass ratio of the two components. Joy, for example, employed this method in his work on the orbit of U *Sagittae* (*Ap. Jour.* **71**, 336, 1930). Here the larger (and fainter) star passes nearly centrally in front of the smaller primary and the total eclipse of the latter lasts about 100 minutes. With the 100-in. reflector enough spectrograms were secured in this short time interval to permit the slope of the velocity curve to be determined with considerable accuracy. The number of stars in which this method may be employed is, however, small. *Contrib. Mt. Wilson Obs.*, #401.

[See *UOC*, #68, Feb. 26, 1926, p. 354.—J.T.K.]

at random, that the average inclination would be 57°3, in accordance with the formula

$$i_0 = \frac{2}{\pi}\int_0^{\frac{\pi}{2}} \int_0^{\frac{\pi}{2}} i \sin i\, di\, d\phi = 1$$

1 radian!

The average value of $\sin^3 i$, however, would not be $\sin^3 57°3$ (= 0.65) but approximately 0.59 in accordance with the formula

$$\sin^3 i_0 = \frac{2}{\pi}\int_0^{\frac{\pi}{2}} \int_0^{\frac{\pi}{2}} \sin^4 i\, di\, d\phi = \tfrac{3}{16}\pi = 0.59"$$

Campbell, whom we have just quoted, and Schlesinger, who, from a slightly different formula obtains the same value for $\sin^3 i_0$, point out that while this mean value holds for orbits in general, it would not be permissible to use it for the spectroscopic binary stars whose orbits have so far been computed. For, to quote again from Campbell, "there is the practical consideration that binary systems whose orbital planes have large inclinations are more readily discoverable than those whose inclinations are small . . . Under ordinary circumstances, and when dealing with a considerable number of orbits, a compromise value of $\sin^3 i = 0.65$ might in fairness be adopted." For 18 systems which he actually considers he adopts the higher value 0.75 because six of them are eclipsing binaries, with inclinations quite certainly between 60° and 90°.

Schlesinger, assuming "that the chance of discovery is proportionate to $\sin i$," obtains $\sin^3 i = 0.68$ for a mean value. We may then adopt, for convenience in computation,

$$\sin^3 i = 0.667 = \tfrac{2}{3},$$

since comparatively few eclipsing binaries are among the number under discussion.

Both spectra are visible in 103 of the 321 pairs in Table II and for these the computers of the orbits have given the values $m \sin^3 i$, $m_1 \sin^3 i$, or, for some of the eclipsing binaries, the values m and m_1. Table 9 lists these pairs with their spectral classes and mass values. The most massive pair, by far, is BD + 57°28,* Class B5, and the least massive is probably the eclipsing pair S *Antliae*, Class F0, with masses 0.52☉ and 0.29☉ for the two components, respectively. Smaller minimum mass values are

---

* [See p. 251; also cf. Krueger 60, p. 242, a Visual Binary; also (46) Dra, B4745, Spec. Binary: *Lick Obs. Bull.* 483, I, #275 (non-eclipsing).—J.T.K.]

TABLE 9.—MASSES: SPECTROSCOPIC BINARIES

Star	Spec.	$m \sin^3 i$	$m_1 \sin^3 i$	2 Spectra	
				m	m_1
$+57°28$	B5	113.2	44.9		
* Boss 46	B0	17.57	16.37		
* TV Cas	B9	......	.....	1.83	1.01
π Cas	A5	1.35	1.34		
γ And	B3	1.50	1.10		
Boss 373	F5	1.16	1.06		
κ Ari	A0	0.14	0.13		
ι Tri, br	G0	1.12	1.12		
ι Tri fr	F4	0.91	0.86		
$+59°609$	B5	18.88	9.17		
Boss 816	B8	2.87	2.76		
o Per	B1	5.42	3.79		
A Per	F5p	1.01	0.88		
* $+33°785$	B3	4.86	4.29		
Boss 1001	B9	0.56	0.55		
$+7°676$	B5	7.0	3.7		
Boss 1213	B9	2.5	2.2		
* TT Aur	B5	6.7	5.3		
α Aur	G0	1.19	0.94		
Σ 674A	F5	1.40	1.33		
Boss 1275	A0	1.71	1.50		
* η Ori	B1	11.2	10.6		
ψ Ori	B2	5.53	4.19		
Boss 1457	A0	0.63	0.44		
Boss 1464	B2	10.3	3.9		
β Aur	A0p	......	.....	2.38	2.34
$-3°1413$	B5	6.2	4.1		
* WW Aur	A0	2.2	1.9		
$+6°1309$	B0p	75.6	63.3		
29 CMa	Oe	32.2	24.3		
Boss 1906	B8	4.3	2.3		
Boss 1945	F5	1.05	0.85		
* α Gem C	M1e	0.63	0.57		
$+34°1657$	F0	1.53	1.32		
$+20°2153$	A0	1.39	1.35		
Boss 2484	A0	1.48	1.27		
* S Ant	F0	0.52	0.29		
o Leo	F5	1.30	1.12		
* W UMa	G0	0.67	0.48		
Boss 2830	F2, A3	0.28	0.24		
ω UMa	A0	3.50	0.60		
Boss 2987	A2	0.12	0.08		
Boss 3138	B3	8.2	4.4		
θ' Cru	A5	0.74	0.61		
$+74°493$	G5	0.80	0.70		
Boss 3323	A5	4.62	2.37		
Boss 3354	A0	2.47	2.08		
* RS CVn	F8	1.79	1.66		
ζ' UMa	A2p	1.70	1.62		
α Vir	B2	9.6	5.8		
Boss 3555	F5	2.34	1.92		
Boss 3635	F5	1.36	1.29		
39 Boo ftr	F5	1.27	1.03		

TABLE 9.—(*Continued*)

Star	Spec.	$m \sin^3 i$	$m_1 \sin^3 i$	m	m_1
* UCrB	B8	......	.....	4.27	1.63
ζ CrB br.	B8	13.35	13.06		
β′ Sco	B1	13.0	8.3		
σ CrB br.	G0	0.94	1.07		
+17°3053	A0	2.19	1.35		
Boss 4247	F2	1.11	0.99		
ε Her	A0	1.6	1.0		
* U Oph	B8	......	.....	5.31	4.66
* u Her	B3	7.5	2.9		
* TX Her	A5	......	.....	2.04	1.77
Boss 4423	F0	0.88	0.82		
+14°3329	A3p	1.83	1.62		
* Z Her	F5p	1.5	1.3		
Boss 4602	F5	0.46	0.41		
Boss 4622	F0	1.04	1.01		
Boss 4643	A2	1.72	1.18		
* RX Her	A0	2.08	1.85		
+65°1276	A3	1.97	1.87		
+49°2871	F5, A	1.48	1.47		
Boss 4788	A0	0.95	0.90		
−10.4926	B5	7.10	4.43		
+16.3758	F5	1.26	1.26		
* RS Vul	B8	......	.....	5.26	1.64
U Sag	B9	......	.....	6.7	2.0
+37°3413	A0	1.18	0.84		
* Z Vul	B3	......	.....	5.25	2.37
Boss 4947	A0	0.91	0.65		
* σ Aql	B3	5.3	4.4		
Boss 5026	F5	1.46	1.44		
+35°3970	B0	13.85	12.90		
θ Aql	A0	0.52	0.38		
Boss 5173	A2	2.27	2.06		
+45°3139	B1	2.90	2.35		
* Y Cyg	B2	......	.....	17.4	17.6
Boss 5375	B3	1.79	1.67		
+32°4134	A0	1.87	1.08		
+27°4107	F0	0.97	0.77		
Boss 5575	A3	1.62	1.54		
Boss 5579	A0	0.96	0.95		
Boss 5591	A5	1.19	1.17		
Boss 5629	B3	20.8	13.6		
* RT Lac	G5	1.9	1.0		
Boss 5683	F5	0.65	0.61		
Boss 5764	B5	0.87	0.71		
Boss 5834	B3	6.01	3.87		
Boss 5846	G0	1.47	1.38		
* +64°1717	B3	11.4	9.8		
+58°2546	B3	4.8	2.9		
Boss 6142	B0	18.5	12.7		
Boss 6148	F5	1.70	1.67		
Boss 4745, 46(c)Dra	A0	0.12	0.10	(perhaps the least massive star known)	

The asterisk preceding star names in the first column indicates that the star is an eclipsing binary.

listed, it is true, but the factor $\sin^3 i$ may, in these cases, also be far below the average value.

It will be noted that two pairs, one in Class B0–B2 ($+57°28$), the other in Class B3–B5 ($+6°1309$), are extraordinarily massive and cannot, therefore, be used in deriving mean mass values for stars of those classes. Omitting them, we have the mean values given in Table 10.

TABLE 10.—MEAN MASS VALUES FOR SPECTROSCOPIC BINARY STARS

Class	Noneclipsing				Eclipsing			
	N	$m \sin^3 i$	$m_1 \sin^3 i$	m_1/m	N	$m \sin^3 i$	$m_1 \sin^3 i$	m_1/m
O	1	32.2	24.3	0.75	..	.....	.....	....
B0–B2	10	10.79	8.09	0.75	1	17.4	17.6	1.01
B3–B5	16	7.44	4.77	0.64	1	5.25	2.37	0.45
B8–A3	27	2.08	1.61	0.77	8	3.75	2.12	0.57
A5–F4	11	1.33	1.04	0.78	2	1.28	1.03	0.80
F5–G2	18	1.26	1.16	0.92	3	1.24	1.15	0.93
G5	1	0.80	0.70	0.88	1	1.9	1.0	0.53
M_1	..	.....	.....	....	1	0.63	0.57	0.93

In compiling this Table, I have taken the mass values for all stars noted as eclipsing binaries to be the true masses, although for a number of them the figures in Table 9 are entered as minimum values.

Inspection of that table shows that in only two systems (Y *Cygni*, B2 and σ *Coronae Borealis,btr*, G0) is m_1 slightly more massive than m, and that in only 17 others is there practical equality between the masses of the two components. The general rule is that the secondary is definitely the less massive star. We shall see that this holds true, too, for the visual binaries for which the mass ratio has been computed.

From Tables 9 and 10 it is clear that binaries of classes O to B5 are decidedly more massive than those of later classes and that there is a fairly definite progression in the average mass values as we pass from O to G, though too much stress must not be laid upon the particular figures in Table 10, since there is a large range in the individual values for every class.

Conclusions, moreover, that are drawn from systems in which the spectra of both components are recorded cannot, legitimately, be extended to all spectroscopic binary systems, for the double-line systems are selected, in the sense that it is only in systems with relatively large values of K that the spectrum of the second component is visible. The sum $(K + K_1)$ enters by its cube in Eq. (4) and the mass, therefore, in general increases very rapidly with K.

The value of the function $m_1^3 \sin^3 i/(m + m_1)^2$ is frequently omitted by the computer of orbits for it gives very little definite information. Equation (7) affords a ready means of computing the function for any system, but I have not considered it necessary to carry out the computation, for a glance at the numbers recorded in Table II* shows at once that no conclusions could be based upon any means that might be taken. There is nothing novel in these conclusions; they simply confirm, on the basis of more extensive data, conclusions reached by several earlier investigators. As early as 1911, for example, Ludendorff found, from the systems then available for study, that those of Class B were, on the average, about three times as massive as those of classes A to K.

The last two columns of Table I* give the parallaxes and masses of 83 visual binary star systems. The parallaxes for the brighter stars were taken, with but one or two exceptions, from Schlesinger's *Catalogue of Bright Stars;* those for the stars too faint to be listed in that catalogue, from parallax data kindly sent to me from the Yale University Observatory. It is to be noted that the latter are not Schlesinger's values but my own deductions from the data. Taking them all at face value we have the following summary:

TABLE 11

Class	N	$(m + m_1)$	M
B	1	10.65	−0.10
B8 to A3	21	4.03	1.04
A5 to F3	11	2.59	2.18
F5 to G2	37	2.43	3.25
G5 to K2	16	2.14	5.25
Ma, b	2	0.62	10.70

The final column gives the mean absolute magnitudes of the stars.

The means for classes A, F, and G agree well with those for the corresponding classes of spectroscopic binaries in Table 10. The

* In the Appendix.

numbers for classes B, K, and M are too small to give the means any weight.

Several of the individual mass values in Table I relate to triple or quadruple systems. It is known that one component in each of the systems Ho212 (13 *Ceti*), A2715 (*μ Orionis*), *κ Pegasi*, and OΣ82, and both components in the systems *Castor* (AB) and *ξ Ursae Majoris* (AB) are spectroscopic binaries. Further, invisible companions have been suspected in the system 70 *Ophiuchi* and *ζ Cancri* (AB) and a fainter companion to the companion of *Sirius* has been reported by several observers. It is not at all improbable that other systems may be found to have similar additional components when later measures give us more accurate orbits. In some instances, the mass of the invisible companion is known to be very small, but even so, when the data become more extensive and reliable, account must be taken of all of these extra bodies in any discussion of the masses of the visual binary stars. At present it will suffice to call attention to their existence and to the fact that allowance for them would modify slightly the figures in Table 11. The uncertainties still attaching to the values of the parallax are, however, far more important, for many of the parallaxes are small and changes in their value, within the probable error of measure, will make large changes in the computed masses since the parallax enters the formula by its cube. Changes in the orbit elements P and a will have far less effect for, to a large degree, they will offset each other, since in general they vary in the same sense.

It may be remarked that the comparatively small range in mass in the visual binary systems might have been predicted from the fact that, in general, long-period orbits have the larger values of a, short-period orbits, the smaller ones. A large percentage of the known visual orbits are comparable in size to the orbits of the major planets in the solar system.

The parallaxes utilized in Table 11 do not depend upon the fact that the stars to which they relate are binary systems, but it is to be noted that when, in a visual binary we have not only the orbit elements but also spectrographic measures of the relative radial velocities of the two components, we have the data for an independent determination of the parallax, as See pointed out many years ago. Hussey used this method to derive the parallax of *δ Equulei*, and Wright, to derive that of *α Centauri*, their values agreeing closely with those given in the table. The computation is readily made by means of the following formulas, adapted by Wright from the work of Lehmann-Filhés:* Let

R = the astronomical unit, expressed in kilometers.

α = the semi-major axis of the binary, expressed in kilometers, and a'', the same element expressed in seconds of arc.

n = the mean angular motion of the star, in the visual orbit, in circular measure per second of time.

ΔV = the observed difference in the radial velocity of the two components.

Then

$$\left.\begin{aligned} n &= \frac{2\pi}{86400 \times 365.26 \times P} \\ \alpha &= \frac{\Delta V \sqrt{1 - e^2}}{n \sin i[e \cos \omega + \cos (v + \omega)]} \\ \pi'' &= \frac{a''}{\alpha} \cdot R \end{aligned}\right\} \quad (8)$$

The micrometric measures connecting the two components of a visual double star afford data for the computation of the relative orbit only, and give us no direct information about the position of the center of gravity of the system or the mass ratio of the two components. This information can be obtained only from measures connecting one, or both, of the components with independent stars. Such measures, covering a sufficient time interval, afford the data for the computation of the absolute orbit of the component concerned, and thus, by comparison, of the mass ratio.

The classic illustration is the star *Sirius*. Bessel, in his discussion of the proper motion of the bright star, based upon the meridian-circle observations, noted as early as 1834 that it was not moving uniformly along a straight line but was describing a wavy line across the sky. He inferred the existence of an unseen companion, the two components revolving about their common center of gravity in a period of fifty years.† The faint companion discovered by Alvan G. Clark in 1862 fully confirmed this prediction, and the combination of the micrometer,

---

* I have made slight changes in Wright's notation as given in *L.O.B.* **1**, 4, 1904.

† For a more detailed statement, see p. 237.

meridian-circle, and parallax measures permits the computation of the mass of each component and also of the linear dimensions of the orbits.

When a series of micrometric or photographic measures connecting the components of a binary with an independent star is available, the relative masses can be determined in a very simple manner.*

Let AB be the binary system, C an independent star, and let ρ, θ and ρ', θ', respectively, be the distance and position angle of C referred to A and of B referred to A. Then the apparent rectangular coordinates of C and B referred to axes drawn from A as origin in position angles θ_0 and $(90° + \theta_0)$ will be

$$x = \rho \cos (\theta - \theta_0) \qquad\qquad x' = \rho' \cos (\theta' - \theta_0)$$
$$y = \rho \sin (\theta - \theta_0) \qquad\qquad y' = \rho' \sin (\theta' - \theta_0)$$

Now if we let K equal the mass ratio $B/(A + B)$, the coordinates of the center of gravity of AB will be Kx', Ky', and since the motion of C with respect to this point must be uniform, we have

$$x = a + b(t - t_0) + Kx'; \qquad y = a' + b'(t - t_0) + Ky', \qquad (9)$$

t_0 being any convenient epoch.

Each set of simultaneous observations of AB and AC furnishes an equation of condition in x and one in y for the determination of the five constants a, b, a', b', K. No knowledge of the period or other elements of the binary system is involved, the accuracy of the determination of K depending entirely upon the amount of departure from uniformity of motion of B relatively to A. In *Lick Observatory Bulletin* 208 I published a list of systems specially suited to the application of this method and urged the desirability of measuring them systematically.

The late Lewis Boss deduced the mass ratios for a number of systems and published his results as an appendix to his *Preliminary General Catalogue of Stars for* 1900.0. Taking his values and a few obtained by other investigators and applying them to the masses for the systems, as given in Table I,† we have the following data on the masses of the components in visual binary systems:

* Russell, *Ap. Jour.* **32**, 363, 1910.
† In the Appendix.

TABLE 12

Star	Spec.	m_1/m	m	m_1
η Cass.................................	F8	0.76	0.72	0.55
40 Erid. BC............................	A	0.45	0.44	0.21
Sirius..................................	A0	0.39	2.40	0.96
Procyon................................	F5	0.36	1.17	0.43
ζ Cancri AB...........................	G0	1.00	1.24	1.23
ε Hydrae AB...........................	F8	0.86	2.02	1.74
ξ Urs. Maj. Aa, Bb....................	G0	1.00	0.83	0.83
γ Virginis.............................	F0	1.00	1.19	1.19
α Centauri.............................	G0	0.85	0.95	0.81
ξ Bootis...............................	G5	0.87	0.73	0.63
ζ Herc.................................	G0	0.45	1.22	0.52
Melb 4, AB............................	K2	0.75	0.67	0.51
μ Herc BC.............................	Mb	0.80	0.46	0.37
70 Oph.................................	K0	0.78	0.80	0.72
Krueger 60............................	Ma	0.67	0.24	0.16
85 Pegasi..............................	G0	1.86	0.35	0.65
* [K Pegasi AB (A is a Sp. Bin.).............	F5	0.60	3.30 (A+a)	1.90 —J.T.K.]

The evidence available at present leads to the conclusion that the fainter component in the system 85 *Pegasi* is the more massive one, but Boss considered the uncertainties so great that he finally gave the two components equal masses. The results for the other systems indicate that the fainter star is the less massive one, a conclusion which is in harmony with that derived from the spectroscopic binary stars.

DYNAMICAL[†] PARALLAXES OF THE VISUAL BINARY STARS

Equation (1), page 217, written in the form

$$p = \frac{a}{\sqrt[3]{(m_1 + m_2)P^2}}$$

where p is the parallax, may obviously be used to compute the parallaxes of systems with known orbits for which a value of the mass[‡] can be determined or assumed from independent data; but the number of such systems is small and is not increasing very rapidly. It has, however, been known for many years that two or more sets of elements for a given system may have but little resemblance to each other as a whole and yet give

* [*Lick Obs. Bull.* 483, Tab. I, #342 R, p. 22, Luyten, 1934.—J.T.K.]

† The term "hypothetical" was used in earlier years to describe these parallaxes.

‡ The Sun's mass is, as usual, taken as the unit in this discussion.

approximately the same value for the ratio a^3/P^2, which enters our equation. The reason is, as Jackson says, that the various sets of elements "give nearly the same arc for that portion of the orbit which has been observed and that this arc is sufficient to determine the gravitational attraction between the two stars." In fact, in order to define the relation between the parallax and the mass of a system, all that is needed is an observed arc long enough for the computation of a satisfactory value of the double areal velocity $\rho^2(d\theta/dt)$.

Comstock* was the first, apparently, to apply this principle, using it to derive the masses of systems in slow orbital motion for which parallaxes were available. Russell,† Hertzsprung,‡ and Jackson and Furner§ later developed formulas for determining dynamical parallaxes on the basis of assumed average values for the mass $m_1 + m_2$. Hertzsprung, in 1911, adopting the value $(m_1 + m_2) = 1$, derived "minimum hypothetical" parallaxes and concluded that, statistically, the ratio of the true to the minimum hypothetical parallaxes, does not vary greatly and can be expressed by

$$\log \frac{p}{p_{h,min.}} = +0.27 \pm 0.14$$

Jackson and Furner, the first to publish an extensive list of dynamical parallaxes, used $(m_1 + m_2) = 2$ for systems with orbits, and $1/\sqrt[3]{m_1 + m_2} = 0.855$ for the much larger number with observed arcs too short for the computation of even preliminary elements.

In 1923, Russell, Adams, and Joy¶ published their comparison of 327 dynamical parallaxes, computed by Russell on the assumption that the mass of each system equals that of the Sun, with the spectroscopic parallaxes derived at Mount Wilson. They grouped the stars according to spectral class, separating giants

---

* *Publ. Washburn Obs.* **12**, 31, 1908.

† Determinations of Stellar Parallax, *A.J.* **26**, 147, 1910; *Science* (*N.S.*) **34**, 523, 1911.

‡ *Über Doppelsterne mit eben merklicher Bahnbewegung*, *A.N.* **190**, 113, 1911.

§ Jackson and Furner: The Hypothetical Parallaxes of 556 Visual Double Stars, with a Determination of the Velocity and Direction of the Solar Motion, *Mon. Not. R.A.S.* **81**, 2, 1920.

¶ A Comparison of Spectroscopic and Dynamical Parallaxes, *Publ. A.S.P.* **35**, 189, 1923.

from dwarfs from F6 to M, taking absolute magnitude = 3.0 as the dividing point. They also computed the absolute magnitude for each pair, both from the dynamical and from the spectroscopic parallaxes. The relationship between absolute magnitude and mass was striking; stars of all spectral classes and giants as well as dwarfs, "fell into line." "It is evident," they wrote, "that statistically considered, the mass of a binary system is a function of its absolute magnitude." The theoretical explanation of the mass-luminosity relationship, has been given by Eddington. In his more recent work on dynamical parallaxes, Russell* has developed formulas which include a factor, n, depending upon the mass-luminosity relationship and has drawn up tables from which its value may be obtained.

For pairs with orbits, his formula is

$$p = nd_1 = naP^{-\frac{2}{3}}$$

and for physical pairs with only a short observed arc, he writes

$$h = nh_1, \qquad h_1 = l\sqrt[3]{\frac{sw^2}{4\pi^2}} = 0.418\sqrt[3]{sw^2}$$

where s is the observed distance, w the observed relative motion in seconds of arc a year, and l a factor (derived from a statistical discussion not given in detail) which is designed to make the mean values of d_1 and h_1 equal. The values of d_1 and h_1 (except for the factor of proportionality) are derived directly from the data of observation. To find n, three tables, A, B, and C, are provided. Table A gives the correction to be applied to the observed visual magnitude of a pair to reduce it to the "standardized bolometric magnitude m." This correction, of course, depends upon, and varies with, the spectral class (that of the primary star is taken in general) or assumed temperature. The bolometric absolute magnitude, M_1, then follows from

$$M_1 = m + 5 + 5 \log d_1 \text{ (for pairs with orbits)}$$
$$= m + 5 + 5 \log h_1 \text{ (for other physical pairs)}$$

With M_1 as argument, take out n_0 from Table B, and with M_1 and ΔM_1 the difference of magnitude between the two components, as arguments, take A from Table C. Then

$$n = n_0 A. \tag{1}$$

* On the Determination of Dynamical Parallaxes, *A.J.* **38**, 89, 1928.

TABLE A

Sp.	Temp.	Corr.	Sp.	Temp.	Corr.	Sp.	Temp.	Corr.
B0	23000°	$-0^m.9$	gG0	5600°	$0^m.0$	dG0	6000°	$+0^m.1$
B5	15000	-0.1	gG5	4700	-0.4	dG5	5600	0.0
A0	11000	$+0.2$	gK0	4200	-0.7	dK0	5100	-0.2
A5	8600	$+0.3$	gK5	3400	-1.5	dK5	4400	-0.6
F0	7400	$+0.3$	gM2	3100	-2.0	dM0	3400	-1.5
F5	6500	$+0.2$	gM7	2700	-2.6	....	....	.....

TABLE B

M_1	n_0	M_1	n_0	M_1	n_0
-6	0.065	0	0.417	6	0.880
-5	0.097	1	0.496	7	0.961
-4	0.132	2	0.575	8	1.046
-3	0.189	3	0.652	9	1.138
-2	0.251	4	0.728	10	1.238
-1	0.337	5	0.803	11	1.345

TABLE C

ΔM	$M_1 = -4$	-2	0	$+2$ and fainter
0	1.00	1.00	1.00	1.00
1	1.02	1.01	1.01	1.01
2	1.05	1.04	1.03	1.03
3	1.08	1.07	1.06	1.05
4	1.11	1.09	1.08	1.07
5	1.13	1.12	1.11	1.10
6	1.14	1.13	1.12	1.12
7	1.15	1.14	1.14	1.14
8	1.16	1.15	1.15	1.15
9	1.16	1.15	1.15	1.16
10	1.16	1.16	1.16	1.18
12	1.17	1.17	1.18	1.19

In 1929, Russell and Miss Charlotte E. Moore published the dynamical parallaxes of 1,777 double stars,* derived by the method just described, and in 1933, Miss Moore computed the dynamical parallaxes of 323 of the pairs of my own discovery, from observational data which I provided.†

* *A.J.*, **39**, 165, 1929.
† *Lick Obs. Bull.* **16**, 96, 1933, #451.

Mr. R. O. Redman,* in a paper published just before Russell's, also gave the results of an investigation planned to improve dynamical parallaxes by making the masses conform to the mass-luminosity relation instead of adopting a mean standard mass. His discussion differs from Russell's in its details and results in more laborious processes for the actual computations of parallax. Finsen† has recently made an instructive comparison of the formulas developed by Comstock, Jackson, Hertzsprung, and Russell, and has added a formula for use in the case of binaries whose periods are known, though only a small actually observed arc is available. Several pairs of this kind are given in double star catalogues.

Dynamical parallaxes are, statistically, of a high order of accuracy, particularly when the mass-luminosity relation has been taken into account, but it does not follow that the dynamical parallax of an individual star can be taken as the measure of its distance. Comparison of the dynamical parallaxes computed by Russell and Miss Moore with the parallax values entered in Table I,‡ for example, shows that the mean of the differences is only $+0\rlap{.}''00016$, but individual differences range from $+0\rlap{.}''009$ to $-0\rlap{.}''008$, with a few, for the nearer stars, that are much larger.

DENSITY OF THE BINARY STARS

Although every short-period spectroscopic binary star would be an eclipsing binary to an observer in the plane of its orbit, as Stebbins and others have remarked, the methods outlined in Chap. VII to determine the density of an eclipsing binary from the orbit elements cannot be applied to spectroscopic binaries in general, and still less to the visual binaries. But from the relations that have been established theoretically between the absolute magnitude, diameter, and temperature of a star, confirmed as they have been in many critical cases by interferometer measures and by the investigations on eclipsing binaries, it is possible to determine the diameters and the masses of stars, and hence their densities.

---

* A Statistical Study of the Effect of the Mass-Luminosity Relations on the Hypothetical Parallaxes of Binary Stars, *Mon. Not. R.A.S.* **88**, 33, 1927.

† The Determination of Dynamical Parallaxes of Double Stars, *Mon. Not. R.A.S.* **92**, 47, 1931.

‡ Appendix.

The fact that a star is a component of a binary system has no bearing either upon the principles involved in these methods, or upon their application and for this reason they are not treated here. It may be remarked, however, that the evidence now favors the conclusion that the densities of stars of the main sequence, from Class B to Class G, whether they are single stars or components in a spectroscopic or visual binary system, are very similar to those found for the eclipsing binaries. There are, of course, a few exceptions among components of binary systems, as, for example, the very dense companion to *Sirius* which will be discussed in detail in Chap. IX.

MULTIPLE STARS

In 1781, Herschel noted that the brighter star of the 5″ pair, ζ *Cancri*, discovered by Tobias Mayer in 1756, was itself a double star with an angular distance of only 1″ between its nearly equal components. In the years that have followed, a large number of such triple systems, and not a few that are quadruple, or multiple, have become known. During the Lick Observatory double star survey, for example, I catalogued at least 150 such systems previously unknown, and Prof. Hussey's work yielded a proportionate number. The triple was formed, in more than half of these cases, by the discovery of a close companion to one of the components of a wider pair previously catalogued by other observers, and in some cases there is no question but that the closer pair had been overlooked at the earlier date because it was below the resolving power of the telescope.

The spectrograph has also revealed many triple and multiple systems; sometimes, as in 13 *Ceti* or κ *Pegasi*, by showing that one component of a visual binary is itself a binary too close to be seen as such with the telescope; again, as in *Algol*, by showing that the short-period spectroscopic binary revolves in a larger orbit with a third invisible star.

In 1918 I estimated that 4 or 5 per cent of the visual binaries are triple or quadruple systems if components known only spectroscopically or through the perturbations they produce are included as well as visible additional companions. The compilation of the *New General Catalogue of Double Stars* offered opportunities to check that estimate. I did not make a complete count, but was confirmed in my opinion that this estimate is

very little, if at all, too liberal. It seems to be a general rule
that the distance between the components of the close pair
in such systems whether visual or spectroscopic is small in
comparison with that which separates the pair from the third
star. However, there are exceptions to the rule. Thus we
have in Hu 66, BC = 0″.34, A and BC (= OΣ 351) = 0″.65; in
A 1079, AB = 0″.23, AB and C = 0″.48; in A 2286, AB = 0″.34,
AB and C = 0″.94; in A 1813, AB = 0″.20 AB and C = 0″.70;
and in Hu 91, BC = 0″.15, AB (= OΣ 476) = 0″.54. Some
allowance must, of course, be made for the effect of perspective; the orbit plane of the closer pair may not coincide with
the plane in which the third star revolves. But it is unlikely that
this will modify the relative apparent angular distances greatly.

The system of *Castor* affords an extreme example of the
contrasting distances between the close and wide pairs in a
quadruple star; each component of the visual pair is a spectroscopic binary, the revolution periods being respectively three
and nine days while the period of the orbit described by these
two pairs is certainly greater than 300 years! The motion of
the third star with respect to the closer pair in a triple *visual*
system has in no instance been observed over an arc long enough
to permit the computation of a reliable orbit.

The various conclusions drawn in the present chapter as to
masses and densities of the binary stars and as to the relations
between the orbit elements, rest upon comparatively small
numbers of pairs, but some of them, none the less, may be
accepted as definitely established. Others may require modification, when additional data become available.

References

From the many papers published in recent years on subjects discussed
in the present chapter, I have selected the following, in addition to those
quoted in the footnotes, as representative.

LUDENDORFF, H.: Weitere Untersuchungen über die Massen der spektroskopischen Doppelsterne, *A.N.* **211**, 105, 1920.

HERTZSPRUNG, E.: On the Relation between Mass and Absolute Brightness
of Components of Double Stars, *B.A.N.* **2**, 15, 1923.

JACKSON, J.: The Masses of Visual Binary Stars of Different Spectral Types,
Mon. Not. R.A.S. **83**, 444, 1923.

SHAJN, G.: The Movement of the Line of Nodes in Spectroscopic Binaries
and Variables and its Consequence, *Ap. Jour.* **57**, 129, 1923.

EDDINGTON, A. S.: On the Relation between the Masses and Luminosities
of the Stars, *Mon. Not. R.A.S.* **84**, 308, 1924.

BRILL, A.: Strahlungsenergetische Parallaxen von 123 visuellen Doppelsternen, *Veröff. Univ. Sternwarte Berlin-Babelsberg*, **7**, I, 1927.

LUNDMARK, K.: Statistical Concerning the Binary Stars, *Ark. f. Mat. Astr. och. Fysik*, **20A**, 12, 1927.

PITMAN, J. H.: The Masses and Absolute Magnitudes of Binary Stars, *A.J.* **39**, 57, 1929.

SHAJN, G.: On the Mass-Ratio in Binary Stars and the Hypothesis of a Secular Decrease of Mass, *A.N.* **237**, 57, 1929.

KREIKEN, E. A.: Many papers: *e.g.*, *Mon. Not. R.A.S.* **89**, 589, 1929; *B.A.N.* **4**, 239, 1928; **5**, 71, 1929; *A.N.* **238**, 373, 1930.

CHAPTER IX

SOME BINARY SYSTEMS OF SPECIAL INTEREST

Having studied the orbit elements of the binary stars in their more general relations, it will be of interest next to consider the various systems in themselves, the extent, and the limitations, of our knowledge of their motions and physical conditions. Selection is here an obvious necessity, and in making my choice I have been influenced in part by the historical associations connected with certain systems, in part by the peculiarities of the orbit. Some of the systems are among those for which our knowledge is relatively full and exact; others present anomalies still more or less baffling to the investigator.

α CENTAURI

Our nearest known stellar neighbor, α *Centauri*, is a system of more than ordinary interest. One of the first half dozen double stars to be discovered—the very first among the stars of the southern heavens—it also divides with 61 *Cygni* the honor of being the first whose approximate distance, or parallax, became known. It consists of two very bright stars, 0.3 and 1.7 magnitude, respectively, which revolve in a strongly elliptic orbit so highly inclined to the plane of projection that at times they are separated by fully 22″, at others by less than 2″.

Accurate micrometer measures of relative position begin only with Sir John Herschel, in 1834, but meridian circle observations date back to Lacaille's time, 1752. Since these early dates the system has been observed regularly with meridian circle, micrometer, and heliometer, and the position of its components has been measured on photographic plates. The material is therefore ample for a very good determination of the orbit elements and of the proper motion of each component and excellent use has been made of it by Roberts, See, Doberck, Lohse, and, in 1926, by Finsen, whose elements are quoted in Table I. Finsen's period is 1.25 years longer than that found by

Lohse, but his other elements differ little from the earlier set and we may regard his results as definitive. The parallax is known with equal precision; the value resulting from the excellent heliometer measures by Gill and Elkin having been confirmed by later discussions of meridian observations by Roberts and others and by Wright's results from measures of the relative radial velocities of the components, to which reference has been made on an earlier page. Schlesinger* gives the value $0''.760$ and assigns the proper motions $-3''.604$ in right ascension and $+0''.739$ in declination to the system of the two stars. The spectrograph has also given us the radial velocity† of the center of mass of the system, -22.2 km/sec.

Taking Finsen's elements and the parallax value just quoted, we find that the semimajor axis of the system is 23.2 A.U., but since the eccentricity of the orbit is 0.52, the distance between the components at periastron is but 11.2 A.U. only a little greater than *Saturn's* mean distance from the Sun, whereas at apastron it is 35.3 A.U., a value about midway between those of *Neptune* and *Pluto* from the Sun.

In 1904, when Wright measured the radial velocities of the two components of α *Centauri*, he found that the brighter star was approaching the Earth with a velocity of 19.10 km/sec, and the fainter one, with a velocity of 24.27 km/sec. That is, *relatively to the center of mass of the system*, the primary was receding from the Earth, the companion approaching it. The companion's position angle at that date was approximately 207°, and the nodal point of the orbit is 25°.4; hence, on the system of notation we have adopted (Chap. IV), the sign of the inclination is negative.‡

The mass of the system corresponding to the adopted values of the parallax and orbit elements is 1.96 times that of the Sun, and all investigators of the proper motions of the two components agree that the brighter star is very slightly the more massive of the two. Besides being practically equal to the Sun in mass, it belongs to the same spectral class (G0) and has nearly the same absolute magnitude, 4.73 as compared with 4.85. It is therefore almost a replica of the Sun. The fainter component belongs to Class K5, and its absolute magnitude is

---

* *Catalogue of Bright Stars*, p. 110, 1930.

† Moore, *Publ. Lick Obs.* **18**, 115, 1932.

‡ It was incorrectly stated to be positive, in the first edition.

6.10. Combining the values for proper motion and radial velocity, we find a space velocity of 25.2 km/sec, but little greater than that of the velocity of our Sun.

A new chapter in the story of this system was opened when Innes, in 1915, discovered that "Proxima Centauri," a faint star of 10.5 apparent magnitude (15.0 absolute) had approximately the same proper motion as the bright star, although a little more than 2° distant from it. It proved also to have very nearly the same parallax, and is no doubt physically connected with the two bright stars though too distant to affect their orbital motions. "Proxima" is a little nearer to the Sun (4.16 light years) than α *Centauri* (4.30 light years) and is therefore our nearest known stellar neighbor.

SIRIUS

Several references have been made to *Sirius* on the earlier pages of this volume, but it will not be amiss to give a more connected account of the star here. It was in 1834 that Bessel noticed that the proper motion of *Sirius*, the brightest star in the sky, was variable. Six years later he noted a similar phenomenon in the proper motion of *Procyon*, and by 1844 he had worked out the nature of the variation sufficiently to become convinced that it was due in each instance to the attraction of an invisible companion. His famous letter to Humboldt on the subject has often been quoted: "I adhere," he wrote, "to the conviction that *Procyon* and *Sirius* are genuine binary systems, each consisting of a visible and an invisible star. We have no reason to suppose that luminosity is a necessary property of cosmical bodies. The visibility of countless stars is no argument against the invisibility of countless others."

Peters examined the existing meridian circle observations in 1851 and concluded that they supported Bessel's hypothesis; ten years later, T. H. Safford repeated the investigation and "assigned to the companion a position angle of 83°.8 for the epoch 1862.1." The most complete discussion, however, was that of Auwers, who "placed the question beyond doubt by determining the orbits and relative masses of the bright star and the invisible companion; but before the results were published, Mr. Alvan G. Clark discovered the companion, in 1862, near its predicted place." Bond's measures for the epoch

1862.19, in fact, placed the companion 10ʺ.07 from the primary in position angle 84°.6.

Since that time it has described more than an entire revolution and the orbit elements, now known with high precision, agree as well as could reasonably be expected with Auwers's, computed before the companion's discovery. Thus, Volet's orbit, computed in 1931, which differs very little from my own, published in 1918, has the revolution period 49.94, whereas Auwers gave 49.42 years.

The eccentricity of the true orbit is greater than that for the orbit of α Centauri, but the inclination of the orbit plane is considerably less and the apparent ellipse is therefore a more open one, the maximum apparent separation of the components being about 11ʺ.2 and the minimum a little less than 2ʺ. The bright star is so exceedingly brilliant, however, that it is impossible to see the faint companion with any telescope when it is near its minimum distance. Thus, periastron passage occurred early in 1894, but the last preceding measure was Burnham's in the spring of 1892 when the angular separation was 4ʺ.19, and the little star was not again seen until October, 1896, when my first measure gave an apparent distance of 3ʺ.81. The photometric magnitude of *Sirius* (and also its photographic magnitude, since it is a star of Class A0) is −1.6. Estimates of the apparent magnitude of the companion are subject to great uncertainty because they are all affected by the presence of the intensely brilliant primary. Visual observers, in recent years, have adopted the value 8.5, and Wendell's value from measures with a double-image Rochon prism photometer* is 8.44. This value has recently been confirmed by Kuiper† from measures made with the Leiden 10-in. refractor, fitted with objective gratings. On the other hand, Vyssotsky,‡ using the 26-in. refractor of the McCormick Observatory and (a) coarse objective gratings, and (b) a rotating sector, derives the value 7.1 for the photovisual magnitude.

The question of the precise magnitude of this star is an important one, because of its relation to the question of the star's

---

* *Harvard Annals* **64**, No. VI, 1909.

† *B.A.N.* **6**, 197, 1932. More recently, Kuiper using the 12-in. refractor at the Lick Observatory and suitable gratings, found the value 8.42, in full agreement with his Leiden result (*Publ. A.S.P.* **46**, 99, 1934).

‡ *Publ. A.S.P.* **42**, 155, 1930; *Ap. Jour.* **78**, 1, 1933.

density. The mass of the system corresponding to the parallax and orbit elements in Table I is 3.36 times that of the Sun and this, with Boss's value for the mass ratio,* 0.39, gives 0.94⊙ for the mass of the companion. The presence of the bright primary makes accurate determination of the spectral class difficult, but Adams finds that it is a little earlier than F0, and it is now usually called A7. It is the best known representative of the peculiar group called "white dwarfs." Taking the apparent magnitude as 8.4, and assuming the companion to have the surface temperature of a normal star of its spectral class, the density is found to be nearly 50,000 times that of water. The density corresponding to Vyssotsky's apparent magnitude determination, 7.1, is only about one-sixth as great.

It was pointed out by several writers a number of years ago that a star of great density should produce an "Einstein shift" in its spectrum far greater than the one predicted in the spectrum of the Sun. In a single star this prediction cannot be tested observationally for there is no way to distinguish between an Einstein shift and the shift arising from the star's radial velocity. In a double star system, like that of *Sirius*, however, for which we know the parallax, the orbit elements and the mass ratio, the radial velocity of the faint component for any date can be computed from the observed radial velocity of the primary. Allowance can then be made for it and any residual Einstein shift detected. The brilliance of *Sirius* makes the observations of the spectrum of its companion extremely difficult, as I have already noted, but Adams† with the 100-in. reflector at Mount Wilson secured spectrograms, the measures of which, after allowance for the radial velocity and the blend effect from the scattered light of the bright star, gave a displacement corresponding to +19 km/sec, and Moore,‡ using the Mills spectrograph attached to the 36-in. Lick refractor, later found precisely the same displacement. The theoretical value, according to Eddington, is +20 km/sec.

These observations evidently support the greater value for the density of the companion and hence the value 8.4 for the apparent magnitude, but further investigation is desirable.

* *Preliminary General Catalogue*, p. 265, 1910.
† *Proc. Nat. Acad. Sci.* **11**, 382, 1925.
‡ *Publ. A.S.P.* **40**, 229, 1928.

Accepting the value 8.4 for the apparent magnitude, it follows that the primary is 10,000 times as bright as its companion, whereas it has only two and a half times its mass and is less than 1/50,000 part as dense. And yet the two stars, presumably, had a common origin. No satisfactory theory has been advanced to account for such a system. If we adopt Vyssotsky's value, 7.1, the contrasts are not so great, but the difficulties in the way of an explanation are not lessened.

There is another question relating to this system that must be considered: Is a third body present? Fox, on one night in 1920, suspected one less than a second of arc from B, the Clark companion, and van den Bos, Finsen, and other observers at the Union Observatory felt certain that they saw such a companion, about a magnitude fainter than B, on several nights in 1926, 1928, and 1929. On other nights, however, when they rated the definition as equally good, they did not see it, and Innes, in publishing the observations,* added that "in view of the negative evidence, it would be wrong to assert that the companion C exists without any doubt."

On the negative side, it is also to be said that neither Burnham nor Barnard, both noted for remarkable keenness of vision, saw such a companion at any time in the course of their many measures of the system with the 36-in. Lick and 40-in. Yerkes refractors. My own eyes are not so keen as theirs were, but I must add that I have never seen one, though I have measured the system annually since 1896, often under the most favorable observing conditions. Although negative evidence is always less convincing than positive testimony, I think it fair to return the Scotch verdict "not proven" on the question of the direct observation of this companion.

There is, however, another method of investigating the problem, and that is to ascertain whether the measures of the system AB give evidence of perturbations that might be explained by a third body. Zagar† and Volet,‡ to name only the two most recent writers on the subject, have made thorough investigations using different methods and both agree not only that such

* *The Observatory* **52**, 22, 1928.

† F. Zagar, II terzo corpo nel sistema Sirio, *R. Oss. Astr. Padova* Nr. 23, 1932.

‡ *Ch. Volet*, Recherche des perturbations dans le système de Sirius, *Bull. Astron.* **8**, 51, 1932.

perturbations exist, though of small amplitude, but also give approximately the same hypothetical orbit for the disturbing body, on the assumption that it is a companion to B. Unfortunately, the computed position angles of C, the third body, differ from those observed in 1920, 1928, and 1929 by amounts ranging from 70° to 170°. The 1926 observation is the only one in reasonable agreement with the theory. It is, however, impossible to say definitely, as Volet points out, that the hypothetical close companion attends component B; it may attend the brilliant primary A, in which event it would be quite impossible to observe.

KRUEGER 60

The system known as Krueger 60, though the closer pair was really discovered by Burnham in his careful examination of all the double stars noted by Krueger in the course of his meridian circle observations, offers a strong contrast to the two we have been considering, not only in its appearance but in many of its physical characteristics, but like them it is remarkable for its large proper motion and its large parallax. *Sirius* and *α Centauri* are two of the brightest stars in the sky and are also of great absolute brilliance; Krueger 60 is only of the ninth magnitude, despite its large parallax, and is among the feeblest of known stars in its actual radiating power.

The companion has now made very nearly one complete revolution since its discovery in 1890, and since 1900, when Doolittle called attention to the rapid orbital motion, has been very well observed, Barnard, in particular, making a remarkable series of measures—often on 18 to 21 nights a year—extending from 1900 to 1921. The orbit elements, therefore, while not so accurate as those of *Sirius*, are very well known. The parallax of the system is even better known, and the proper motion is also accurately determined.

It happens that several independent stars are in the same field of view with Krueger 60, one, of 9.6 magnitude, being less than 30″ distant in 1890, and but little over 1′ now. Since the apparent orbit of the binary is a fairly open one, the minimum angular distance between the components exceeding 1″.4, the conditions are specially favorable for the determination of the mass ratio of the two components (see Chap. VIII). Our knowledge of the physical conditions in the system is therefore far more complete than is the case for the average system with good orbit elements.

The parallax, 0″257, and my orbit elements computed in 1925 ($P = 44.27$ years, $a = 2″46$)give the mass $0.45 \odot$; using Huffer's later elements ($P = 44.52$ years, $a = 2″362$) and the same parallax, the computed mass is $0.40 \odot$. These are probably the limiting values. Alden,[*] in 1925, found the mass ratio to be 0.835. With Huffer's elements, this gives the mass of A as $0.22 \odot$, that of B, $0.18 \odot$. The latter, which is probably correct to within one or two units of the second decimal place, is the smallest mass so far established for any star.

Estimates of the magnitudes, as is usual in double star systems, vary considerably. The combined magnitude is given as 9.0 in the BD, and 9.1 in the Astronomische Gesellschaft Catalogue, but on the International (photovisual) Scale, Kuiper finds it to be 9.64, and the difference of magnitude of the two components, 1.56. This would give 9.9 and 11.4 as the apparent magnitudes of A and B, respectively. The corresponding absolute magnitudes are 11.9 and 13.4. According to Adams, the spectrum of A is Mb, and it is probable that the spectrum of B is of even later type. Both stars therefore belong to the class of red dwarfs, and the fainter one is one of the least luminous stars known. We may agree with Russell that they are nearing "the very end of their evolutionary history."

It is worth noting that Krueger 60 is one of the eight known visual binary systems within five parsecs or about 16 light-years distance. It is because it is so near us, relatively speaking, that we know anything about it. The mean parallax for stars of apparent magnitude 9.0 is, according to Seares, 0″0039. Remove Krueger 60 to the corresponding distance (more than 800 light years) and it would be beyond the resolving power of any existing telescope, and the combined image of the two components would be of about the eighteenth magnitude.

61 CYGNI

There are a number of wide double stars whose components have large proper motions of nearly the same amount. If the *directions* of the motion are different, the measures soon enable us to decide whether the pair is a physical, or, like Σ634 (ADS 3864), merely an optical one. But when the directions differ but little

* *Pop. Astron.* **33**, 164, 1925.

and the apparent relative motion is small or nearly rectilinear, it is not always easy to classify the pair on the basis of the micrometer measures alone. Consider, for example, Σ1321 (ADS 7251). The two components,* both 8.1 magnitude, have an angular separation of a little less than 20″ and the relative motion in 92 years has been but 23° and 1.″4. When the positions of B with respect to A are plotted, they lie along a straight line within the error of measure. But the large proper motions differ so little that we may adopt the value 1.″683 in 247°.6 for both components, and the parallax, $+0.″165$, is the same for each. Unquestionably they constitute a physical system. This is also true of 34 Groombridge (ADS 246), though the two components, separated nearly 40″, differ in brightness by more than two magnitudes and their relative motion in 50 years is but 3°.5 and less than 1.″0, for they have the same large parallax, $+0.″282$, and proper motion, 2.″89 in 82°.5.

Other examples might be given (*e.g.*, Σ2398 = ADS 11632†), but the best known pair of this class is undoubtedly 61 *Cygni*, (Σ2758 = ADS 14636) which is famous also as the first star for which an approximately correct value of parallax was determined. This bright pair (magnitudes 5.57, and 6.28) has been known since the time of Bradley who, as quoted by Sir John Herschel, gave the position for the date 1753.8 as 54°36′ *nf* 19.″628. Herschel listed the measures made to the end of the year 1822 and argued from them and from the large proper motion assigned to the pair by Piazzi and Bessel that the two stars constitute a binary system‡ as otherwise in the course of "nearly 70 years, during which they have been observed, one of them would doubtless have left the other behind, without supposing a coincidence too extraordinary to have resulted from accident." Nor did he fail to point out that the data make "61 *Cygni* a fit object for the investigation of parallax."

This early argument notwithstanding, the question of the character of the pair long remained an open one, for it developed that the proper motions of the two components are not quite identical, Auwers giving the values 5.″191 in 51°.52 and 5.″121 in 53°.68 for A and B, respectively, and the numerous observations since 1830 for many years gave little evidence of departure

---

* [+53° 1320/21, HD 79210/11, in U Ma.—J.T.K.]

† [+59° 1915, in Draco.—J.T.K.]

‡ *Observations of 380 Double and Triple Stars in the Years 1821, 1822 and 1823*, by J. F. W. Herschel and James South, p. 367, London, 1825.

from relative rectilinear motion. C. F. W. Peters,* it is true, computed a set of orbit elements in 1885, finding $a = 29''48$, $P = 782.6$ years, and $e = 0.17$, but the observed arc was entirely too short for accurate orbit computation and as late as 1905 Burnham clearly intimated that he thought the pair an optical one. In that same year, however, Östen Bergstrand, from a thorough examination of all available data, including a special series of photographs taken by himself in the years 1899 to 1903, demonstrated the physical relationship of the two stars by showing not only that they have the same parallax, but also that the path of B relatively to A is concave.† This was confirmed by Schlesinger and Alter, in 1910.‡

More recently provisional sets of elements have been computed by P. Baize§ and by Alan Fletcher.¶ The former, using graphical methods, finds a nearly circular orbit ($e = 0.013$) with a period of 756 years and a semimajor axis equal to $32''8$. The latter, adopting a mass value of 1.126 from the mass-luminosity relationship (Baize's elements give 2.28) and using special analytical methods, finds an orbit of marked eccentricity ($e = 0.404$) with a period of 696.63 years and a semimajor axis equal to $24''525$. This shows how wide the range of possible solutions still is. It is probable that the components are nearly equal in mass, but whether they are each equal to the Sun or have only half its mass is still in doubt. After another half century it will be possible to reach more definite conclusions.

The system is, in any event, one of vast dimensions, its orbit having a semimajor axis at least twice as great as that of *Pluto*, but it must be emphasized that orbits of this size are by no means exceptional. There are certainly far more visual binaries with orbital dimensions of this order than there are of systems like *δ Equulei*, which by way of contrast, we shall next consider.

δ EQUULEI

Until it had, recently, to yield its place to δ31, to which Dawson in his preliminary orbit computation assigns a period

---

* Bestimmung der Bahn des Doppelsterns 61 Cygni, *A.N.* **113**, 321, 1886.
† Untersuchungen über das Doppelsternsystem 61 Cygni, *Nova Acta R. Soc. Sci. Upsaliensis*, Ser. IV, Vol. 1, n. 3, 1905.
‡ See Chapter IV, page 121.
§ Le Système double de 61 Cygni, *Bull. Soc. Astron. de France* **41**, 20, 1927.
¶ The Binary System 61 Cygni, *Mon. Not. R.A.S.* **92**, 121, 1931.

4.56 years*, δ *Equulei* was the visual binary of shortest known period. This, of course, excludes *Capella*, which has been measured with the interferometer, and the pair ξ *Ursae Majoris* Aa, one of whose components is invisible, but is known not only from the variable radial velocity of A but also from the perturbations it produces in the relative orbit of the pair AB.

For many years, the period of δ *Equulei* was supposed to be 11.4 years, and the orbit nearly circular, for the two components are nearly equal in brightness, and the pair is below the resolving power of existing telescopes at times of minimum angular separation. Hussey, in 1900, however, showed conclusively that the period is only half as long, 5.7 years, and the orbit a fairly elongated ellipse ($e = 0.39$). Another system resembling δ *Equulei* in that the two components had been mistaken for each other after passing the point of minimum separation, is ξ *Scorpii* AB. The accepted orbit, prior to 1905, had a period of about 105 years and an eccentricity of about 0.13, but my measures with the 36-in. refractor in 1904 and 1905 proved this to be incorrect. I found that the true period is only 44.7 years and the orbit really a very eccentric one ($e = 0.75$).

Returning to δ *Equulei*, we note that the orbit elements are well determined, the period in particular, since the pair has made 14 revolutions since its discovery by Otto Struve in 1852. The semimajor axis is 0."27 and this, since the parallax† is 0."066, corresponds to about 4 A.U. The orbit is therefore decidedly smaller than that of *Jupiter* and resembles the larger and more eccentric minor planet orbits. The mass of the system is 2.11 times that of the Sun and the two components probably are nearly equal in mass. Each is therefore approximately equal to the Sun in mass, but since the absolute magnitudes of the two are, respectively, 4.4 and 4.5 and the spectral class is F5, they are brighter than the Sun and shine with a whiter light.

TWO MULTIPLE SYSTEMS

Two of the best known double stars in the northern heavens are *Castor* (α *Geminorum*), discovered by Bradley and Pound

---

* See footnote, p. 205, for Kuiper's discovery of a visual binary with period of less than 2 years.

† Schlesinger's *Bright Stars*. Maxwell (*Publ. Lick Obs.* **16,** 311) found 0."048 from the orbit and the relative radial velocity of the components. This gives $a = 5.6$ A.U., which is a little larger than that of *Jupiter*.

in 1719, and ξ *Ursae Majoris*, discovered by Sir William Herschel on May 2, 1780. Both pairs are among those used by Herschel in the papers, presented to the Royal Society in 1803 and 1804, in which he gave observational as well as theoretical reasons for his belief that many double stars are physical systems, with components in orbital motion. ξ *Ursae Majoris* was also the first, and *Castor* perhaps the second pair for which an orbit was computed. Savary, in 1830, used the former system to illustrate his method of orbit computation,* and Sir John Herschel, in 1833, used both pairs, among others, to illustrate his very different method. The orbital motion in ξ *Ursae Majoris* is far more rapid than that in *Castor*, and for that reason these early orbits computed for it were more successful than Herschel's orbit of the latter pair.

Struve began to measure ξ *Ursae Majoris* in 1826 and from that time on the visual observations have been numerous and well distributed. The two components differ but one magnitude in brightness, and the angular distance between them, even at minimum, is but little less than one second of arc. The pair is therefore also well suited for photographic measurement, and, in fact, the photographic measures are more accurate than the visual ones, as appears from the series made at Potsdam by Hertzsprung and Münch in the years 1914 to 1923, and from the one by Przybyllok, at Königsberg in the following years.

Ultimately, an orbit of a system of this character based entirely upon photographic measures will probably be more accurate than one resting upon visual observations, but it is not so certain that modern photographic measures used in combination with earlier visual ones, particularly if the latter were made with small telescopes, will give a better orbit than visual measures alone, unless very great care is exercised in making the combination. Van den Bos did not overlook this point when, in 1928, he computed the orbit of ξ *Ursae Majoris*, which has now described nearly two revolutions since Struve's first measures, and his elements, which differ but little from those of Nörlund (1905), may be regarded as practically definitive. He gives $P = 59.863$ years, $e = 0.4128$, and $a = 2''.5355$.

If this were a simple binary system there would be no occasion, other than its association with the early methods of orbit computation, to single it out for special notice. It is, however, not

* See Chap. IV.

a binary, but a quadruple system. Wright* in 1900, noted that the radial velocity of the brighter star is variable, and Nörlund, in his investigation of the orbit of the visual pair in 1905, discovered a perturbation with an amplitude of $0''.05$ and a period of about 1.8 years. This he attributed to the presence of a third body, but he was apparently unaware of Wright's discovery. Wright, in 1908, showed that the radial-velocity observations confirmed Nörlund's period, for which van den Bos gives the more precise value, 1.8321 years. In a sense, as Hertzsprung has remarked, this may be called the shortest period established for a binary star on the basis of micrometrical observations.† This short-period orbit proves to be elliptic, ($e = 0.50$) and to be highly inclined to the plane of projection, the inclination, whose sign is fixed by the radial velocity measures, being $-84°.5$. The unseen companion, a, is therefore in retrograde motion, about A, just as B is. Apparently, the general rule is that the wide and close pairs in a triple or quadruple system revolve in the same direction, but this is not without exception. It is not followed in four of 21 systems which van den Bos examined.

In 1918, the Lick observers announced that the fainter component, B, of the visual system is also a spectroscopic binary of short period. Berman‡ has recently made a thorough investigation of the orbit of this pair and finds it to be circular, with a revolution period of only 3.9805 days. The orbital inclination is probably too small to permit even a partial eclipse, and van den Bos finds that, notwithstanding its high inclination, the pair Aa is also not an eclipsing binary.

Van den Bos investigated the question of the distribution of masses in this system; with the advantage of the knowledge of the orbit of Bb, Berman has repeated the investigation. Taking the value $0''.126$, the mean of the 10 modern results, for the parallax, and van den Bos's elements of the visual pair, he finds the total mass to be 2.27 times that of the Sun. Adopting 0.77 as the best value the present data will give for the mass ratios, the mass of Aa is 1.280, of Bb, 0.990. Taking van den Bos's value for the mass ratio a/A he finds the mass of A to be $0.93 \odot$, that of a, $0.35 \odot$. The mass ratio b/B may have, according to Berman, any value between ½ and ⅕.

* *Ap. Jour.* **12**, 254, 1900.

† Prior to 1935.

‡ *Lick Obs. Bull.* **15**, 109, 1931, #432.

The combination of two such unlike short-period binaries as the components of a 60-year-period system presents a problem of unusual interest to the student of the origin of the binary stars, as Berman has not failed to remark.

Turning next to *Castor*, we find an even more remarkable multiple system, for not only are the bright stars, A and B, of the historic double, the visible members of short-period spectroscopic binaries, but a third star, of the ninth magnitude, 73″ distant in 165°, which has the same parallax and proper motion as the bright pair, is also a short-period binary. The system Bb was discovered by Belopolsky, at Pulkova, in 1896, the system Aa, by Curtis, at Lick, in 1904. Curtis's investigations* showed that B and its faint companion revolve in practically circular orbits in a period of 2.928285 days, whereas A and its invisible companion travel in elliptic orbits ($e = 0.5033$) and have a period of 9.2218826 days. Curtis, moreover, on the basis of the observed data and what seemed to be reasonable assumptions, concluded that the fainter system Bb was about six times the more massive one. Luyten† has recently given reasons for adopting the more moderate mass ratio of two to one as the maximum possible, but even that is an anomalous result, for there are few exceptions (and those not above suspicion) to the rule that in binary systems, both visual and spectroscopic, the brighter component is the more massive one. Luyten, himself, regards the true mass ratio as still unknown, and a careful review of all of the published data leads me to the same conclusion.

In 1920, Adams and Joy‡ announced the fact that the ninth-magnitude companion to *Castor*, which we may call *Castor* C, is a short-period binary, and in 1926 Joy and Sanford§ computed its orbit from the measures of radial velocity. Before their paper was sent to press, van Gent's paper¶ appeared, with an orbit of the pair as an eclipsing variable based upon photometric observations. The combined data show that the components of Cc revolve in circular orbits with an inclination of 86°.4 in a period of 0.814266 day. It also appears‖ that the brighter

---

* *Lick Obs. Bull.* **4**, 55, 1906.

† *Publ. A.S.P.* **45**, 86, 1933; *Publ. Minn. Obs.* **2** (1), 3–13, 1934.

‡ *Publ. A.S.P.* **32**, 158, 1920.

§ *Ap. Jour.* **64**, 250, 1926.

¶ *B.A.N.* **3**, 121, 1926.

‖ See Table 1, Chap. VII, p. 200.

component, C, has a mass 0.63 ☉, the fainter one, c, a mass 0.57 ☉, that the densities of the two are, respectively, 1.40 and 1.80 ☉, their radii, 0.76 ☉ and 0.68 ☉ and the distance between their centers 2.7 × 10⁶ km. In other words, our knowledge of this latest known of the four orbital systems in this great multiple group, three spectrographic and one visual, is by far the most accurate and complete.

Our knowledge of the first known of the group, the visual binary pair, on the other hand, is the most incomplete. The majestic scale of the relative orbit, with a semimajor axis nearly twice as great as the mean distance of *Pluto* from the Sun, is, of course, responsible. Many hundreds of measures have been made since 1826, when Struve began his series, but in the interval to 1931 the companion had described an arc of but 53°. The earlier measures, back to 1719, give only the direction of B from A, with occasional rough estimates of distance. It is now evident that the point of maximum separation in the third quadrant was passed some 25 or 30 years ago, and the range of possible orbit solutions is therefore much smaller than it was in 1900, but orbits with periods ranging from 340 to 477 years still represent the latest measures about equally well. As so frequently happens, however, the mass of the quadruple system Aa–Bb is better known than the orbit elements. It is less than was thought some 20 years ago, and is probably about five times the mass of the Sun.

It may be noted that while there is no question of the physical relationship of the distant system Cc to the bright quadruple system, there is no hope at all of securing evidence of its orbital motion about the center of gravity of Aa–Bb for many centuries, for, on the most favorable assumptions, the revolution period must be of the order of 25,000 years.

CAPELLA

In 1899, Campbell, at the Lick Observatory, and Newall, at the University Observatory, Cambridge, England, independently discovered the fact that Capella is a spectroscopic binary star, with the spectra of both components visible. Campbell's announcement was published in the *Astrophysical Journal* for October, 1899, and Newall's, in the November, 1899, number of the *Monthly Notices, R.A.S.* In March 1900, Newall[*] pub-

* *Mon. Not. R.A.S.* **60**, 418, 1900.

lished a paper on the binary in which he showed that the period
is approximately 104 days, that the two components are nearly
equal in mass and not very unequal in brightness and argued
that the inclination of the orbit exceeded 27°.   Reese,* in 1901,
published a more detailed investigation, based upon spectrograms
secured at the Lick Observatory in the period September 1, 1896
to September 27, 1900.   His value for the period is 104.022 days,
for the eccentricity, 0.0164, and for K, the semiamplitude of
the velocity curve of the primary star, 25.76 km.   He gave
1.26 as the approximate value for the ratio $K^1/K^2 = M^1/M^2$.

Interesting as these facts are, they would not, taken alone,
call for special comment.   But Anderson,† in 1920, successfully
applied the interference method of measurement developed by
Michelson to observations of *Capella*, using a new type of
interferometer which he had himself devised, and these measures
were continued later in that same year and early in 1921 by
Merrill who utilized the entire series for the computation of an
orbit of the system,‡ adopting, however, Reese's period, which
Sanford§ had shown to be very nearly correct.   He found the
orbit a little more nearly circular than Reese gave it, his value
for e being 0.0086.

Important results arose from the combination of the interferometer with the spectrographic orbit data.   This permitted
the derivation of the values of a and i, separately, fixed the
algebraic sign for i, and, most important of all, gave an extremely
accurate value of the parallax of the system, and hence also
values of the masses of the two components and of the separation,
in linear measure, of their centers $(a_1 + a_2)$.   These values are:

$$a = 0.''05360, \qquad i = -41.°08, \qquad (a_1 + a_2) = 126{,}630{,}000 \text{ km}$$
$$\pi = 0.''0632, \qquad m_1 = 4.2\odot, \qquad\qquad m_2 = 3.3\odot$$

The visual magnitude of *Capella* is 0.21 and since the two
components differ in brightness by $0.^{m}5$, their magnitudes¶ are,
respectively, 0.74 and 1.24, which, with the given parallax,
correspond to the absolute magnitudes −0.26 and +0.24.
Both components are therefore giant stars.

* *Lick Obs. Bull.* **1**, 32, 1901.
† *Ap. Jour.* **51**, 257, 1920.
‡ *Ap. Jour.* **56**, 40, 1922.
§ *Publ. A.S.P.* **34**, 178, 1922.
¶ According to the accurate formula, not the approximate values tabu-
lated on p. 54.

The maximum angular separation of the components measured with the interferometer is 0."0550, a fact that fully accounts for the failures to separate the two components with the most powerful telescopes. Interferometer measures, however, are made visually, and, in a sense, we may therefore refer to *Capella* as the *visual* binary of shortest known period.

Merrill's value of the parallax of *Capella* is probably as accurate as any stellar parallax value we have. This fact, and the completeness and accuracy of our knowledge of the other data relating to the system, led Eddington to adopt the brighter component, which belongs to spectral class G0, as the foundation for the numerical application of his theory of the *Internal Constitution of the Stars*, including the mass-luminosity relation. Assuming the effective temperature to be 5200°, Eddington finds the absolute bolometric magnitude of this component to be -0^m36, which is 5.26 magnitudes brighter than the Sun. From these values he derives the total radiation of the star ($127 \times \odot$), its radius ($13.74 \times \odot$), and its mean density 0.00227 gm per cubic centimeter and then proceeds to further conclusions as to the star's internal structure and temperature, which do not come within the scope of this volume.

THE MASSIVE BINARY HD 698 (= BD. + 57°. 28)

As long ago as 1904, Hartmann,[*] in examining the spectrograms of δ *Orionis* (Class B0), secured at Potsdam in the years 1900 to 1903, discovered that the calcium line *K* differed from the other lines in the spectrum (mostly due to hydrogen and helium) in two important particulars. It was narrow and sharp, whereas the other lines are more or less diffuse, and it gave a nearly constant velocity, with a mean value about equal to the velocity of the center of mass of the system, instead of showing as the other lines did, variable velocity with a range of about 200 km/sec. The calcium line, apparently, did not originate in the star.

In explanation, Hartmann assumed the existence of a calcium cloud stationary in space (at least so far as radial velocity is concerned) lying between us and the star. This was plausible, since the *Orion* region is known to be one filled with nebulous matter and the mean velocity, +18.7 km/sec, from the calcium line was nearly the same as that of the Sun's velocity of recession from the *Orion* region.

[*] *Ap. Jour.* **19**, 268, 1904.

Questions, however, soon arose, for it appeared—particularly from Slipher's researches*—that the calcium lines in other stars of the *Orion* type, that is, of classes O to B2, widely distributed around the sky in low galactic latitudes, exhibited similar anomalous phenomena, and Miss Heger (Mrs. C. D. Shane), in 1919 and 1921, showed that, in some of these stars at least, the sodium *D* lines behaved in like manner.

The theory now accepted to account for the observed facts is the one advanced by Eddington† in 1926. He postulated the existence of a uniformly distributed interstellar cloud of extremely low density, and showed that it was competent to produce the observed absorption in the spectra of all stars distant enough to give sufficient depth to the cloud. More recent evidence, based upon direct observation, has been given by O. Struve,‡ Gerasimovic,§ and particularly, Plaskett and Pearce,¶ that practically establishes the fact of the existence of Eddington's hypothetical cloud. For it appears that the intensities of the interstellar lines increase with the distance of the stars, that the cloud, like the stars, rotates about the galactic center, and that the mean distance of the cloud is about half the average distance of the stars.

One difficulty remained. While it was not to be expected that the interstellar lines of calcium and sodium would show in the spectra of stars of classes F to M, since they would be masked by the broad, diffuse stellar lines, it was hard to explain why they did not appear in the spectra of at least some of the binaries of Class A in which the range in variable velocity is large. Pearce's investigation of the system HD 698, of spectral class B9sek‖ and visual magnitude 7.08 removes this difficulty.

Merrill and Humason,** in the course of their study of stars with bright hydrogen lines, found the radial velocity of this star to be variable. Their announcement was made in 1925, and Pearce⸸ has now computed the orbit of the pair, on the basis of spectrograms secured at the Dominion Astrophysical

* *Lowell Obs. Bull.* **2**, 1, 1909.

† Bakerian Lecture: Diffuse Matter in Interstellar Space, *Proc. Roy. Soc.* **A, 111**, 424, 1926.

‡ *Ap. Jour.* **65**, 163, 1927; **67**, 353, 1928.

§ *Ap. Jour.* **69**, 7, 1929.

¶ *Mon. Not. R.A.S.* **90**, 243, 1930.

‖ It may be well to explain that the letter *s* signifies sharp lines, the letter *e*, emission lines, and the letter *k*, the presence of interstellar calcium lines.

** *Ap. Jour.* **61**, 389, 1925.

⸸ *Mon. Not. R.A.S.* **92**, 877, 1932.

Observatory. He finds the spectrum of the primary to be that of a star of high intrinsic luminosity for Class B9, and that of the secondary (apparently a normal star of Class B5) to be relatively faint and measurable only at times of maximum separation of the lines. The interstellar calcium absorption line, K, is also present and was measured on 18 of the 40 plates.

Before commenting upon the K line let us note the orbit elements derived from the measures of the lines for the primary star. The period is 55.904 days, the eccentricity 0.033, neither value being in any way exceptional. The semiamplitudes of the velocity curves, too, while large ($K = 85.5$ km, $K_1 = 215.5$ km), are not extraordinary, a statement that may also be made of the mass ratio they give, $m_2/m_1 = 0.40$. But the minimum mass values are remarkable, $m \sin^3 i$ being $113.2 \odot$, and $m_2 \sin^3 i$, $44.9 \odot$. These are the largest mass values so far found in any binary system, and it is to be remembered that the inclination is less than 90°, since the pair is not an eclipsing variable, and that the true masses therefore are even greater than those given.

Turning now to the calcium line K, we note that Pearce found a blend of the interstellar line with the stellar K line of the primary through about 41 days of the 56-day period, the blended velocities varying from $+38$ km/sec to -52 km/sec. But for a few days when the stars were passing through the nodes, the three lines, from the primary star, the secondary star, and the interstellar source, were clearly separated, and the interstellar lines from 12 observations at these favorable times gave a constant velocity of -13.9 km/sec. The velocity of the center of mass of the binary system is -24.5 km/sec. These results for a Class A star afford strong support for Eddington's theory of the origin of the interstellar lines in spectroscopic binary star spectra.

ALGOL *

β *Persei*, or *Algol*, as it is more commonly called, has been known as a variable star since 1670, when Montanari not only noted the fact of variation in light but actually observed it at

---

* [Kopal, Zdenek; A Study of the Algol System, *Ap. Jour.* **96** (3), 399–420, Nov. 1942.

Elements of the Third Orbit: P: 1.873 yrs.; e: 0.26; i (provisional): 72°; Mass: $1.0 \pm 0.3 \odot$.

Semimajor axis of relative orbit $(a_1 + a_3)$: 36×10^7 km; apparent separation at maximum elongation: $0''.10$.—J.T.K.]

minimum brightness* on November 8, but the general character
of its light variation was first established by Goodericke, in 1783.
He found that the successive minima occurred at intervals of
about 2^d 20^h 49^m, the descent to, and recovery from, minimum
covering about eight or nine hours, and that for the rest of the
period the light remained sensibly constant. He explained the
phenomena by assuming that a dark companion, revolving
about a common center with *Algol*, produced a partial eclipse of
the bright star once in each revolution, but this hypothesis,
though essentially correct, as we now know, was not generally
accepted and, in fact, was almost forgotten, until Pickering†
revived it in 1880, and Vogel,‡ in 1889, found the star to be a
spectroscopic binary, with a period equal to that of its light
variation.

The star has been the subject of so many memoirs that it would
be impossible to give even a full reference list of them here, to
say nothing of an adequate account of the work they represent
or of the theories advanced in them. We must limit ourselves
to a general description of the more significant advances made
in our knowledge of the system.

Argelander§ was the first to demonstrate the existence of
fluctuations in the period between successive light minima,
and Chandler's¶ more extensive studies, utilizing all available
observations from Goodericke's time to 1888 (and in his later
work to 1897), not only confirmed this conclusion but led him to
explain them as arising from a long-period inequality which he
ascribed to the influence of a third body in the system.

His formula for the period failed, however, to represent later
epochs of minima, and that has also been the fate of more
recently derived formulas, including Hellerich's (1919). There
still remain small periodic and irregular variations not fully
accounted for by theory.

Belopolsky's discovery, in 1906, of a variation in the radial
velocity of the center of mass of the eclipsing system in a period
of the order of 1.8 years, was the next step in advance. The
work of Curtiss in 1908, and, more conclusively, that of Schlesinger in 1912, established the existence of the third body called

* See Porro's note, *A.N.* **127**, 41, 1891.

† *Proc. Amer. Acad.* **16**, 1, 371, 1880.

‡ *Publ. Potsdam Obs.* **7**, 111, 1889.

§ *Bonn-Beob.* **7**, 343, 1869.

¶ *A.J.* **7**, 165ff, 1888; **22**, 39, 1901.

for by this variation. Curtiss gave 1.899 years for the revolution period, Schlesinger, 1.874. The latter also found the semi-amplitude of the velocity curve to be 9.14 km, and the orbit to be nearly circular. The revolution of the eclipsing pair about the center of mass in this long-period orbit, produces an oscillation in the times of minimum light, which, as Schlesinger points out may amount to a displacement of five minutes in either direction.

Meanwhile, Stebbins had perfected his selenium photometer, so that in the years 1909 and 1910, he was able to measure the brightness of stars to the third magnitude with far greater accuracy than had been possible by visual or photographic methods. Applying it to the study of *Algol*, he discovered the existence of a secondary minimum in its light curve, with a depth of but 0.06 magnitude and showed, moreover, that the light varied continuously between minima. Ten years later he repeated the investigations with the far more sensitive photoelectric-cell photometer. The new light curve was, naturally, more accurate than the earlier one, but confirmed the secondary minimum and the continuous variation in the light. It also showed an effect resulting from the ellipsoidal shape of the components. The orbit of the eclipsing system was shown to be practically circular.

The rotation of a star upon its axis has the effect of broadening the lines of its spectrum unless the axis is directed toward us since one limb is receding, the other approaching us relatively to the motion of the star's center. This effect, which has received special attention from O. Struve in his studies of the emission lines in Class B stars, is particularly pronounced in the case of eclipsing binary stars, since the receding limb of the component entering eclipse is the visible one, whereas the approaching limb is the visible one on emerging from eclipse. Rossiter studied this effect in *β Lyrae*, and McLaughlin, in *Algol*, in 1923 and 1924. In both cases it was found to be well marked, the residuals before minimum light in *Algol*, with which we are here concerned, all being positive and those after minimum negative, as theory requires. The observed range of the effect was 35 km. Using Stebbins's values for the relative dimensions of the system and for the inclination of the orbit to compute the range, McLaughlin found it necessary to assume the brighter star to be five times as massive as the fainter one to secure agreement with the observed value. On this assumption, with the observed range of the rotation effect, it becomes possible to compute the absolute dimensions in the system, the mass and density of each component, and also the parallax.

Combining McLaughlin's spectrographic results with Stebbins's photometric ones we have the following data for the eclipsing system:

Period (Hellerich's value)................	$2^d.867301$
Duration of principal minimum...........	$9^h.66$
Inclination of orbit (cos $i = 0.142$)........	$81°.8$
Distance between centers ($ab + af$)........	10,522,000 km
Radius of bright body...................	$3.12 \odot$
Radius of faint body....................	$3.68 \odot$
Mass of bright body.....................	$4.72 \odot$
Mass of faint body......................	$0.95 \odot$
Density of bright body..................	$0.16 \odot$
Density of faint body...................	$0.02 \odot$

The corresponding dynamical parallax of *Algol* is $+0.''031$.

It is specially to be noted, however, that nothing is yet known of the spectrum of the third star or of any effect it may have upon the photometric measures of the eclipsing pair.*

McLaughlin, in his closing paragraphs, refers to the difficulty of obtaining a reliable trigonometric parallax for *Algol*, because of its revolution in an orbit about two-thirds as large as the Earth's orbit in a period of less than two years. This is a point to which Wright called attention as long ago as 1904, in his note on the parallax of α *Centauri* and which he elaborated more fully in 1921 in his note† "On Spectroscopic Binaries and the Determination of Parallax." It is, obviously, one to be specially noted by parallax observers.

References

It is impossible‡ and, happily, unnecessary to list here the many papers that have been consulted in the preparation of this chapter. Footnote references have been given to a number of the more important ones, and the extensive catalogues of double stars, of spectroscopic binary stars, and of variable stars will help any reader who wishes to look up more fully any of the systems that have been described.

* It should be noted that M. A. Danjon in his photometric study of *Algol* (*Annales, Strasbourg Obs.* **2**, 148, 1928) reaches conclusions differing in many particulars from those described above. These conclusions, however, await confirmation.

† *Publ. A.S.P.* **33**, 47, 1921.

‡ The references to the literature on *Algol* alone would fill four quarto pages of fine print! It is hardly necessary to add that not all of these papers were read in preparing my note.

CHAPTER X

STATISTICAL DATA RELATING TO THE VISUAL BINARY STARS IN THE NORTHERN SKY

The visual binary stars for which orbits have been computed or in which the observed arc suffices for the computation of dynamical parallaxes may be utilized, as has been shown in Chap. VIII, in the study of the relations between the orbit elements and for the investigation of stellar mass. It is obvious, however, that even if they were not selected stars, they would not afford an adequate basis for a study of the number of the visual binaries, of their distribution (apparent or real), or of the absolute magnitudes of their components. The data required for a thoroughly satisfactory investigation of these and similar problems would include a complete enumeration of all binary systems to a definite limiting stellar magnitude, and measures (a) of the angular distances of all pairs for a given epoch, (b) of the photometric magnitudes and spectral classes of both components, and (c) of the parallaxes of the systems.

The first step in an approximation to this ideal material is to make a survey of all stars in the sky to a definite magnitude with sufficiently powerful telescopes used under good observing conditions. All previously known pairs must be noted and all new pairs falling within predetermined limits of magnitude and angular separation identified and measured. The Lick Observatory survey and the surveys of the southern sky which are still in progress at Johannesburg and Bloemfontein, all described in my historical sketch, were undertaken with the definite purpose of providing the basis for such statistical studies.

The Lick Observatory survey was completed in 1915, and the results obtained for the sky area north of the equator will now be presented. The data consist of all known double stars as bright as 9.0 BD magnitude* which fall within the distance limits set by the following working definition of a double star

---

* BD magnitudes were taken because photometric magnitudes to the limit 9.0 were not available.

proposed by me in 1911:[*]

(1) Two stars shall be considered to constitute a double star when the apparent distance between them falls within the following limits:

1″ if the combined magnitude of the components is fainter than 11.0

3″ if the combined magnitude of the components is fainter than 9.0 BD.

5″ if the combined magnitude of the components lies between 6.0 and 9.0 BD.

10″ if the combined magnitude of the components lies between 4.0 and 6.0 BD.

20″ if the combined magnitude of the components lies between 2.0 and 4.0 BD.

40″ if the combined magnitude of the components is brighter than 2.0 BD.

(2) Pairs which exceed these limits shall be entitled to the name double star only when it has been shown (*a*) that orbital motion exists; (*b*) that the two components have a well defined common proper motion, or proper motions of the 61 *Cygni* type; (*c*) that the parallax is decidedly greater than the average for stars of corresponding magnitude. †

In all, there are 5,400 pairs, more than half of which were discovered in the course of the survey (766 by Hussey, 2,057 by

* [See pages 35 and 268. Aitken's working definition (1911) is:

$$\log \rho = 2.5 - 0.2m$$

which gives 5″ for 9.0 magnitude.

Also, see ADS, p. IX, separation limits for ADS

$$\log \rho = 2.8 - 0.2m$$

App. m	ρ	App. m	ρ
1.0	400″	7.0	25″
2.0	250″	8.0	16″
3.0	160″	9.0	10″
4.0	100″	10.0	6″
5.0	63″	11.0	4″
6.0	40″	12.0	2″.5—J.T.K.]

† The definition, with correspondence relating to it, will be found in the *Astronomische Nachrichten* (**188**, 281, 1911). Comstock and E. C. Pickering there suggest limits based upon the apparent magnitude, the former using the formula $s = c(\frac{2}{3})^m$, the latter, the formula, $\log s = c - 0.2m$, where s is the distance in seconds of arc between the components, m, the apparent magnitude, and c an arbitrary constant. If the values of c in the two formulae are so chosen as to give the limit 5″.0 for stars of magnitude 6.0, the formulae will give the limits 0″.75 and 1″.25, respectively, for stars of 9.0 magnitude. From the theoretical point of view either formula gives more logical limits than the ones in my definition, but there were practical considerations, fully stated in the article referred to, which led to the adoption of the latter.

Aitken). A given system is counted only once though it may have three, or even four or more, components. In the multiple systems the closer pair is, in general, the one counted, but in a few cases in which the close pair is very faint, the principal bright pair is taken.

The first question to consider is whether the data are homogeneous, for it is obvious that they can make no claim to be exhaustive. However carefully an observer may work, some pairs which he might discover with a given telescope will surely escape him. His eye may be fatigued, unnoticed haze or momentary bad seeing may blur out a faint companion star, or it may chance that at the date of examination the two components are so nearly in conjunction as to be below the resolving power of the telescope. The number of known double stars can only be regarded as the lower limit to the number which might be discovered. Homogeneity was earnestly sought for, care being taken to work only when in good physical condition and when the seeing was good, the practical test being the power to recognize very close and difficult pairs at a glance. But variations in the conditions are inevitable when the working program requires years for its execution and doubtless such variations have affected the present results. Careful comparison, however, shows no discernible difference in the thoroughness of the work done at different seasons of the year or in different parts of the sky, and it may fairly be said that the results of the survey represent the capacity of the combination of telescope and observer under average good atmospheric conditions at Mount Hamilton. If the work had all been done with the 36-in. refractor the resulting data might be considered quite homogeneous. Unfortunately, a considerable part of it, including practically the entire area north of $+60°$ declination, was done with the 12-in. telescope, and it becomes necessary to consider the relative efficiency of the two instruments.

I have applied two tests: first, the comparison of the most difficult pairs discovered with each instrument; second, the reexamination with the 36-in. of some 1,200 stars previously examined with the 12-in. telescope. I find that, under the usual observing conditions, a pair with nearly equal components separated by only 0″15, or a companion star as faint as 14.5 magnitude and not less than 1″5 from its primary is practically certain of detection* with the 36-in.; with the 12-in., the corresponding limits in the two cases are $0''25$ and 13 to 13.5 magnitude. Twelve new double stars were added by the reexamination of the 1,200 stars. From these tests, taking into account the proportion of the whole work done with the 12-in. telescope, I conclude that about 250 pairs would have been added if the entire northern sky had been surveyed with the 36-in. Since all or nearly all of the brighter stars had been examined repeatedly by other observers using powerful telescopes, it is fair to assume that comparatively few of these undiscovered pairs are brighter than 7.0 BD magnitude.

According to Seeliger's count of the BD stars there are 100,979 as bright as 9.0 magnitude in the northern hemisphere. Of these, 5,400, or 1 in 18.7 on the average, have actually been found to be double within the limits set above. If we add only 200 pairs, the ratio becomes 1:18.03. A definite answer is

TABLE 1.—THE DISTRIBUTION OF DOUBLE STARS IN RIGHT ASCENSION AND DECLINATION

R.A. Decl.	0^h–1^h	2^h–3^h	4^h–5^h	6^h–7^h	8^h–9^h	10^h–11^h	12^h–13^h	14^h–15^h	16^h–17^h	18^h–19^h	20^h–21^h	22^h–23^h
0°–9°	6.3	6.3	7.4	6.0	6.0	5.9	5.5	6.4	5.4	6.0	5.3	4.9
10–19	5.4	5.4	6.4	6.2	5.5	5.5	4.8	6.1	4.5	6.0	5.4	5.2
20–29	5.2	5.6	5.9	5.1	4.8	6.4	5.2	4.8	5.4	6.2	4.9	4.2
30–39	6.0	5.5	5.9	4.4	4.3	4.8	5.4	4.1	5.0	5.6	5.2	4.8
40–49	6.7	5.0	5.0	4.5	4.5	6.2	3.2	5.6	5.5	4.2	5.2	4.9
50–59	6.2	6.2	8.0	5.2	4.8	3.6	4.4	6.0	4.6	4.4	6.8	4.9
60–69	4.6	5.0	7.1	2.9	4.3	4.4	2.6	4.1	3.6	4.1	5.3	6.8
70–79	5.9	3.8	4.2	3.5	3.1	2.6	2.8	2.2	3.4	4.9	5.0	6.5
80–89	(0^h–5^h)	3.7		(6^h–11^h)		3.3	(12^h–17^h)		3.4	(18^h–23^h)		3.9

The figures give the percentages of double stars among stars to 9.0 BD magnitude; the average percentage for the whole northern sky is 5.35.

thus given to my first question: *At least one in every 18, on the average, of the stars in the northern half of the sky which are as bright as 9.0 BD magnitude is a close double star visible with the 36-in. refractor.*† There is no reason to doubt that the ratio is

* Unless the primary is brighter than 7.0 magnitude.

† [Research and observation since 1935 lead to the conclusion that at least half the stellar population consists, not of single stars like our sun, but of members of systems; that is, practically one out of every two stars is a binary or multiple system. Also, in spite of the high frequency of spectroscopic binaries among bright stars, W. H. van den Bos assures us that in space the spectroscopic binary is a rare exception, the visual binary the rule.—J.T.K.]

equally high in the southern half of the sky. In fact, preliminary counts made by van den Bos lead him to estimate the ratio in that hemisphere as high as one in 17.

Table 1 exhibits the distribution of the 5,400 double stars in right ascension and declination as compared with the distribution of the BD stars to 9.0 magnitude, the figures giving the percentage of double stars in each area. There are obvious irregularities in the table but no evidence of systematic differences that can be regarded as seasonal effects. The percentages are as high in the sky areas surveyed in winter as in those surveyed in summer. There is a falling off in the percentage in the high declinations, especially in the regions well removed from the Milky Way, which is doubtless due in part to the fact that the area north of 60° was almost entirely surveyed with the 12-in. telescope. The broken line in the table represents very roughly the position of the central line of the Milky Way, and it will be noted that the percentages near this line are, in general, above the average.

The distribution with respect to the plane of the Milky Way is more clearly brought out when the stars are tabulated according to galactic latitude. This has been done in Tables 2 and 3, in the former of which the stars are divided into classes according to magnitude and the latitudes into zones each 20° wide,

TABLE 2.—THE DISTRIBUTION OF DOUBLE STARS BY MAGNITUDE CLASSES AND ZONES OF GALACTIC LATITUDE

Zone \ Mag.	to 6.5	6.6–7.0	7.1–7.5	7.6–8.0	8.1–8.5	8.6–9.0	Total
I	19	13	14	29	40	84	199
II	43	28	50	68	114	193	496
III	60	43	56	79	148	254	640
IV	96	54	81	132	232	401	996
V	121	88	133	249	376	653	1,620
VI	84	51	81	134	221	395	966
VII	28	23	18	54	90	154	367
VIII	7	6	5	12	31	55	116
Total	458	306	438	757	1,252	2,189	5,400

beginning at the north galactic pole. Zone V therefore includes the area from +10° to −10° galactic latitude, and zone IX, which ends at the south galactic pole and lies entirely below the equator, is not represented. As was to be expected, the numbers in every column of this table are largest in zone V and fall to minima in zones I and VIII. The question is whether this condensation toward the Milky Way is greater than that of all the stars. Table 3 provides the answer. Since the zones are not of equal area, and since only the first one lies wholly in the northern hemisphere, the fairest comparison is that afforded by the relative densities per square degree of double stars and of all stars of the corresponding magnitudes. The double star densities were determined by dividing the figures in Table 2 by the number of square degrees in each zone area; the figures were then reduced to a common standard by making the density in each column unity in zone V, the Milky Way zone. Seeliger has published corresponding data

TABLE 3.—DENSITY OF DOUBLE STARS BY MAGNITUDE CLASSES AND GALACTIC LATITUDE COMPARED WITH THE DENSITY OF BD STARS TO 9.0 MAGNITUDE (AFTER SEELIGER)

Mag. Zone	to 6.5		6.6–7.0		7.1–7.5		7.6–8.0		8.1–8.6		8.6–9.0	
	BD	D.S.	BD	D.S.	BD	D.S.	BD	D.S.	BD	D.S.	BD	D.S.
I	0.551	0.395	0.431	0.374	0.518	0.266	0.404	0.304	0.419	0.261	0.382	0.325
II	0.572	0.456	0.445	0.410	0.497	0.484	0.424	0.351	0.441	0.390	0.404	0.380
III	0.639	0.480	0.554	0.474	0.599	0.407	0.509	0.307	0.512	0.380	0.484	0.377
IV	0.790	0.789	0.689	0.610	0.765	0.606	0.730	0.529	0.720	0.614	0.728	0.613
V	1.000	1.000	1.000	1.000	1.000	1.000	1.000	1.000	1.000	1.000	1.000	1.000
VI	0.912	0.822	0.787	0.687	0.842	0.721	0.772	0.639	0.799	0.694	0.789	0.716
VII	0.572	0.395	0.427	0.446	0.467	0.231	0.480	0.370	0.521	0.407	0.527	0.401
VIII	0.428	0.307	0.315	0.361	0.352	0.199	0.373	0.255	0.462	0.435	0.527	0.445

for all of the BD stars and the two sets of values are entered in Table 3 in the columns D.S. and BD, respectively. It is clear that the density curves of double stars rise to sharper maxima in the zone V than the corresponding curves of stars in general do.

This fact is exhibited in a more striking manner if we tabulate, as in Table 4, the percentages of double stars in five areas, the Milky Way zone, the 20° zone on either side of it and the areas north of +30° and south of −30° galactic latitude.

The increased percentage in zone V must be accepted as real. Table 3 shows that stars of all magnitude classes participate in it, and an examination of my charts leads to the conclusion that it cannot be an observing effect, for some areas of all galactic latitudes were examined in summer, others in winter; the area north of +60° declination, examined almost exclusively with the 12-in., extends from −3° to +27° galactic latitude and the areas of high galactic latitude, both north and south, were examined mainly with the 36-in. refractor. It appears, therefore, that among stars as bright as 9.0 BD magnitude *close visual double stars are relatively more numerous in low than in high galactic latitudes.*

TABLE 4.—PERCENTAGES OF DOUBLE STARS

Galactic latitude	BD stars to 9.0	Double stars	Percentage of double stars
+90° to +30°	26,948	1,335	4.95
+30 +10	19,355	996	5.15
+10 −10	26,477	1,620	6.13
−10 −30	17,831	966	5.13
−30 −70	10,368	483	4.66

This apparent concentration of double stars toward the galactic plane is certainly to be explained, in part, by the far greater extension of the stellar system in that plane than in the direction perpendicular to it. Possibly this is the full explanation, perhaps the observed increase in double star density is entirely a perspective effect; but in that event it would seem that in zone V, the galactic zone, we might expect a relatively higher percentage of very close pairs than of pairs of greater separation. Table 5, however, in which the 5,400 pairs are grouped according to galactic latitude and angular separation, shows that the percentage increase toward zone V is substantially the same in all the angular distance categories up to 5″.00.

Let us consider next the relation between the angular separation and magnitude. This is shown in Table 6 where the pairs are arranged with these qualities as arguments. The

TABLE 5.—THE DISTRIBUTION OF DOUBLE STARS IN GALACTIC LATITUDE BY DISTANCE CLASSES

Dist. Zone	0″.00– 0″.50 No.	%	0″.51– 1″.00 No.	%	1″.01– 1″.50 No.	%	1″.51– 2″.00 No.	%	2″.01– 3″.00 No.	%	3″.01– 4″.00 No.	%	4″.01– 5″.00 No.	%	5″.01 and over No.	%
I	41	11	31	10	25	14	24	16	39	17	15	9	14	10	10	20
II	101	26	92	30	56	30	56	38	61	26	65	40	48	33	17	34
III	139	36	99	32	90	49	65	44	101	43	61	37	53	36	32	64
IV	225	58	175	57	131	71	104	70	133	57	112	68	74	51	42	84
V	388	100	306	100	184	100	149	100	233	100	164	100	146	100	50	100
VI	247	64	152	50	119	65	105	70	144	62	101	62	72	49	26	52
VII	82	21	77	25	52	28	36	24	42	18	32	20	29	20	17	34
VIII	33	8	18	6	14	8	12	8	12	5	9	6	12	8	6	12

TABLE 6.—THE DISTRIBUTION OF DOUBLE STARS BY ANGULAR
DISTANCE AND MAGNITUDE

Dist.⧹ Mag.	to 0."50	0."51– 1."00	0."00– 1."00	1."01– 2."00	2."01– 3."00	3."01– 4."00	4."01– 5."00	5."01 and over
≤ 6.5	75	63	138	83	62	41	31	99
6.6–7.0	82	52	134	59	42	40	21	14
7.1–7.5	103	67	170	99	64	48	31	29
7.6–8.0	178	132	310	164	107	85	63	26
8.1–8.5	310	223	533	285	173	128	111	21
8.6–9.0	508	413	921	532	317	217	191	11
Totals	1,256	950	2,206	1,222	765	559	448	200

Percentages

Dist.⧹ Mag.	to 0."50	0."51– 1."00	0."00– 1."00	1."01– 2."00	2."01– 3."00	3."01– 4."00	4."01– 5."00	5."01 and over
≤ 6.5	.....	...	39	23	17	12	9	...
6.6–7.0	.....	...	45	20	14	14	7	...
7.1–7.5	.....	...	41	24	16	12	7	...
7.6–8.0	.....	...	42	22	15	12	9	...
8.1–8.5	.....	...	43	23	14	11	9	...
8.6–9.0	.....	...	42	25	14	10	9	...
Totals	.....	...	42	23	15	11	9	...

sums of the numbers in the first two columns of the table are
entered in the third, thence the numbers are given for uniform
steps in angular distance to the final column. Every line of
columns three to seven exhibits a marked increase in the number
of pairs as the angular distance diminishes.

This is still more apparent when the figures in these five columns are expressed as percentages of the total number of pairs
under 5".0 separation in each magnitude class. If we may
assume that the stars of a given magnitude class, for example,
from 8.6 to 9.0, are, on the average, at the same distance from
us, then this observed increase in the number of pairs as the
angular distance diminishes is not a mere perspective effect
but represents a *real increase in the number of pairs as the angular
distance diminishes.*

The table also indicates that the Lick Observatory survey
was as thorough for the fainter stars (to 9.0 BD magnitude)
as for the brighter ones, for the percentages in each column
in the lower division of the table are not far from uniform and
there is a fair agreement between the ratios of the figures in each
line of the first two columns of the upper half of the table. This
was to be expected, for the pairs most likely to be missed in a

survey are those in which the difference in magnitude of the two components is large and bright pairs of that character are at least as difficult objects as pairs in which the primary is of 9.0 magnitude.* When the two components are of equal brightness, on the other hand, a 9.0 magnitude pair is but little more difficult than one of 6.0 magnitude, unless the angular distance is below 0.″15; in fact, I find that 123 of the 379 pairs with angular distance less than, or equal to, 0.″25, and 385 of the 877 pairs with angular distances between 0.″26 and 0.″50, discovered in that survey are of the BD magnitude class 8.6–9.0.

These statements are of significance also in connection with the figures entered in Table 7, which shows the percentage of double stars of each BD magnitude class.

TABLE 7.—PERCENTAGE OF DOUBLE STARS BY MAGNITUDE CLASSES

Magnitude	BD stars	Double stars	Percentage of double stars
to 6.5	4,120	458	11.1
6.6–7.0	3,887	306	7.9
7.1–7.5	6,054	438	7.2
7.6–8.0	11,168	758	6.8
8.1–8.5	22,898	1,251	5.5
8.6–9.0	52,852	2,189	4.1

The drop in percentage as we pass from the brighter to the fainter magnitudes cannot be attributed to lack of completeness in the data, for it follows from what has been said above, that the pairs overlooked in the survey are quite as likely to belong to the brighter magnitude classes as to the fainter ones; but we must not forget that this table, as well as the preceding ones, is based upon the apparent magnitudes only; whether the observed progression holds also for the absolute magnitudes we shall not know until we have more knowledge of the parallaxes of the stars involved. The very high percentage of spectroscopic binaries, among stars as bright as or brighter than 5.5 apparent magnitude, and particularly among stars of classes A and B, may possibly be significant in this connection, though we cannot as yet say definitely that the percentage is not as great among the fainter stars.

It will be of interest to inquire whether the results for the relative numbers and apparent distribution of the visual binary

* This holds true unless Δm exceeds six magnitudes.

stars given by the survey just reviewed find any support from the data given in the *New General Catalogue of Double Stars within 120° of the North Pole,* or from other available data. In 1932, I made a single count of the double stars in the new catalogue which are included within the limits of the curve defined by the formula log $\rho = 2.5 - 0.2m$. This formula gives 5".0 as the angular separation corresponding to a pair of 9.0 magnitude. I found 12,708 such pairs. Of these, 4,761 pairs are fainter than 9.0 magnitude and must be omitted in our present inquiry because no adequate double star survey has yet been made of the stars below 9.0. Further, it must be said that the survey is not complete even to 9.0 for the entire sky down to −30° declination. Making a very generous estimate of the number of such stars actually examined, I again find that *at least* one in every 18 is a close double star within the resolving power of good modern telescopes.

Table 8 shows the distribution of these 7,947 pairs by magnitude and angular separation, the data being given in more condensed form than was adopted in the earlier tables to minimize the effect of errors in the rapid count of the different categories.

TABLE 8

Ang. sep. / Mag.	<0".51	0".51– 1".00	1".01– 2".00	2".01– 5".00	5".01– Curve	Total
< 6.00	66	69	63	156	317	671
6.01–7.00	136	98	134	214	302	884
7.01–8.00	305	244	346	522	341	1,758
8.01–9.00	879	793	1,035	1,564	363	4,634
Totals	1,386	1,204	1,578	2,456	1,323	7,947
Percentages	17.4	15.2	19.9	30.9	16.6	100.0

The number of pairs under 0".51 in angular distance exceeds the number with distances between 0".51 and 1".00; the number under 1".00 is about one-third, the number wider than 5".0 is but one-sixth of the whole. These figures support the earlier finding that the number of double stars increases as the angular distance diminishes.

The fact that the tables presented above are based upon the apparent magnitudes, the observers' estimates (often very inexact) of the difference in magnitude of the two components of a pair, and upon measures of the angular distances made at many different epochs and with telescopes both large and small, is to be emphasized. If accurate photometric measures of magnitude (and of Δm) were available, and fairly reliable measures of all angular distances, it would be desirable to set up tables with the arguments log distance, m, and Δm. Such tables would give a far better picture of the actual distribution of the double stars.

It is well known that four of the ten stars nearest to the Sun are visual binaries: *α Centauri, Sirius, Procyon,* and 61 *Cygni.* This, no doubt, is an exceptional percentage, but it is of interest to quote some figures sent me by van Maanen who has recently made a study of the nearest stars.* Within a distance of 5 parsecs (approximately 16 light years), he finds that 8 double star systems (with 18 components) and 21 single stars (including the Sun) are known; in the volume of space between the limits 5 and 10 parsecs, 16 double or multiple systems (38 components) and 62 single stars, and in the volume between 10 and 20 parsecs, 91 double or multiple systems (197 components) and 281 single stars. In all, 617 individual stars (including the Sun) are known to us in the volume of space within a radius of 20 parsecs. Of these, 364 are single stars; the remaining 253 are components of 115 double or multiple systems. Counting each such system as a unit, then, one star in four is a visual double or multiple. Van Maanen proceeds to show that there are probably about 2,000 individual stars in this volume of space that have not yet been recognized as inhabitants. The chances are that the percentage of components of double star systems is not so great among these fainter stars as among those already known. Counts like these cannot be compared directly with the results given by our double star survey, but they nevertheless indicate that our estimate of the frequency of double stars is a very conservative one.

The spectral classes of the stars have been ignored in the preceding tables. It will be of interest now to take them into account, as far as possible. In 1917, through the courtesy of the Director, the late E. C. Pickering, and of Dr. Annie J. Cannon, of the Harvard College Observatory, I had the privilege of comparing my list of 5,400 double stars with the great card

* *Publ. A.S.P.* **45**, 247, 1933.

catalogue of stellar spectra later published as the *Henry Draper Catalogue*. This comparison provided the spectral classification of 3,919 of the 5,400 pairs. Of the remaining 1,481, only 15 are as bright as 8.0 (BD), 218 lie between 8.1 and 8.5, and 1,248 between 8.6 and 9.0. The published volumes of the *Henry Draper Catalogue* were available when I prepared the copy for my *New General Catalogue of Double Stars within 120° of the North Pole* (briefly the ADS), and I utilized them to enter all known spectra of the double stars I catalogued. I have made a single count of these, taking the spectrum of the primary star only, in cases where the spectra of additional components are entered, and find the total to be 9,190.

The pairs in the ADS, include all double stars to −30° declination, falling within the very generous distance limits set by the curve $\log \rho = 2.8 - 0.2m$, which gives the angular distance 10″.0 for a 9.0 (BD magnitude) pair.

Table 9 shows the distribution according to spectral class of the 9,190 ADS pairs with known spectra, of the 3,919 pairs in the northern half of the sky which fall within the much narrower limits set by my "working definition," and of the 222,570 stars in the *Henry Draper Catalogue*, as given in *H.C.O. Circular* 226.

TABLE 9
Numbers

	B	A	F	G	K	M	All
Visual pairs in n. hem..	157	1,251	532	1,093	837	49	3,919
Visual pairs in ADS...	268	2,910	1,220	2,461	2,126	205	9,190
Stars in HDC.........	3,567	64,259	21,120	46,552	73,208	13,864	222,570
Ratio ADS:HDC.....	1:13	1:22	1:17	1:19	1:34	1:68	....

Percentages

	B	A	F	G	K	M	All
Visual pairs in n. hem..	4.0	31.9	13.6	27.9	21.4	1.2	100.0
Visual pairs in ADS...	2.9	31.7	13.3	26.8	23.1	2.2	100.0
Stars in HDC.........	1.6	28.9	9.5	20.9	32.9	6.2	100.0

Table 10, in similar manner, shows the distribution of the spectroscopic binary stars in Moore's Third Catalogue (Table I), omitting the Cepheid variables and other stars whose variation in radial velocity does not satisfy Otto Struve's criterion. Since these binaries are practically all bright stars—nearly all brighter than 5.5 visual magnitude—their distribution in spectral class is compared with that of the HDC stars as bright as 6.25 magnitude (*H.C.O. Circ.* 226).

TABLE 10
Numbers

	B	A	F	G	K	M	All
Spec. Bin.	227	360	104	115	149	26	981
HDC Stars to 6.25	719	2,018	680	656	1,984	538	6,595
Ratio Spec. Bin. to HDC	1:3	1:6	1:7	1:6	1:13	1:21	.....

Percentages

	B	A	F	G	K	M	All
Spec. Bin.	23.1	36.7	10.6	11.7	15.2	2.7	100.0
HDC Stars to 6.25	10.9	30.6	10.3	9.9	30.1	8.2	100.0

The upper part of each table records the actual numbers of stars counted, the lower part their percentage distribution among the spectral classes. It is evident that the count of the 3,919 visual parts made in 1917 gave a good representation of the apparent distribution of the visual binary stars among the different spectral classes, for the count of the 9,190 pairs exhibits very closely the same percentage distribution.

It appears from the frequency ratios in Table 9 that visual binary stars are relatively more numerous among stars of classes B, F, and G, than among the stars of the other three classes, the small ratios for classes K and M being specially striking. From Table 10 it is equally clear that among the stars as bright as 6.25 magnitude, spectroscopic binaries are most numerous among stars of Class B and least numerous among stars of Class M. The strong contrast between the frequency ratios for classes B and M in both tables is perhaps their most striking feature. It may be of interest to add that my count shows that the visual binaries of classes B and A in the ADS are strongly concentrated toward the galactic plane, whereas those of classes F and M are quite uniformly distributed over the sky, and those of classes G and K are more frequent among stars of high than of low galactic latitude.

Such general statistics are of interest and have also a certain degree of significance, as have also the statistical relations between the magnitudes, spectral classes and colors of the components of the visual binary stars. The relation between the colors of the components of double stars and their difference in magnitude was recognized by Struve and every observer since his time has noted that fact that when the two components are about equally bright they are almost without exception of the same or nearly the same color, and that the color contrast increases with the difference in magnitude of the components. Professor Louis Bell argued that this is a subjective effect since the fainter star is generally the bluer one. Doubtless this subjective effect is often present but it is by no means the sole cause. There are real and very striking differences in the spectral classes of the components of double stars and these are definitely correlated to the color differences and also to the differences in magnitude. The absolute magnitude of the primary also enters as a factor. Thus Lau,* in two papers written as early as 1917 and 1918, respectively, found that the companions to giant stars are bluer, the companions to dwarf stars redder than their primaries.

Several writers have investigated the relations between magnitude and spectral class, in the components of double stars, among them Dr. F. C. Leonard.† His thorough analysis of the data for 238 pairs clearly showed (1) that when the two components are of equal or nearly equal magnitude, they differ little in spectral class, except in the case of a few giant stars like γ *Circini;* (2) that when the primary is a giant of spectral class F0 or later, the companion belongs to an earlier spectral class; and (3) that when the primary is a dwarf star, or a giant star of spectral class earlier than F0, that is, when the primary is a star of the main sequence, the companion belongs to a later spectral class. These results prove that the color relationships observed by Lau correspond to actual differences of spectral class. Since they are also in harmony with the mass-luminosity relationship, they indicate that the components of double stars are normal stars, having the same properties as ordinary single stars of corresponding mass and magnitude.

* *A.N.* **205**, 29, 1917; **208**, 179, 1918.

† Leonard, *Lick Obs. Bull.* **10**, 169, 1923. See also Peter Doig's paper (*Mon. Not.* **82**, 372, 1922) and G. Shajn's (*Bull. Poulkova Obs.* **10**, 276, 1925). Their conclusions are similar to Leonard's.

As has already been noted, one of the weakest points in these statistical investigations aside from the unavoidable incompleteness of the data, is that the apparent magnitudes of the components of double stars are so unreliable. What is needed is the accurate determination of Δm (and therefore of difference in absolute magnitude) of all pairs to a given magnitude limit (for the primary star). Some years ago, Dr. G. P. Kuiper, with the aid and encouragement of Prof. Ejnar Hertzsprung, began to make such a determination, using suitable wire gratings over the 10-in. refractor at Leiden, to reduce the first-order spectra of the primary stars to a brightness within one-half a magnitude of the image of the secondary star. He is following out this program at the Lick Observatory at the present time, with the object of including in his observations every star as bright as 6.5 visual magnitude on the Harvard scale, that has a companion within 30″. He is at the same time determining the spectral classes of the components, using a slitless spectrograph attached to the Crossley reflector. When completed, this program will afford a sound observational basis for a study of the relationships between Δm and the difference of spectral class in these bright pairs.

The various results as to the number and distribution of the binary stars given above are all, as I have said, of interest and of significance, though they rest, admittedly, upon data neither homogeneous nor complete. Some will be confirmed when additional data become available, others may have to be abandoned. One of the most significant findings is perhaps, that the components of the binary stars are normal stars, resembling in all essentials the single stars of corresponding magnitude and spectral class.

Among other investigations that lead to this same conclusion we may refer to Oort's* "A Comparison of the Average Velocity of Binaries with That of Single Stars," in which he finds no indication of any difference between the two; and Wallinquist's† "The Solar Motion as Derived from the Radial Velocities of the Visual Binary Stars." His value for the position of the solar apex, derived from a discussion of 536 systems, mainly with angular distance between components under 5″, agrees closely with the generally accepted value.

---

* J. H. Oort, *A.J.* **35**, 141, 1924.

† A. Wallinquist, *Ann. Bosscha Sterrenwacht* **4**, 21, 1929.

References

Many papers have been written in the past fifteen years on questions related to those discussed in this chapter.   In addition to those already referred to in the footnotes, a few representative papers are listed here.

JACKSON, J.: *Mon. Not. R.A.S.* **83**, 4, 1922.

LUNDMARK, K., and W. J. LUYTEN: On the Relation between Absolute Magnitude and Spectral class as Derived from Observations of Double Stars, *A.J.* **35**, 93, 1923.

LUYTEN, W. J.: On Some Statistical Properties of Double Stars in Space, *Proc. Nat. Acad. Sci.* **16**, 252, 1930.

GYLLENBERG, W.: The Binary Stars and the Stream Motions, *Med. Lunds. Obs. Ser.* **1**, No. 132, 1932.

Also a series of papers by E. A. Kreiken in the *Monthly Notices*.

CHAPTER XI

THE ORIGIN OF THE BINARY STARS

The problem of the origin of the binary stars may be considered from two quite different points of view. We may question by what conceivable process or combination of processes a single star or, alternately, a primal nebulous mass, can develop into a binary system of any kind whatever; or, we may pass in review the whole vast series of spectroscopic and visual double and multiple systems and ask what theory is competent to account not only for the origin of any one binary system but also for the great variety in content, form, and dimensions the known systems actually exhibit. Obviously, the second point of view makes the severer demand upon any theory that may be propounded, whether we regard all binaries as objects of a single genus, as I am disposed to do, or separate the very close, short-period spectroscopic binaries from those of longer period and from the visual binaries.

We may summarize briefly the more important conclusions that have been reached in the discussion of the observations of the visual double stars in the northern half of the sky and from the study of the known orbits of the visual and spectroscopic binary systems presented in the three preceding chapters.

1. A large proportion of the stars are binary systems. On the average, at least one in 18 of those as bright as 9.0 magnitude is a binary visible in our telescopes and coming within the limits set by the "working definition" of a double star; at least one in every three or four of those as bright as 5.5 magnitude is a binary revealed by the spectrograph. *These are minimum values.* Both visual and spectroscopic binaries within these magnitude limits remain to be discovered, our knowledge of the fainter stars is still very incomplete, and the angular distance limits set by the "working definition" are necessarily arbitrary. Unquestionably, many double stars with greater angular distances are binary systems. On the evidence before us, we may safely say that one-third, and probably two-fifths of the stars are binary or multiple systems.

2. A considerable percentage of these systems have three or more components. It is well within the truth to say that one in 20 of the known visual binaries has at least one additional member either visible or made known by the spectrograph, and many systems are quadruple or even more complex. Many of the purely spectroscopic systems are also triple or multiple. It is a fact of undoubted significance that, as a rule, triple systems, whether visual or spectroscopic, consist of a close binary pair and a companion relatively distant.

3. The masses of the spectroscopic binaries of Class B are decidedly greater than those of the spectroscopic binaries of later classes, and, among the *double-line binaries* (*i.e.*, those in which the spectra of both components are visible) there is some evidence of a progressive decrease in the average mass values with advancing spectral class. Evidence of the same kind, though less marked, exists for the visual binaries for which both orbits and parallax values are available, for the average masses of the visual binaries of classes A, F, and G agree very well with those of the spectroscopic binaries of the corresponding classes. It is to be noted, however, that double-line spectroscopic binaries and visual binaries with known orbits and parallaxes are necessarily selected systems.

4. The rule, both in visual and in spectroscopic binaries, is that the fainter component is the less massive one, but the mass ratio is rarely less than one-half and the average, as far as can be determined from the available data, is about three-fourths.

5. Spectroscopic binaries are relatively more numerous among stars of classes B and A, and visual binaries among stars of classes B, F, and G, than among stars of the other spectral classes. The small number of systems of either type among stars of Class M is specially striking.

6. When the primary star of a visual binary is a giant of spectral class later than F0, the companion belongs to an earlier spectral class; when the primary is a star of the main sequence (*i.e.*, a giant of spectral class earlier than F0, or a dwarf) the companion belongs to a later spectral class, the difference in spectral class, in both cases, increasing with the difference in magnitude of the two components.

7. There is a close correlation between the length of period, or size of system, and the degree of ellipticity in the orbit. The visual binaries, with periods to be reckoned in years or even in

centuries, have an average eccentricity slightly above 0.5; the spectroscopic binaries, with periods to be reckoned, for the most part, in days or even in fractions of a day, have an average eccentricity of less than 0.2, and in each class the average eccentricity increases with the average length of period. We have, apparently, one unbroken progression or series of orbits from systems in which the two components revolve in a fraction of a day in circular orbits and practically in surface contact, to systems in which the components, separated by one, two, or many hundreds of times the distance from the Earth to the Sun, revolve in highly elliptic orbits in periods of hundreds and even of thousands of years. The scatter of the values of *e* in any given period group is large, but, statistically, we may regard the correlation as securely established.

These facts and relations, as well as others less conclusively demonstrated as yet, must all be taken into account when we look at the question of the origin of the binary stars from the second point of view indicated in the opening paragraph of this chapter. We have now to see whether any of the theories so far advanced are satisfactory from this point of view. At least three theories have been developed that merit consideration.

The capture theory, apparently first advanced by Dr. G. Johnston Stoney, in 1867, is based upon the hypothesis that two stars, originally independent, might approach each other under such conditions that each would be swerved from its path and forced to revolve with the other about a common center of gravity. This theory, in its original form, has been completely abandoned, but the consequences of the near approach of two stars have been the subject of extensive discussion in more recent years. Chamberlin and Moulton, for example, have argued that, under appropriate initial conditions, such an approach might result in a system of planets like our own. This is probably the best theory that has been developed to account for the origin of the solar system, and if it may be accepted, then we may agree that the close approach of two stars, under somewhat different conditions, might result in a planetary system in which the disparity in mass between the central star and its largest planet would be far less than it is between the Sun and *Jupiter.* That is the assumption MacMillan* makes in arguing

* *Science* **62**, 63, 96, 121, 1925.

that, in certain cases, a planetary system might ultimately develop into a binary star system.

Assume, for example, that, as the solar system traverses space, the Sun and the planets grow in mass from the infall of atoms, molecules or larger particles, sometimes very slowly, at others (as the system passes through a region filled with nebulous matter) more rapidly, and that, on the whole, the Sun's gain by this process is offset by its loss of mass through radiation. Then the mass of *Jupiter*, to consider only the largest planet, would steadily increase relatively to that of the Sun and the distance between the two bodies would decrease. If, in this manner *Jupiter* were to acquire sufficient mass to become a dwarf red star while the Sun just held its own in mass, we should have a double star system, the other planets being absorbed, ultimately, either by *Jupiter* or by the Sun. MacMillan describes the process in more detail, but in a recent personal letter says that *Jupiter* could not become equal to the Sun in mass before it merged with it. Indeed it is doubtful if it could exceed one-tenth the mass of the Sun without having the two bodies drawn together.

It is hard, therefore, to see a double star future for the solar system, for we have found that even in the closest spectroscopic binaries the mass ratio rarely falls below one-half. But even if we grant that a binary star might develop, in the course of eons, from a planetary system in which the original mass distribution was more favorable, the process, at best, could account for only an occasional spectroscopic binary with quite unequal components. Once formed, there would, it is true, be a tendency toward equality in mass of the two components, as time went on, for the rate of radiation from a star is proportional to a power higher than the first,* but we have already noted MacMillan's conclusion that in a system so formed the two stars are likely to fall together when the mass ratio approaches unity. If we assume this danger to be averted through tidal interaction and loss of mass by both bodies through radiation, then, statistically, the masses of the visual binaries with periods measured in decades or in centuries should be smaller than those of the spectroscopic binaries, with periods measured in days. This, however, we have shown not to be the case (Tables 10 and

---

* Jeans, *Mon. Nat.* R.A.S. **85**, 209, 1925.

11, Chap. VIII). We must, I fear, decide that the theory does not meet the requirements.

The fission theory which we have next to examine, assumes that a star in its primal nebulous stage, or possibly at a later one, divides under the stress of its own gravitation, radiation pressure, and rotational forces or under the strain of some external disrupting force or forces.

The behavior of a rotating, homogeneous, incompressible, fluid mass, in equilibrium and free from external disturbance, was investigated by Maclaurin and Jacobi about a century ago and later by Poincaré, G. H. Darwin, Liapounoff, Jeans, and others. It was found possible, under certain assumptions, to follow, mathematically, the transformations of figure as the rotating mass contracts under its own gravitation and heat radiation from the initial sphere through a succession of spheroids and ellipsoids until a pear-shaped figure is reached. It seems probable, though it could not be demonstrated mathematically, that fission into two masses would follow, the masses revolving at first in surface contact and in circular orbits.

The stars and, in all probability, the antecedent nebulae, are neither homogeneous nor incompressible, but it has been argued, first, I believe, by See, and later by Darwin and Jeans, that a nebula (or even a star in its earliest stage) might none the less pass through a similar series of changes and ultimately form a stable double star system. Once formed, the forces of tidal interaction and of the disturbances ("knocking about") produced by the attractions of other stars, were invoked to account for the development of the systems with longer periods and elliptic orbits.

Sir James Jeans, in particular, has advocated this theory, and readers are referred to his writings cited at the end of the chapter for his mathematical development of it. But Jeans himself has confirmed Liapounoff's conclusion* that the pear-shaped figure is unstable and has pointed out that if a double star system results, it, too, will be unstable unless the mass ratio of the two components is less than one-third. It has also been shown by Moulton, Russell, and Jeans that even were a stable double star system to result from fission, the mutual tidal actions

---

* Liapounoff, *Mem. Imp. Acad. Sci. St. Petersburg* **17**, 1905;
Jeans, *Phil. Trans. Roy. Soc. A* **217**, 1, 1917.

of the two components could never greatly increase either the major axis or the eccentricity of the orbit. Quite recently William Markowitz* made a statistical investigation of the possibility that short-period spectroscopic binaries might develop into long period systems and in his work he had the benefit of advice from Profs. MacMillan, Moulton, and Otto Struve, He found that the necessary increase in the values of P, a, and e could not result from contraction, secular decrease of mass, or close encounters with other stars nor yet from the combination of all three. Jeans had earlier concluded that pairs with periods in excess of about 55 days could not result from the process of fission, and that a different origin must be sought for them.

A separation of the binaries at the 55-day period point or at any other is negatived, in my judgment, by the fact that there is no apparent correlation between period and mass,† and also by the fact that there is a definite correlation between eccentricity and period. If the fission theory is incompetent to explain the origin of the longer period binaries, that fact alone leads us to abandon it entirely.

The separate nuclei theory remains to be considered. This was first suggested by Laplace more than a hundred years ago. In Note VII to his *Système du Monde*, he remarks:

"Such groups (as the *Pleiades*) are a necessary result of the condensation of nebulae with several nuclei, for it is plain that the nebulous matter being constantly attracted by these different nuclei must finally form a group of stars like the *Pleiades*. The condensation of nebulae with two nuclei will form stars in very close proximity, which will turn one around the other similar to

---

* *Ap. Jour.* **75**, 69, 1932.

† In 1924, 1925, Jeans and E. W. Brown both found that, theoretically, the semimajor axis (a) and therefore the period (P) would increase if one or both components of a binary system were losing mass by radiation. Jeans found that the eccentricity (e) would also remain constant, whereas Brown's conclusion was that it, too, would increase though at a lower rate.

In a note in *Nature* for April 21, 1934, A. E. H. Bleksley states that a recent investigation of his own confirms Jeans's results. He concludes that the "*semiaxis major is inversely proportional to the mass of the system*" throughout the life of a binary. He adds that a statistical study of all available material shows that this relation appears to hold for the visual binaries of known orbit but not for the short-period spectroscopic binaries, and he suggests that there is a difference in origin between the two groups. No details are given.

those double stars whose relative motions have already been determined."*

The modern writer who has adopted this theory most explicitly is the very man who first formulated the fission theory, Dr. See. His discussion of the binary stars in the second volume of his *Researches on the Evolution of the Stellar System* is devoted more particularly to the development of the systems after their initial formation but on page 232 we find the statement, "It is evident . . . that the resulting mass-ratio in a system depends on the supply of nebulosity and the original nuclei already begun and slowly developing in the nebula while it was still of vast extent and great tenuity," and, on page 584, the even more definite statement, "When a double star had been formed in the usual manner by the growth of separate centers in a widely diffused nebula. . . . "

The separate nuclei theory apparently affords sufficient latitude for the explanation of any binary system except, perhaps, the very close, short-period spectroscopic binaries. To account for these, the effect of a resisting medium has been invoked, Markowitz, for example, finding that, unless the two components are radiating mass more than 2.5 as fast as they are gathering it in, the values of P, a, and e of the system are decreasing. But even if we grant a tendency toward such a decrease, it is hardly conceivable that it would account for the transformation of, say, hundred-year-period systems into systems with periods of a single day, or of ten days, especially in view of the fact that no correlation appears to exist between mass and period.

The fundamental objection to the separate nuclei theory is that we really do not explain anything; to use Moulton's words, "we only push by an assumption the problem of explaining the binary systems a little farther back into the unknown."

Russell's specific objection, based upon his study of the triple and quadruple systems, is also of great force. Why should these systems almost invariably consist of a comparatively close binary pair attended by a third star or by another close binary pair at a distance relatively great? As Russell says, "Not only is there no apparent reason for it, but if we try to retrace in imagination the history of such a system, through stages of greater and greater diffusion as we penetrate

* See *Essays in Astronomy*, p. 501 (edited by E. S. Holden, New York, D. Appleton & Company, 1900).

farther into the past (keeping in mind that the moment of momentum of the whole system must remain constant), it is hard to form any idea of the history of the nuclei which will finally form a close and rapidly revolving pair, attended by a distant companion."

The general conclusion of our discussion is that, although the observational data that have been accumulated clearly indicate the common origin of the binary stars, no theory of that origin and of the subsequent development of the observed systems that has so far been formulated can be regarded as satisfactory.

It is the duty of the observers to supply us with the data required for the formulation and test of such a theory. Observations of the various classes of binary systems, visual, spectroscopic and eclipsing, must be continued indefinitely, by the methods described in earlier chapters or by improved methods, to provide the data needed for orbit computation. More orbits of all these classes of systems are, of course, demanded. We must have a number sufficiently great to insure confidence that conclusions based upon our discussions are not affected by selection in the data.

But that is not all. We are quite as much in need of accurate values of the parallaxes of the systems and of accurate determinations of the magnitudes and spectral classes of the fainter as well as of the brighter components. A knowledge of the masses, the mass ratios, the absolute magnitudes, and the spectral characteristics of the components in these systems is quite as important as a knowledge of the orbital elements for the solution of the problem of the origin and evolution of the binary stars.

References

The following list contains only a few of the many papers that have been read in preparing this chapter. References to others will be found in them, and also in some of the papers cited at the end of Chap. VIII.

DARWIN, G. H.: The Genesis of Double Stars, *Darwin and Modern Science*, pp. 543–564. Cambridge University Press, 1910.

———: Presidential Address, British Association for the Advancement of Science, *Report B. A. A. S.* 1905, p. 3.

JEANS, J. H.: The Motion of Tidally Distorted Masses with Special Reference to Theories of Cosmogony. *Mem. R.A.S.* **62**, part 1, 1917.

———: On the Density of Algol Variables, *Ap. Jour.* **22**, 93, 1905.

———: The Evolution of Binary Systems, *Mon. Not. R.A.S.* **79**, 100, 1918.

———: The Origin of the Binary Stars, *Scientia* **31**, 11, 1922.

————: Astronomy and Cosmogony, pp. 198–307, Cambridge University Press, 1928.

MOULTON, F. R.: On Certain Relations among the Possible Changes in the Motions of Mutually Attracting Spheres when Disturbed by Tidal Interactions; and, Notes on the Possibility of Fission of a Contracting Rotating Fluid Mass, *Publication* 107, *Carnegie Institution of Washington*, pp. 77–160.

————: *Introduction to Astronomy*, revised edition, pp. 543–548

RUSSELL, H. N.: On the Origin of Binary Stars, *Ap. Jour.* **31**, 185, 1910.

SEE, T. J. J.: Die Entwickelung der Doppelstern-Systeme, *Inaugural Dissertation*, 1892.

————: Researches on the Physical Constitution of the Heavenly Bodies. *A.N.* **169**, 321, 1905.

————: *Researches on the Evolution of the Stellar Systems*, **2**, Chap. 20, 1910.

MACMILLAN, W. D.: The Problem of Two Bodies with Diminishing Mass, *Mon. Not. R.A.S.* **85**, 904, 1925.

SHAJN, G.: On the Mass-Ratio in Double Stars, *Mon. Not. R.A.S.* **85**, 245, 1929; *A.N.* **237**, 57, 1929.

MARKOWITZ, W.: The Evolution of Binary Stars, *Ap. Jour.* **75**, 69, 1932.

————: Some Statistical and Dynamical Aspects of the Fission Theory, *Ap. Jour.* **78**, 161, 1933.

APPENDIX

The two tables printed on the following pages list the visual and spectroscopic binary star orbits that have been used in the preparation of the present volume. In compiling them, all orbits available to me by September, 1933, have been examined. The visual orbits listed in Table I have been taken from my card catalogue of orbits, the orbits of the spectroscopic binaries, from the card catalogue of variable radial velocities which Dr. J. H. Moore keeps up to date.* I am deeply indebted to Mrs. Moore for her kindness in copying off the necessary data. Both sets of orbits have been checked by examination of the original publications.

The abbreviations used for publications cited in the footnotes and at the end of the chapters in the volume will, I think, be readily understood. In the following tables, however, it has been necessary to use the shortest possible form, and it may be well to state that *A.N.*, *A.J.*, *Ap. Jour.*, *M.N.*, *P.A.*, *B.A.N.*, *P.A.S.P.*, and *R.A.S.C.*, stand, respectively, for *Astronomische Nachrichten*, *Astronomical Journal*, *Astrophysical Journal*, *Monthly Notices of the Royal Astronomical Society*, *Popular Astronomy*, *Bulletin of the Astronomical Institutes of the Netherlands*, *Publications of the Astronomical Society of the Pacific*, and *Journal of the Royal Astronomical Society of Canada*. "*Observatory*," has been abbreviated to *O.*, *D.A.O.*, *D.O.* and *A.O.* standing, respectively, for the Dominion Astrophysical, the Dominion and the Allegheny Observatories. *C.A.* represents the *Cape* (of Good Hope) *Annals*. The other abbreviations need no explanation.

---

* [Dr. Moore died on March 15, 1949. See p. 40.—J.T.K.]

TABLE I.—ORBITS OF VISUAL BINARY STARS

	Star	α (1900) δ	Mag.	Sp.	P	n	T	e	a	ω	i	Ω	Authority	π	$(m + m_1)$
1	Σ3062	0ʰ01ᵐ0 + 57°53'	6.5, 7.5	G5	105ʸ55	d	1836.07	0.466	1″44	98°7	±46°1	37°4	Doberck, A.N. 173, 257, 1906	0″032	8⊙18
2	Σ2	03.8 + 79 10	6.8, 7.1	A3	215.	d	1890.8	0.472	0.64	337.1	±70.9	166.5	Russell, P.A. 25, 667, 1917	0.011	4.26
3	OΣ4	11.5 + 35 56	8.2, 8.9	G0	108.	r	1908.0	0.543	0.41	......	0.	12.5	Luyten, P.A.S.P. 45, 183, 1933	.....	.....
4	A111, AB	27.0 − 5 44	9.3, 9.3	G5	10.5	r	1919.75	0.405	0.18	30.45	±37.85	125.5	Aitken, P.A.S.P. 35, 258, 1923	0.034	1.64
5	I260	27.0 − 63 31	4.7, 6.7	A2	41.3	r	1923.57	0.668	0.477	4.6	±44.2	113.6	Van den Bos, B.A.N. 3, 259, 1927	.....	.....
6	Ho212	30.1 − 4 09	5.7, 6.5	G0	6.88	d	1932.79	0.725	0.242	66.8	+53.45	38.7	Aitken, Pub. L.O. 12, 5, 1914	0.052	2.13
7	β395	32.2 − 25 19	6.4, 6.6	K0	25.0	d	1924.50	0.171	0.66	152.7	+76.0	112.8	Aitken, Pub. L.O. 12, 7, 1914	0.069	1.40
8	η Cas	43.0 + 57 17	3.6, 7.2	F8	478.7	d	1888.7	0.495	11.92	82.8	−35.9	102.4	Volet, J.O. 16, 107, 1933	0.180	1.27
9	β232	44.8 + 50 05	8.5, 9.0	F5	91.2	d	1914.8	0.326	0.368	317.6	±45.6	129.2	Kuiper, B.A.N. 5, 231, 1930	.....	.....
10	Σ73	0 49.6 + 23 05	6.1, 6.7	K0	124.2	r	1815.93	0.708	0.97	76.5	±41.2	105.7	Jackson, Grve. Cat. 205, 1921	0.028	2.70
11	δ31, AB	1 30.4 − 30 26	7.8, 8.0	G5	4.56	r	1927.97	0.30	0.173	319.4	±14.6	143.4	Dawson, A.J. 43, 15, 1933	.....	.....
12	p Eri	36.0 − 56 45	6.0, 6.1	G5	218.9	r	1806.14	0.721	8.025	301.40	±65.74	1.03	Dawson, A.J. 32, 144, 1919	0.170	2.20
13	Σ186	50.7 + 1 21	6.9, 6.9	G0	158.4	d	1891.7	0.69	1.00	216.7	±69.7	41.0	Volet, J.O. 16, 107, 1933	0.035	0.93
14	β513	53.7 + 70 25	4.7, 7.1	A3	63.3	d	1904.8	0.385	0.66	341.6	+31.5	90.5	Bennot, P.A. 33, 306, 1925	0.028	3.27
15	OΣ238	1 57.8 + 41 51	5.4, 6.6	A0	55.0	r	1892.0	0.82	0.346	201.2	±76.6	113.5	Hussey, Pub. L.O. 5, 43, 1901	0.015	4.06
16	Σ228	2 07.6 + 47 01	6.4, 7.3	F0	149.6	d	1897.2	0.29	0.917	318.9	±63.2	96.3	Kuiper, B.H.N. 5, 232, 1930	0.028	1.57
17	A1928	34.7 − 0 17	8.9, 8.9	G0	19.0	d	1919.0	0.50	0.17	335.0	±44.8	67.0	Aitken, P.A.S.P. 39, 45, 1927	.....	.....
18	β524, AB	2 47.4 + 37 56	5.6, 6.7	F0	33.33	r	1895.0	0.60	0.16	325.0	±33.5	127.1	Aitken, Pub. L.O. 12, 20, 1914	0.017	0.75
19	Σ412, AB	3 28.5 + 24 08	6.6, 6.7	F0	270.4	r	1917.3	0.555	0.49	348.0	±40.6	97.0	Aitken, L.O.B. 11, 66, 1923	0.006	7.47
20	40 Eri, BC	4 10.7 − 7 49	9.9, 11.6	A	247.92	d	1848.93	0.402	6.894	326.96	±71.55	150.96	Van den Bos, B.A.N. 3, 128, 1926	0.202	0.65
21	OΣ79	14.2 + 16 17	7.0, 8.8	G0	88.9	d	1897.8	0.625	0.57	129.8	±56.2	66.0	Aitken, Pub. L.O. 12, 30, 1914	0.027	1.19
22	β744	17.4 − 25 58	6.6, 6.6	F0	64.86	d	1924.80	0.565	0.521	329.0	±32.9	151.1	Van den Bos, B.A.N. 3, 261, 1927	.....	.....
23	β1185	20.0 + 18 38	8.2, 8.8	G0	28.9	r	1917.8	0.20	0.25	301.6	±75.65	24.3	Aitken, L.O.B. 11, 70, 1923	.....	.....
24	Σ554	24.4 + 15 25	5.7, 9.0	F0	148.3	r	1888.30	0.79	1.036	157.92	±71.0	8.88	Van den Bos, M.N. 81, 474, 1921	0.026	2.88
25	β883	45.7 + 10 54	7.7, 7.7	F5	16.61	d	1923.64	0.445	0.19	......	0.	224.2	Aitken, Pub. L.O. 12, 35, 1914	0.034	0.63
26	β552	4 46.2 + 13 29	7.0, 10.0	F5	88.2	d	1882.85	0.519	0.627	316.3	±50.4	122.0	Jackson, Grve. Cat. 209, 1921	0.018	5.43
27	A2715	56.9 + 9 39	4.3, 6.6	A2	17.5	r	1929.25	0.76	0.27	43.	+70.	39.	Bourgeois, Ap. Jour. 70, 256, 1929	0.035	1.29
28	β895	6 13.6 + 28 28	7.9, 7.9	A3	45.7	d	1914.31	0.88	0.255	289.9	±60.7	22.7	Van den Bos, B.A.N. 2, 25, 1923	0.026	.....
29	OΣ2149	30.2 + 27 22	6.9, 9.4	G0	103.	r	1923.0	0.72	0.77	285.	±69.0	77.0	Van Biesbroeck, Pub. Y.O. 5, 206, 1927	0.025	2.76

30		6 40.8 − 16 35	−1.6, 8.4	A0	49.94	r	1894.02	0.588	7.62	145.87	+44.49	43.77		0.375	3.36
30	Sirius	6 40.8 − 16 35	−1.6, 8.4	A0	49.94	r	1894.02	0.588	7.62	145.87	+44.49	43.77	Volet, Bul. Astr. 7, 24, 1931	0.375	3.36
31	I65	6 53.7 − 35 22	6.8, 7.0	F5	16.5	d	1926.8	0.586	0.315	269.7	±56.3	116.4	Finsen U.O.C. 86, 259, 1932		.....
32	Σ1037	7 06.7 + 27 24	7.2, 7.2	F5	120.4	r	1920.57	0.932	0.870	254.1	+39.0	31.4	Van Biesbroeck, M.N. 85, 478, 1925	0.024	3.28
33	Castor	7 28.2 + 32 06	2.0, 2.8	A0	340.	r	1963.	0.43	5.84	276.5	+34.0	35.	Luyten, A.J. 42, 179, 1933	0.074	4.25
34	Procyon	7 34.1 + 5 29	0.5, 13.5	F5	40.23	d	1926.73	0.31	4.26	65.7	+30.6	127.8	Spencer Jones, M.N. 83, 403, 1928.	0.310	1.60
35	β101	7 47.2 − 13 38	5.8, 6.4	G0	23.34	d	1915.94	0.75	0.69	74.65	+79.8	99.7	Aitken, Pub. L.O. 12, 51, 1914	0.072	1.62
36	β581	7 58.8 + 12 35	8.6, 8.6	G5	44.0	d	1909.75	0.39	0.38	292.3	+47.7	116.1	Aitken, L.O.B. 12, 47, 1925	0.033	0.82
37	ζCnc, AB	8 06.5 + 17 57	5.6, 6.3	G0	59.60	r	1930.62	0.314	0.949	189.08	+29.4	10.33	Makenson, A.J. 42, 153, 1933	0.046	2.47
38	ζCnc, Cc*	8 06.5 + 17 57	6.0,	G0	17.64	r	1909.99	0.221	0.236	268.32	+56.72	80.8	Makenson, A.J. 42, 153, 1933		.....
39	εHya, AB	8 41.5 + 6 47	3.7, 5.2	F8	15.3	d	1931.57	0.65	0.23	270.0	+49.95	104.4	Aitken, Pub. L.O. 12, 59, 1914	0.024	3.76
40	Σ3121	9 12.0 + 29 00	8.0, 8.0	K0	34.0	d	1912.30	0.33	0.669	127.52	+75.0	28.25	See, Evol. Stel. Sys. 94, 1895	0.051	1.95
41	ωLeo.	23.1 + 9 30	5.9, 6.7	G0	116.74	d	1840.82	0.56	0.844	122.10	+66.2	44.28	Doberck, A.N. 173, 251, 1906	0.026	2.51
42	ψArg.	26.8 − 40 02	3.8, 5.8	F5	34.90	d	1936.79	0.37	0.914	219.2	−56.2	116.8	Dawson, A.J. 36, 23, 1924	0.067	2.08
43	φUMa	45.3 + 54 32	5.1, 5.5	A2	112.663	r	1883.58	0.497	0.343	9.24	+22.86	157.89	Dick, Dissertation, 1921	0.014	1.16
44	AC5	9 47.6 − 7 38	5.7, 6.1	A2	72.76	r	1953.30	0.60	0.41	133.1	+37.14	17.95	Schoenberg, A.N. 178, 189, 1908	0.015	3.86
45	ξUMa, AB	11 12.8 + 32 06	4.4, 4.9	G0	59.863	r	1935.027	0.413	2.536	127.18	+57.20	101.40	Van den Bos, Mem. Copen. Acad. 12, 2, 1928	0.126	2.27
46	ξUMa, Aa	12 .8 + 32 06	4.41,	G0	1.832	r	1909.752	0.531	0.051	320.0	−84.5	309.4	Van den Bos, Mem. Copen. Acad. 12, 2, 1928		
47	O2234	25.4 + 41 50	7.6, 8.0	F8	84.734	d	1883.532	0.422	0.347	218.37	+54.08	151.63	Riechert, A.N. 219, 227, 1933		.....
48	OΣ235	26.7 + 61 38	5.7, 7.1	F5	71.9	d	1909.0	0.40	0.78	135.0	+43.6	78.5	Aitken, Pub. L.O. 12, 72, 1914	0.040	1.43
49	β794	11 48.3 + 74 19	7.1, 8.4	F8	82.0	d	1912.16	0.52	0.42	243.9	+36.9	32.5	Voronov, Tashkent O.C. 10, 1933		.....
50	Σ1639	12 19.4 + 26 08	6.6, 7.8	A5	361.	r	1888.10	0.926	1.00	300.9	+43.6	78.4	Jackson, Grw. Cat., 212, 1921	0.012	4.44
51	γCen.	36.0 − 48 25	3.1, 3.2	A0	80.4	r	1930.2	0.86	0.917	196.9	+71.9	6.3	Van den Bos U.O.C. 79, 49, 1929	0.032	3.81
52	γVir.	12 36.6 − 1 57	3.6, 3.7	F0	177.75	r	1836.38	0.859	3.615	236.15	+30.65	13.8	Lohse, Pub. Potsdam O. 20, 101, 1908	0.085	2.38
53	42 Com.	13 05.1 + 18 03	5.2, 5.2	F5	25.87	d	1911.74	0.522	0.665	278.6	+89.87	12.6	Russell, P.A. 25, 667, 1917	0.058	2.25
54	Σ1768	33.0 + 36 48	5.2, 7.1	F0	220.4	r	1860.26	0.856	1.205	118.6	+47.4	52.8	Jackson, Grw. Cat., 213, 1921	0.024	2.61
55	β612	34.6 + 11 15	6.2, 6.2	F2	23.05	d	1930.27	0.52	0.225	357.95	+50.4	33.85	Aitken, Pub. L.O. 12, 85, 1914	0.016	5.23
56	Σ1785	44.5 + 27 29	7.9, 8.2	K2	155.71	d	1916.91	0.449	2.475	200.06	+47.66	156.58	Rabe, A.N. 231, 121, 1927	0.062	2.62
57	β1270	13 58.8 + 8 58	8.5, 8.6	F5	38.1	d	1911.58	0.41	0.21	24.4	+20.5	126.1	Aitken, L.O.B. 11, 79, 1923	0.017	1.30
58	Σ1834	14 16.6 + 48 58	7.9, 8.0	F8	295.6	r	1901.73	0.823	0.93	169.2	+82.04	110.6	Van den Bos, Proc. Amater. Acad. 30, 72, 1921		.....
59	β1111, BC	18.5 + 8 54	7.4, 7.4	A0	40.53	d	1918.38	0.238	0.235	144.35	+40.8	43.95	Aitken, P.A.S.P. 31, 286, 1919	0.012	4.57
60	A570	27.9 + 27 07	6.6, 6.8	A2	28.45	r	1924.88	0.171	0.202	219.9	+35.8	170.9	J. Young, P.A.S.P., 35, 221, 1923	0.012	5.89

* Spectroscopic Binary.

TABLE I.—ORBITS OF VISUAL BINARY STARS.—(*Continued*)

	Star	α (1900) δ	Mag.	Sp.	P	n	T	e	a	ω	i	Ω	Authority	π	$(m + m_1)$
61	α Cen.	14h32m.8 − 60°25'	0.3, 1.7	G0	80y.089	d	1875 759	0.521	17".665	52°.132	+79°.233	25°.445	Finsen, U.O.C. **63**, 343, 1926	0".760	1⊙.76
62	ζ Boo.	36.4 + 14 09	4.4, 4.8	A2	130.	r	1898.0	0.96	0.62	180.	+39.7	129.	Hertzsprung, A.N. **203**, 393, 1916	0.013	6.42
63	Σ1879	41.4 + 10 05	7.5, 8.5	F8	177.9	r	1868.14	0.623	0.789	148.3	+51.2	70.6	Jackson, Grw. Cat. 215, 1921	....	....
64	OΣ285	41.7 + 42 48	7.7, 8.2	F5	88.5	r	1882.64	0.553	0.33	137.7	+25.6	41.7	Jackson, Grw. Cat. 216, 1921	....	1.36
65	ξ Boo.	14 46.8 + 19 31	4.9, 6.8	G5	151.425	r	1909.36	0.510	4.874	23.8	+40.8	168.3	Doberck, A.N. **214**, 89, 1921	0.155	....
66	Σ1909	15 00.5 + 48 03	5.3, 6.1	G0	204.74	d	1793.48	0.445	3.578	25.03	+83.07	58.73	Doberck, A.N. **182**, 27, 1909	0.078	2.30
67	η CBr	19.1 + 30 39	5.6, 6.1	G0	41.623	d	1892.385	0.276	0.907	219.91	−59.025	23.72	Silbernagel, A.N. **234**, 441, 1928	0.063	1.72
68	μ Boo.	20.7 + 37 42	7.2, 7.8	K0	224.	r	1864.6	0.53	1.30	339.0	+42.0	177.2	Comstock, A.J., **33**, 139, 1921	0.032	1.34
69	γ Lup.	28.5 − 40 50	3.6, 3.8	B3	104.3	r	1905.7	0.314	0.78	2.9	+88.1	91.5	Dawson, A.J., **33**, 109, 1921	0.016	10.65
70	OΣ298	32.5 + 40 08	7.4, 7.7	K0	55.109	d	1882.594	0.568	0.802	16.88	+64.05	3.80	Buchar, Pub. Inst. Ast. Prague **2**, 9, 1928	0.044	1.99
71	γ CBr	38.6 + 26 37	4.0, 7.0	A0	101.	r	1842.7	0.42	0.62	125.	+82.	111.	Comstock, A.J. **33**, 163, 1921	0.020	2.92
72	π UMi	45.1 + 80 17	7.2, 8.2	F2	115.	r	1902.7	0.80	0.42	165.	+62.25	16.3	Aitken, Pub. L.O. **12**, 100, 1914	....	....
73	ξ Sco, AB	15 58.9 − 11 06	4.8, 5.1	F8	44.70	d	1905.39	0.75	0.72	343.6	+29.1	27.2	Aitken, Pub. L.O. **12**, 102, 1914	0.038	3.41
74	Σ2026	16 11.1 + 7 37	9.1, 9.6	K5	215.0	r	1908.07	0.695	1.53	7.2	+44.1	178.7	Comstock, A.J. **31**, 33, 1918	....	1.47
75	Σ2052	24.5 + 18 37	7.8, 7.8	K0	317.5	r	1920.21	0.77	2.87	114.5	+75.0	93.1	Jackson, Grw. Cat. 218, 1921	0.054	....
76	λ Oph.	25.9 + 2 12	4.0, 6.1	A0	135.29	d	1945.29	0.590	0.942	37.02	+25.17	180.1	Rabe, A.N. **231**, 124, 1927	0.028	2.08
77	ζ Her.	37.5 + 31 47	3.0, 6.5	G0	34.417	r	1933.164	0.455	1.349	146.50	−46.90	52.24	Silbernagel, A.N. **233**, 145, 1928	0.106	1.74
78	D15	40.8 + 43 40	8.9, 9.2	K5	119.9	r	1895.40	0.42	0.91	149.8	+62.6	144.7	Van Biesbroeck Pub. Y.O. **5**, 233, 1927	....	1.63
79	Σ2107	16 47.9 + 28 50	6.7, 8.2	F5	261.82	d	1895.51	0.560	1.012	242.07	+27.06	52.66	Rabe, A.N. **231**, 127, 1927	0.021	2.92
80	Hu1176	17 04.5 + 36 04	6.1, 6.1	A5	15.5	d	1919.9	0.14	0.16	308.4	+56.0	90.8	Aitken, L.O.B. **11**, 83, 1923	0.018	2.92
81	Brs. 0.13, AB	11 4 − 46 32	5.6, 8.4	K0	100.9	d	1912.61	0.168	3.503	315.21	+48.80	175.45	Van den Bos, B.A.N. **2**, 29, 1923	0.140	1.54
82	Mlb. 0.4, AB	12.2 − 34 53	5.9, 8.5	K2	42.2	r	1933.68	0.551	1.83	64.0	+50.4	130.2	Voûte, B.A.N. **2**, 181, 1924	0.143	1.18
83	Σ2173	25.3 − 0 59	5.9, 6.2	G5	46.0	r	1915.2	0.18	1.06	322.2	+80.75	153.7	Aitken, Pub. L.O. **12**, 116, 1914	0.060	2.61
84	β962	34.0 + 61 57	5.3, 10.1	F8	111.	r	1893.3	0.23	1.56	65.5	+67.2	153.8	Russell, P.A. **25**, 667, 1917	0.062	1.29
85	μ Her. BC	42.5 + 27 47	10.5, 11.0	Mb	43.02	d	1922.18	0.18	1.287	174.64	+66.18	60.21	Silbernagel, A.N. **233**, 257, 1928	0.112	0.83
86	r Oph.	17 57.6 − 8 11	5.3, 6.0	F0	223.82	d	1814.79	0.534	1.307	17.75	+66.07	76.20	Doberck, A.N. **170**, 101, 1905	0.022	4.19
87	70 Oph.	18 00.4 + 2 31	4.2, 6.2	K0	87.710	d	1895.965	0.499	4.495	193.352	−58.743	122.184	Pavel, A.N. **212**, 347, 1921	0.198	1.52
88	OΣ341	01.6 + 21 26	7.2, 8.4	G0	19.75	d	1917.85	0.96	0.30	149.0	+77.5	98.0	Aitken, L.O.B. **11**, 85, 1923	....	....

No.	Name	α, δ (1900.0)	m_1	m_2	Sp	P		T	e	a	ω	Ω	i	Authority		
89	99Her	18 03 .2 + 30 33	5.2	9.7	F8	56.0	r	1887.69	0.787	1.03	71.61	±34.20	97.46	Makemson, L.O.B. **14**, 38, 1929	0.053	2.32
90	A88	33 .2 − 3 17	7.1	7.2	F8	12.12	r	1934.34	0.273	0.176	270.0	+62.4	2.4	Aitken, Pub. L.O. **12**, 129, 1914	0.026	2.11
91	β648	53 .3 + 32 46	5.2	8.7	G0	57.0	r	1911.2	0.20	1.24	285.7	±65.5	48.0	Gushee, P.A. **33**, 308, 1925	0.072	1.57
92	Σ2438	55 .8 + 58 05	7.0	7.6	A2	233.0	r	1882.50	0.916	0.53	178.3	0.	......	See, M.N. **68**, 568, 1908	0.009	3.76
93	ΓSgr	56 .2 − 30 01	3.4	3.6	A2	21.17	r	1921.54	0.185	0.565	1.4	±69.4	75.5	Aitken, P.A. **9**, 57, 1901	0.036	8.65
94	γCrA	18 59 .7 − 37 12	5.0	5.0	F8	119.28	r	1878.58	0.309	2.069	165.20	±30.39	48.37	Dawson, *Notes*, 18^b, *SDS*, 1926	0.065	2.27
95	Se. 2, AB	19 07 .8 + 38 37	8.9	8.9	G5	58.	r	1894.0	0.50	0.40	0.0	±68.	90.	Russell, Pub. L.O. **12**, 138, 1914	0.024	1.38
96	Σ2525	22 .5 + 27 07	8.5	8.7	F8	354.9	r	1887.31	0.933	1.205	266.6	±37.5	1.0	Jackson, *Grw. Cat.* 224, 1921		
97	δCyg.	41 .8 + 44 53	3.0	7.9	A0	321.0	r	1941.6	0.188	2.12	201.0	±47.8	87.9	Jackson, *Grw. Cat.* 225, 1921	0.034	2.35
98	ΓSge	44 .5 + 18 53	5.3	6.3	A0	25.20	r	1914.11	0.85	0.362	65.0	±78.1	4.6	Van Biesbroeck, A.J. **29**, 163, 1916	0.018	8.85
99	OΣ387	45 .0 + 35 04	6.9	7.9	K0	128.0	r	1946.7	0.179	0.566	305.0	±51.5	146.4	Jackson, *Grw. Cat.* 226, 1921	0.016	2.70
100	Ho581	19 51 .6 + 41 36	8.0	8.5	G5	25.69	d	1911.37	0.52	0.25	245.0	±39.2	34.6	Van Biesbroeck, Pub. Y.O. **5**, 246, 1927		
101	OΣ400	20 06 .9 + 43 39	7.4	8.4	F5	94.4	r	1885.1	0.48	0.428	340.6	±62.5	143.9	Meier, A.N. **219**, 232, 1923	0.037	3.04
102	βDel.	32 .9 + 14 15	4.0	5.0	F2	26.79	d	1936.62	0.350	0.480	351.2	±62.25	178.55	Aitken, Pub. L.O. **12**, 150, 1914	0.023	1.20
103	4Aqr	46 .1 − 6 00	6.3	7.6	F5	151.7	d	1897.22	0.375	0.695	59.7	±67.4	167.8	Jackson, *Grw. Cat.* 227, 1921	0.019	4.00
104	εEqu.	20 54 .1 + 3 55	5.8	6.3	F5	101.4	r	1920.21	0.702	0.656	339.3	±87.2	105.2	Van den Bos, Letter	0.066	2.11
105	δEqu.	21 09 .6 + 9 36	5.3	5.4	F5	5.70	d	1929.85	0.39	0.27	164.5	±81.0	21.0	Aitken, Pub. L.O. **12**, 158, 1914		
106	ΓCyg.	10 .8 + 37 37	3.8	8.0	F0	49.16	r	1938.46	0.22	0.96	118.0	±42.7	163.0	Van Biesbroeck, Pub. Y.O. **5**, 253, 1927	0.051	2.76
107	24Aqr.	34 .4 − 0 30	7.3	7.8	F8	51.33	d	1925.679	0.910	0.525	87.35	±56.02	4.95	Finsen, U.O.C. **81**, 112, 1929	0.035	1.28
108	κPeg. AB	21 40 .1 + 25 11	5.0	5.1	F5	11.35	r	1931.85	0.49	0.29	106.1	±77.5	109.2	Lewis, *Mem. R.A.S.* **56**, 652, 1906	0.030	7.01
109	Kr60, AB	22 24 .4 + 57 12	9.3	10.8	Ma	44.52	r	1925.54	0.41	2.362	191.8	±12.4	135.5	Huffer, A.J. **40**, 183, 1930	0.257	0.40
110	37 Peg.	25 .9 + 5 35	5.8	7.2	F5	136.	r	1905.0	0.534	0.72	180.0	±84.6	117.0	Van den Bos, B.A.N. **3**, 127, 1926	0.019	2.94
111	83Aqr.	22 59 .9 − 8 14	6.3	6.3	F0	23.82	d	1917.68	0.404	0.245	261.3	±56.35	21.6	Aitken, L.O.B. **9**, 191, 1918	0.021	2.80
112	β80	23 13 .8 + 4 52	8.9	9.8	K0	85.7	d	1904.69	0.773	0.79	288.9	±43.0	174.1	Jackson, *Grw. Cat.* 228, 1921		
113	β1266	25 .5 + 30 17	8.0	8.1	F5	40.	r	1909.8	0.33	0.22	133.	±48.	46.	Aitken, L.O.B. **11**, 97, 1923		
114	Hu298	27 .1 + 6 32	7.3	7.9	F5	30.0	d	1927.47	0.238	0.242	57.5	±52.0	141.6	Finsen, U.O.C. **88**, 319, 1932		
115	Hn60	56 .3 + 39 03	9.2	9.6	G5	144.0	r	1902.8	0.53	0.64	138.0	±50.0	138.3	Van Biesbroeck, Pub. Y.O. **5**, 264, 1927		
116	86Peg.	23 56 .9 + 26 33	5.8	11.0	G0	26.3	d	1936.1	0.46	0.82	266.12	−53.08	115.63	Bowyer & Furner, M.N. **66**, 423, 1906	0.090	1.09

TABLE II.—ORBITS OF SPECTROSCOPIC BINARY STARS

Star	α(1900)δ	Mag.	Sp.	P	T 2,410,000+	ω	e	K	V_0 km/sec	$a \sin i$ million km	$\dfrac{m_1^3 \sin^3 i}{(m + m_1)^2}$	$m \sin^3 i$	Authority
1 33 Peg	0ʰ00ᵐ2 − 6°16′	4.68	K0	72ᵈ93	12530.330	337°71	0.272	16ᵏᵐ43	− 65.6	15.856	0.030⊙		Harper, D.A.O. 3, 341, 1926
2 α And	03.2 + 28 32	2.15	A0p	96.67	7882.40	76.21	0.525	30.75	−11.55	34.790	0.180		Baker, A.O. 1, 17, 1908
3 +57° 28	06.3 + 57 39	7.08	B5	55.904	15634.780	313.3	0.033	85.5	−24.5	65.700		113.2	Pearce, M.N. 92, 877, 1932
4 *Boss 46	12.4 + 50 53	6.12	B0	3.52341	14003.703	133.3	0.037	215.5		165.600		44.9	Pearce, D.A.O. 3, 276, 1926
5 *TV Cas	13.9 + 58 35	7.4-9.0	B9	1.812635	−0.0045	210.16 / 30.16	0	218.45 / 234.59 / 87.92 / 150	−29.34 / + 0.54	10.578 / 11.360 / 2.141 / 3.739		17.57 / 16.37 / [1.83] / [1.01]	Plaskett, D.A.O. 2, 141, 1922
6 α Phe	21.3 − 42 51	2.44	K0	3848.83	6201.85	19.822	0.335	5.76	+75.21	290.000	0.0639		Lunt, C.A. 10, 24G, 1924
7 Boss 82	22.9 + 43 51	5.16	A2	3.95583	8841.590	233.2	0.152	41.7	+ 2.04	2.240	0.0288		Miss Udick, A.O. 2, 190, 1912
8 13 Cet	30.1 − 4 09	5.24	G0	2.08186	15174.857	215.5	0.022	37.1	var.	1.070	0.0114‡		Pago, Ap. Jour. 68, 116, 1928
9 π And	31.5 + 33 10	4.44	B3	143.67	8564.144	350.53	0.573	47.66	+ 8.83	77.200	0.8894	1.35	Jordan, A.O. 2, 45, 1910
10 π Cas	37.9 + 46 29	5.02	A5	1.99408	9970.035	45.1 / 225.1	0.010	117.32 / 118.97	+12.42	3.168 / 3.213		1.34	Harper, D.O. 4, 135, 1917
11 ρ Tuc	38.2 − 66 01	5.46	F5	4.820223	9299.110	269.31	0.024	26.1	+14.1	1.730	0.0089		Neubauer, P.A.S.P. 41, 371, 1929
12 *21 Cas	39.0 + 74 26	5.59	A2	4.46718	13964.657	0	0	71.46	+ 9.97	4.414	0.172		Plaskett, D.A.O. 3, 248, 1926
13 Boss 159	41.1 + 74 18	5.39	B8	33.75	10577.41	269.71	0.405	16.32	− 4.06	7.020	0.0121		Young, D.O. 2, 181, 1915
14 †ζ And	42.0 + 23 43	4.30	K0	17.7673	10037.675	80.60	0.017	25.96	−23.75	6.342	0.0323	1.50	Jones, C.A. 10, 35, 1928
15 ν And	44.3 + 40 32	4.42	B3	4.28294	8155.661		0.0	75.63	−23.91	4.454		1.10	Jordan, A.O. 1, 191, 1910
16 *U Cep	0 53.4 + 81 20	6.9-9.1	A0	2.4929507	13966.644	25.0	0.474	109.9	− 6.0	3.320	0.235		Carpenter, Ap. Jour. 72, 205, 1930
17 α UMi§	1 22.6 + 88 46	2.3-3.4	F8	29.6 yrs.	15648.	332.0	0.63	4.05	−17.4	466.000	0.035		Moore, P.A.S.P. 41, 254, 1929
18 γ Phe	24.0 − 43 50	3.40	K5	193.79	7945.0	267	0.005	15.8	+25.8	42.100	0.079		Wilson, L.O.B. 9, 116, 1918
19 Boss 373	35.7 + 25 14	6.26	F5	4.43474	11940.986	295.58 / 115.58	0.108	81.5 / 88.6	+ 4.6	4.942 / 5.372		1.16	Sanford, Ap. J. 53, 201, 1921
20 φ Per	37.4 + 50 11	4.19	B0p	126.5 / 63.25	8290.42 / 8324.37	347.29 / 257.14	0.428 / 0.107	26.90 / 6.96	+ 3.20	44.803	0.1888	1.06	Cannon, R.A.S.C. 4, 195, 1910
21 ζ Cet	46.5 − 10 50	3.92	K0	16.52	4377.6	85 0	0.586	3.30	+ 9.21	60.750	0.0033		Jones, C.A. 10, 40, 1928
22 α Tri	47.4 + 29 06	3.58	F5	1.73652	10793.821	135.56	0.121	12.10	−12.65	0.287	0.0003		Harper, D.O. 3, 113, 1915

No.	Name													
23	ω Cas	48 .2 + 68 12	5.03	B8	69.92	10426.02	49.97	0.30	29.64	−24.82	27.190	0.164	....	Young, D.O. **2**, 89, 1915
24	β Ari	1 49 .1 + 20 19	2.72	A5	107.0	7632	19.7	0.88	32.6	− 0.6	22.880	0.042	0.14	Ludendorff, Ap. Jour. **25**, 325, 1907
25	κ Ari	2 01 .0 + 22 11	5.08	A0	15.2938	11844.134	359.19	0.608	34.45 / 35.48	+11.48	5.752 / 5.924	....	0.13	Miss Jones, P.A.S.P. **43**, 82, 1931
26	β Tri	03 .6 + 34 31	3.08	A5	31.4009	15191.160	293.9	0.456	26.1	+10.4	9.930	0.0397	....	Struve, Pago, Ap. J. **67**, 336, 1928
27	6 Tri btr	06 .6 + 29 50	(5.5)	G0	14.732	12243.157	5.39 / 185.39	0.043	56.53 / 56.98	−19.09	11.441 / 11.532	....	1.12	Harper, D.A.O. **2**, 129, 1921
28	6 Tri ftr	06 .6 + 29 50	(6.7)	(F4)	2.2365	12246.698	3.68 / 183.68	0.010	95.43 / 101.04	−19.8	2.934 / 3.107	....	1.12	Harper, D.A.O. **2**, 129, 1921
29	δ Tri	10 .8 + 33 46	5.07	G0	9.92912	13309.427	21.50	0.059	8.82	− 5.82	1.200	0.0007	0.91	Pearce, L.O.B. **11**, 131, 1923
30	Boss 523	12 .8 + 1 17	5.82	F8	93.50	13389.995	100.95	0.445	19.43	+25.75	22.371	0.051	0.86	Harper, D.A.O. **6**, 1, 1930
31	Boss 593	31 .2 + 24 13	6.57	F5	9.851	11586.899	129.6	0.146	22.48	+14.42	3.013	0.0113	....	Adams, Joy, Ap. Jour. **49**, 186, 1919
32	Boss 613	36 .2 + 67 24	5.84	A2	2.53636	11895.898	0.93	0.014	55.03	+ 4.22	1.918	0.044	....	Harper, D.A.O. **4**, 313, 1930
33	* RZ Cas	39 .9 + 69 13	6.4-7.7	A0	1.19525	9449.732	154.7	0.052	69.30	−38.32	1.137	0.0412	....	Jordan, A.O. **3**, 137, 1914
34	π Ari	43 .7 + 17 03	5.30	B5	3.854	10370.259	78.27	0.042	24.77	+ 7.81	1.312	0.0061	....	Young, D.O. **4**, 69, 1917
35	+57° 651	2 44 .2 + 57 53	6.27	A0	8.2504	14854.892	212.74	0.227	12.88	− 5.80	1.423	0.0017	....	Harper, D.A.O. **4**, 39, 1927
36,7	* β Per	3 01 .7 + 40 34	2.1-3.2	B8	2.86730 / 1.885 yr.	1.506 / 0.943 yr.	277.5 / 0	0.038 / 0.13	44.1 / 10.0	var. / + 5.7	1.736 / 93.000	0.254	18.88	McLaughlin, Ap. Jour. **60**, 22, 1924
38	*+59° 609	06 .2 + 59 11	7.09	B5	3.36897	14426.705	300.78 / 120.78	0.102	141.65 / 291.79	− 4.19	6.528 / 13.447	....	9.17	Pearce, D.A.O. **4**, 67, 1927
39	+34° 610	09 .8 + 34 19	6.42	A2	5.54348	13080.361	90.66	0.040	62.18	+24.24	4.732	0.138	....	Harper, D.A.O. **6**, 79, 1932
40	Boss 804	25 .4 + 12 36	4.28	K0	960	4889.565	326.32	0.397	8.25	+14.18	99.955	0.0433	....	Harper, D.A.O. **3**, 145, 1924
41	Boss 809	26 .9 + 39 34	5.80	A0	11.422	11925.309	32.47	0.082	95.41	− 3.03	14.935	1.020	2.87	Harper, D.A.O. **4**, 43, 1927
42	Boss 816	29 .4 − 21 58	4.32	B8	6.2236	14447.048	313.	0.20	107 / 103	+15.0	8.970 / 8.640	....	2.76	Struve, Ap. Jour. **63**, 388, 1925
43	o Per	38 .0 + 31 58	3.94	B1	4.41916	8217.924	....	0.00	111.92 / 160.0	+18.46	6.801 / 9.717	....	5.42 / 3.79	Jordan, A.O. **2**, 63, 1910
44	β Ret	42 .9 − 65 07	3.80	K0	1911.5	10086.1	13.8	0.210	5.19	+51.11	133.4	0.0259	1.01	Spencer Jones, M.N. **88**, 644, 1928
45	A Per	49 .2 + 50 24	5.47	F5p	30.4338	13797.270	214.36 / 34.36	0.612	49.38 / 57.10	+25.66	16.343 / 18.898	....	0.88	Harper, D.A.O. **4**, 161, 1928

* Eclipsing variable.
† Ellipsoidal variable.
‡ Elements variable. Those here quoted are for 1927-28 observations.
§ Primary is also 4-day *Cepheid* variable.

TABLE II.—ORBITS OF SPECTROSCOPIC BINARY STARS.—(*Continued*)

	Star	α(1900) δ	Mag.	Sp.	P	T 2,410,000+	ω	e	K (km/sec)	V₀ (km/sec)	a sin i (million km)	$\dfrac{m^3\sin^3 i}{(m+m_1)^2}$	$m\sin^3 i$	Authority
46,7	λ Tau	3h55m1 +12°12′	3.3–4.2	B3	3d.052917	7945.119	77°.5	0.06	56km.18	var.	3.050	0.073⊙		Schlesinger, A.O. **3**, 167, 1914
48	• +33°785	4 00.6 +33 11	6.61	B3	34.60	7831.30		0.0	10.4	− 0.9	4.950	0.004		Plaskett, D.A.O. **3**, 184, 1925
					2.02858	14039.335	30.103	0.0512	164.97 / 187.32	+15.84	4.549 / 5.165		4.86 / 4.29	
49	μ Per	07.6 +48 09	4.28	G0	284	10061.97	301.99	0.0615	20.50	+ 7.83	80.000	0.2539		Cannon, D.O. **2**, 353, 1915
50	† Boss 986	10.7 +50 03	4.57	A2	1.52738	8956.662	271.53	0.017	38.85	var.	0.816	0.0093		Harper, D.A.O. **4**, 309, 1930
51	+16° 577	11.9 +16 41	8.3	G5	5.6100	13102.193	88.6	0.040	58.6 / 63.76	+38.2	4.517 / 4.393		0.56 / 0.55	Sanford, Ap. Jour. **59**, 356, 1924
52	Boss 1001	14.1 −34 03	3.59	B9	5.0105	7562.266	124.33	0.014	64.85	+17.83	4.468	0.1166		Paddock, L.O.B. **8**, 168, 1915
53	O282 btr	17.1 +14 49	7.1	G0	4.00000	12274.812	304.33	0.060	36.1	+37.4	1.980	0.0193		Sanford, Ap. Jour. **53**, 201, 1921
54	Boss 1018	17.7 +16 32	5.68	A2	8.425	9819.0	12.74	0.16	36.5	+36.4	4.170	0.041		Jantzen, A.N. **196**, 118, 1913
55	+72° 227	21.9 +72 20	5.97	A5	4.195	5950.989	190.7	0.043	31.81	+ 8.87	1.831	0.0000		Harper, D.A.O. **4**, 316, 1930
56	θ² Tau	22.9 +15 39	3.62	F0	140.70	8054.723	54.16	0.717	27.12	+42.59	37.471	0.0987		Plaskett, D.O. **2**, 63, 1915
57	e Per	29.7 +41 04	4.46	K0, A3	6270	12892	201	0.45	12.9	+ 4.2	993.500	0.9965		Sanford, P.A.S.P. **43**, 268, 1931
58	Boss 1076	30.2 + 9 57	4.38	A3	3.57122	9734.992		0.0	72.68	+29.23	3.570	0.142		Daniel, A.O. **3**, 93, 1914
59	Boss 1082	32.0 +52 53	5.31	K0	121	11137.55	285	0.019	28.19	−40.47	46.900	0.28		Cannon, D.O. **4**, 175, 1918
60	+7° 676	32.5 + 7 07	6.89	B5	2.2075	14807.936	2.38	0.076	124.9 / 235.8	+25.3	3.780 / 7.137		7.0 / 3.7	Pearce, D.A.O. **6**, 82, 1932
61	Boss 1107	36.2 +22 46	4.33	B5	1.5047	7892.500	182.38	0.087	44.34	+13.55	0.914	0.0135		Parker, Rep. Chief Astr. **1**, 166, 1910
62	+32° 840	42.8 +32 25	5.94	A3	7.0507	16327.626	242.88	0.033	57.81	+20.32	5.602	0.1412		Harper, P.A.S.P. **44**, 260, 1932
63	Boss 1131	42.8 +18 33	6.79	G5	45.454	13030.461	289.66	0.391	13.57	+54.66	7.810	0.0092		Sanford, Ap. Jour. **61**, 321, 1924
64	Boss 1147	45.9 + 5 26	3.78	B3	9.5191	8279.64	26.48	0.027	25.93	+23.27	3.393	0.0172		Baker, A.O. **1**, 107, 1909
65	† Boss 1159	49.0 + 2 17	3.87	B3	3.70045	7921.64	152.27	0.00	57.88	+24.20	2.945	0.0745		Lee, Ap. Jour. **38**, 175, 1913
66	Boss 1161	49.3 +53 36	4.44	A2	3.8846	8281.176	217.14	0.013	35.15	− 8.93	1.877	0.018		Harper, R.A.S.C. **5**, 112, 1911
67	• ζ Aur	4 55.5 +40 56	3.94	K0, B1	973	5122.471	330.13	0.411	23.78	+10.73	294.300	1.0298		Harper, D.A.O. **3**, 151, 1924
68	Boss 1213	5 01.8 − 4 47	5.19	B9	5.52242	13087.575	335.9	0.074	97.0 / 111.0	+30.9	7.300 / 8.400		2.5 / 2.2	Frost, Struve, Ap. Jour. **60**, 313, 1924
69	Boss 1216	02.0 +24 08	5.50	B3	58.31	14221.266	273.88	0.189	36.73	+16.22	28.900	0.280		Hill, P.A.S.P. **42**, 246, 1930

70	*TT Aur	02.8 +39 28	8.0-9.4	(B5)	1.332732	9065.904	......	0.0	196.8 / 246.1	+10.2 /	3.600 / 4.500	...... /	6.7 / 5.3	Joy, Sitterly *Ap. Jour.* **73**, 77, 1930
71	Boss 1244	08.8 +32 35	5.14	A2	3.789	10802.715	19.70	0.033	21.56	-10.74	1.123	0.0039	......	Harper, *D.O.* **3**, 221, 1916
72	α Aur	09.3 +45 54	0.21	G0	104.022	4599.5	117.3	0.016	25.76 / 32.45	+30.17	36.848 / 46.430	......	1.19 / 0.94	Reese, *L.O.B.* **1**, 32, 1901
73	β Ori	09.7 - 8 19	0.34	B8p	21.90	7968.80	254.76	0.296	3.771	+22.62	1.109	0.0001	1.40	Plaskett, *Ap. Jour.* **30**, 26, 1909
74	Σ674 A	11.6 +20 01	6.84	F5	3.4347	14837.932	......	0	95.8 / 101.3	-27.4	4.525 / 4.784	......	1.33	Sanford, *Ap. Jour.* **68**, 42, 1928
75	Boss 1275	14.9 +29 29	5.72	A0	2.15165	11138.241	......	0.000	113.27 / 129.80	-19.70	3.351 / 3.840	......	1.71 / 1.50	Harper, *D.A.O.* **3**, 265, 1926
76	• η Ori	19.4 - 2 29	3.44	B1	7.98922	5720.821	42.3	0.016	144.75	var.	15.901	......	11.2	Adams, Sanford, { *Ap. Jour.* **17**, 68, 1903 / *Ap. Jour.* **64**, 172, 1926 }
77	η Ori A' A''-D	19.4 - 2 29	......	......	9.2 yrs.	5020.0	222.3	0.1	152.4	+19.5	805.000	1.84	10.6	Pago, *Ap. Jour.* **68**, 309, 1928
78	ψ Ori	21.6 + 3 00	4.66	B2	2.52588	7916.36	184.71 / 4.71	0.065	144.12 / 190.0	+12.02	4.995 / 6.570	0.56 / 0.6126	5.53 / 4.19	Plaskett, *Ap. Jour.* **28**, 266, 1908
79	χ Aur	26.2 +32 07	4.88	B1	655.16	10629.78	135.52	0.171	20.53	- 0.15	182.300	0.358	......	Young, *D.O.* **4**, 1, 1916
80	* δ Ori	26.9 - 0 22	2.48	B0	5.732585	12391.584	337.94	0.107	101.53	+21.25	7.958	......	......	Hnatek, *A.N.* **213**, 17, 1920
81,2	* VV Ori	28.5 - 1 14	5.37	B2	1.48540 / ‡‡120	9836.021 / 9819	......	0.00	132.37	+20.77	2.704 / 20.460	0.358	......	Daniel, *A.O.* **3**, 179, 1915
83	Boss 1353	29.3 + 9 25	4.53	B0	8.4 yrs.	8050.5	40	0.30	13.0 / 13.3	+33.2	547.000	0.6958	......	Struve, *Ap. Jour.* **63**, 60, 1925
84	θ² Ori btr	30.5 - 5 29	5.17	B1	21.029	13741.362	105	0.22	93.7	+36.8	27.000	1.795	......	Struve, *Ap. Jour.* **60**, 162, 1924
85	ι Ori	30.5 - 5 59	2.87	Oe5	29.136	7587.991	154.7 / 112.37	0.27 / 0.742	113.68	+21.53	30.560	1.3394	......	Plaskett, Harper, *Ap. Jour.* **30**, 373, 1909
86	ζ Tau	31.7 +21 05	3.00	B3p	138	5769.9	9.8	0.180	14.95	+16.4	27.900	0.0455	......	Adams, *Ap. Jour.* **22**, 118, 1905
87	Boss 1381	32.4 +64 18	5.30	G5	180.8757	13108.42	333.0	0.51	22.4	+ 9.85	47.900	0.1344	......	Lunt, *C.A.* **10**, 19G, 1924
88	Boss 1388	33.5 +25 50	5.00	B3	27.864	10471.607	335	0.55	25.5	+14.8	8.160	0.0280	......	Cannon, *D.O.* **3**, 409, 1916
89	Boss 1399	35.8 - 1 11	5.00	B3	27.160	7961.465	87.02	0.765	93.04	+26.12	22.380	0.6067	......	Plaskett, Harper, *Ap. Jour.* **30**, 374, 1909
90	* Boss 1452	46.0 +59 52	5.26	A0	2.93317	11938.356	359.25	0.030	76.02	-3.86	3.065	0.1337	......	Harper, *D.A.O.* **3**, 159, 1924

* Eclipsing variable.
† Light variable in the same period. Ellipsoidal type of variation without eclipse.
‡‡ Relative orbit.

TABLE II.—ORBITS OF SPECTROSCOPIC BINARY STARS.—(Continued)

	Star	α(1900) δ	Mag.	Sp.	P	T 2,410,000+	ω	e	K	V₀ km/sec	a sin i million km	$\dfrac{m_1^3 \sin^3 i}{(m+m_1)^2}$	m sin³ i	Authority
91	Boss 1457	5^{h}47^{m}0 + 27°35'	4.54	A0	5^{d}969	9362.52	191°.44	0.022	48^{km}9	−17.1	4.011		0.63	Cannon, D.O. 2, 119, 1915
92	Boss 1464	49.1 + 19 44	5.89	B2	7.8271	14141.590	11.44	0.250	71	+7.2	5.826		0.44	Pearce, D.A.O. 6, 59, 1932
93	*β Aur	52.2 + 44 56	2.07	A0p	3.960027††	7100.732	67.0 / 247.0	0.00	74.3 / 194.0	−18.1	7.750 / 20.240		10.3 / 3.9	Baker, A.O. 1, 163, 1910
94	Boss 1492	54.3 − 9 34	5.10	A5	9.3353	9673.815	35.41	0.208	108.96 / 111.04	+22.2	5.934 / 6.047		2.21 / 2.17	Elvey, Ap. Jour. 60, 320, 1924
95,6	μ Ori	56.9 + 9 39	4.19	A2	4.44746	13863.174		0	57.1 / 30.8	var.	7.200 / 2.000	0.1692⊙ / 0.0135		Frost, Struve, Ap. Jour. 60, 192, 1924
					18 yrs.	9292.5	98	0.6	4.0	+43	300.000			Pub. Y.O. 7, 28, 1929
97	Boss 1508	58.0 + 23 16	4.30	G5	9.590	11898.741	203.28	0.2065	11.74	+19.71	1.510	0.0015		Young, D.A.O. 1, 119, 1919
98	Boss 1515	5 59.6 + 38 29	5.31	A3	28.28	10468.197	178.41	0.556	51.38 / 62.51	+16.91	16.550 / 20.140	1.354		Young, D.O. 4, 95, 1917
99	γ Ori	6 01.9 + 14 47	4.40	B2	131.26	7975.16	1.60	0.599	34.09	+22.10	49.270	1.113		Harper, R.A.S.C. 5, 24, 1911
100	Boss 1593	13.6 + 53 30	5.41	F5	6.5013	13634.166	1.58 / 330.60	0.019	31.74	−1.52	2.837	0.2773 / 0.0216		Harper, D.A.O. 3, 189, 1925
101	*R R Lyn	18.0 + 56 20	5.8–6.2	A3	9.944	9341.776	152.9	0.081	67.19	−13.74	9.127	0.3101		Harper, D.O. 2, 167, 1915
102	−3° 1413	18.0 − 3 14	6.58	B5	1.19033	14942.706	9.2 / 189.2	0.036	172.8 / 263.5	+8.3	2.828 / 4.310		6.2 / 4.1	Pearce, R.A.S.C. 26, 345, 1932
103	δ Col	18.4 − 33 23	3.98	G5	868.78	9915.02	117.08	0.695	10.61	−2.6	91.120	0.0405		Jones, C.A. 10, 45, 1928
104	ν Gem	23.0 + 20 17	4.06	B5	9.6 yr.	8580.75	285.	0.20	30.0	+38.45	1417.000	9.24		Harper, D.O. 4, 279, 1919
105	*W W Aur	26.0 + 32 31	6.0–6.5	A0	2.5248	11623.364		0.00	115.6 / 135.1	−5.8	4.010 / 4.690		2.2 / 1.9	Joy, P.A.S.P. 30, 254, 1918
106	+6° 1399	32.0 + 6 13	6.06	B0p	14.414	13031.870	181.95 / 1.95	0.035	206.38 / 246.7	+23.94	40.880 / 48.868		75.6 / 63.3	Plaskett, D.A.O. 2, 147, 1922
107	τ Pup	47.5 − 50 30	2.83	K0	1066.0	10992.8	64.0	0.088	4.14	+36.36	60.500	0.0078		Jones, M.N. 88, 648, 1928
108	A Car	e 47.7 − 53 30	4.38	G5	195.32	11344.0		0.0	24.8	+25.4	66.880	0.313		Wilson, Huffer, L.O.B. 10, 17, 1918
109	+25° 1594	7 03.5 + 25 54	7.01	G0	32.8092	13071.941	82.1	0.080	27.5	+19.7	12.383	0.0705		Sanford, Ap. Jour. 56, 446, 1922
110	*29 C Ma	14.5 − 24 23	4.90	Oe	4.39351	7240.248	37.6 / 217.6	0.156	217.1 / 287.6	−10.6	12.956 / 17.163		32.2 / 24.3	Pearce, R.A.S.C. 26, 345, 1932

No.	Star	α, δ	m	Sp	P	T	ω	e	K	V₀	a sin i	f(m)	M sin³i	Authority
111	τ C Ma	14 .5 − 24 47	4.40	Oe5	154.80	15201.72	102.5	0.36	52.1	+40.4	103.700	1.86	……	Struve, Pogo, Ap. Jour. 68, 335, 1928
112	Boss 1906	14 .7 + 55 28	5.61	B8	2.25960	9031.632	126.1 / 306.1	0.076	106.4 / 199.1	+ 4.2	3.296 / 6.168	……	4.3 / 2.3	Pearce, R.A.S.C. 26, 345, 1932
113	* R C Ma	14 .9 − 16 12	5.8-6.4	F0	1.1359514	7966.576	195.86	0.138	28.64	−39.70	0.443	0.0027	……	Jordan, A.O. 3, 49, 1913
114	Boss 1945	21 .8 + 21 39	5.27	F5	1.93265	13430.048	104.84 / 284.84	0.002	94.56 / 116.76	+24.38	2.513 / 3.103	……	1.05 / 0.85	Harper, R.A.S.C. 20, 15, 1926
115	σ Pup	26 .1 − 43 06	3.27	K5	257.8	10418.6	349.3	0.17	18.55	+87.3	64.800	0.164	……	Wilson, L.O.B. 9, 117, 1918
116	α¹ Gem	28 .2 + 32 06	2.85	A0	2.928285	6828.057	102.52	0.01	31.76	− 0.98	1.279	0.0097	……	Curtis, L.O.B. 4, 55, 1906
117	α² Gem	28 .2 + 32 06	1.99	A0	9.218826	6746.385	265.35	0.503	13.56	+ 6.20	1.485	0.0015	……	Curtis, L.O.B. 4, 55, 1906
118	* α Gem C	28 .2 + 32 06	9.0	(M1e)	0.814266	13746.524	……	0.0	114.0 / 126.7	+ 4.3	1.276 / 1.419	……	0.63 / 0.57	Joy, Sanford, Ap. Jour. 64, 250, 1926
119	+34° 1657	36 .2 + 34 14	6.00	F0	31.50	13854.45	44.0 / 224.0	0.208	45.18 / 52.43	−12.11	19.142 / 22.214	……	1.53 / 1.32	Harper, D.A.O. 3, 269, 1926
120	σ Gem	37 .0 + 29 07	4.26	K0	19.605	5824.019	330.25	0.022	34.21	+45.80	9.220	0.0812	……	Harper, D.O. 1, 276, 1911
121	Boss 2035	39 .8 − 28 43	4.10	A2p	137.626	8188.339	270.00	0.198	7.4	+23.7	13.730	0.0055	……	Neubauer, P.A.S.P. 44, 254, 1932
122	* V Pup	7 55 .4 − 48 58	4.50	B1p	‡‡1.454475	2778.327	72	0.08	……	……	……	……	……	Miss Maury, P.A. 29, 22, 1922
123	ε Vol	8 07 .6 − 68 19	4.46	B5	14.16833	9453.562	……	0.00	66.67	+ 9.68	12.999	0.437	……	Sanford, L.O.B. 8, 127, 1914
124	Boss 2227	19 .6 − 3 26	5.67	F5	1.562975	12650.082	123.92	0.051	30.28	+71.3	0.650	0.0045	……	Sanford, Ap. Jour. 55, 30, 1922
125	+75° 342	25 .2 + 75 04	6.28	A5	4.285	14971.150	101.71	0.109	63.53	− 7.42	3.721	0.1123	……	Harper, D.A.O. 4, 319, 1930
126	Boss 2285	30 .5 + 6 58	6.04	F5	14.296	11599.474	220.80	0.276	22.74	+24.23	4.300	0.015	……	Joy, Abetti, Ap. Jour. 50, 391, 1919
127	+20° 2153	34 .2 + 19 54	7.15	A0	12.9117	15250.803	168.2 / 348.2	0.2	64.0 / 65.6	+32.1	11.134 / 11.395	……	1.39 / 1.35	Sanford, Ap. Jour. 74, 201, 1931
128	ε Hya	41 .5 + 6 47	3.48	F8	5588.	5375	90.0	0.65	8.45	+36.79	493.000	……	[3.33]	Aitken, P.A.S.P. 24, 218, 1932
129	ε Hya C	41 .5 + 6 47	(7.5)	(F5)	9.9047	13800.007	117.6	0.62	35.0	+31.2	3.700	0.0206	……	Sanford, Ap. Jour. 64, 179, 1926
130	+8° 2134	46 .8 + 8 26	6.59	G0	10.2504	14891.018	314	0.1	24.5	+ 3.5	3.436	0.0154	……	Sanford, Ap. Jour. 74, 205, 1931
131	H Vel	53 .3 − 52 21	4.77	B5	0.91470	7967.119	44.33	0.131	46.31	+22.20	0.534	0.0081	……	Neubauer, L.O.B. 15, 104, 1931
132	m Vel	8 56 .4 − 40 52	4.42	F8	74.1469	12728.629	90.0	0.05	17.8	− 7.4	18.130	0.0433	……	Lunt, C.A. 10, 37G, 1924
133	κ Cnc	9 02 .4 + 11 04	5.14	B8	6.393	6486.897	162.3	0.149	67.8	+26.3	5.890	0.200	……	Ichinohe, Ap. Jour. 25, 318, 1907
134	Boss 2447	02 .9 + 27 03	5.96	G5	19.4589	12426.634	252.5	0.206	20.21	+12.3	5.296	0.0157	……	Sanford, Ap. Jour. 55, 35, 1922
135	Boss 2463	06 .4 + 61 50	5.23	F8	16.2382	13049.617	169.25	0.09	34.78	−14.99	7.730	0.07	……	Young, D.A.O. 2, 205, 1923

* Eclipsing variable.
†† Period variable (+0.000010 t).
‡‡ Relative orbit.

TABLE II.—ORBITS OF SPECTROSCOPIC BINARY STARS.—*(Continued)*

	Star	α(1900) δ	Mag.	Sp.	P	T 2,410,000+	ω	e	K	V_0 km/sec	a sin i million km	$\frac{m_1^3 \sin^3 i}{(m+m_1)^2}$	$m \sin^3 i$	Authority
136	Boss 2473	$9^h08^m.5$ − 58°33′	3.56	B3	6^d744	6533.81	115.84	0.18	$21^{km}5$	+23.3	1.960	0.0006⊙		Curtis, *L.O.B.* **4**, 153, 1907
137	Boss 2484	10.8 +47 14	5.70	A0	15.986	9408.027	355.2	0.504	63.34	−13.11	12.026		1.48	Harper, *D.O.* **3**, 391, 1916
138	Boss 2490	11.7 − 5 56	5.40	K0	922	8549.21	175.2	0.293	73.64	− 7.65	13.981		1.27	Jones, *C.A.* **10**, 49, 1928
139	κ Vel	19.0 −54 35	2.63	B3	116.65	6459.00	92.27	0.19	9.98, 46.5	+21.9	121.000, 73.200	0.0832, 1.15		Curtis, *L.O.B.* **4**, 156, 1907
140	• S Ant	27.9 −28 11	6.3–6.8	F0	0.64833872	741.525	96.23	0	81, 148	− 5.0	0.722, 1.320		0.52, 0.29	Joy, *Ap. Jour.* **64**, 287, 1926
141	o Leo	35.8 +10 21	3.76	F5, A3	14.4980	4656.477		<0.02	54.0, 63.1	+27.07	10.775, 12.571		1.302, 1.116	Plummer, *L.O.B.* **5**, 21, 1908
142	* W U Ma	36.7 +56 25	7.9–8.6	G0	0.3336392			0.00	134, 188	− 5	0.610, 0.860		0.67, 0.48	Adams and Joy, *Ap. Jour.* **49**, 189, 1919
143	m Vel	47.9 −46 05	4.56	G5	329.30	6967.60	311.48	0.019	14.07	+11.02	63.700	0.0953		Jones, *C.A.* **10**, 53, 1928
144	Boss 2665	9 51.6 +41 32	5.19	F5	9.283	13498.595	351.09	0.048	15.24	−10.78	1.943	0.0034		Harper, *D.A.O.* **3**, 194, 1925
145	λ Hya	10 05.7 −11 52	3.83	K0	1585.8	8795.1	238.9	0.138	3.74	+19.39	80.800	0.0084		Jones, *M.N.* **88**, 652, 1928
146	Boss 2754	16.9 +66 04	4.92	A0	11.5832	8468.212	171.9	0.381	34.07	− 0.10	5.020	0.0376		Schlesinger, *A.O.* **2**, 139, 1912
147	Boss 2830	33.1 −47 42	4.06	F2, A3	10.210955	10259.381	184.62, 4.62	0.541	42.34, 52	+19.25	4.981, 6.107		0.28, 0.24	Sanford, *L.O.B.* **9**, 179, 1918
148	* TX U Ma	39.5 +46 05	6.87	B8	3.063295	13856.746	252.8	0.205	50.7	−10.1	20.900	0.0389	3.50	Pearce, *R.A.S.C.* **26**, 382, 1932
149	ω U Ma	10 48.2 +43 43	4.84	A0	15.8401	7991.101	11.95, 191.95	0.264	20.64, 120	−18.45	4.336, 25.210		0.60	Parker, *R.A.S.C.* **5**, 377, 1911
150	+82°325	11 02.2 +82 17	7.06	G0	18.8922	13154.071	332.97	0.282	40.01	−46.75	9.975	0.1111		Sanford, *Ap. Jour.* **59**, 359, 1924
151	ξ U Ma ftr	12.9 +32 06	4.87	G0	3.9805	15000.000	320.0	0.00	5.04	−15.90	0.276	0.0000		Berman, *L.O.B.* **15**, 109, 1930
152	ξ U Ma btr	12.9 +32 06	4.41	G0	669.17	8582.0		0.531	7.97	−15.5	62.200	0.0214		Van den Bos, *M.A.R.S.* & *L. Denmark* 8, 1928
153	Boss 2987	13.7 +38 44	4.78	A2	2.5	11412.762	173.4, 353.4	0.11	38.5, 54.5	− 3	1.315, 1.862		0.123, 0.085	Henroteau, *P.A.* **27**, 29, 1919
154	Σ 1561 ftr	33.5 +45 40	8.6	(K4)	23.5415	14303.000	0.00	0.35	25.8	−13.8	7.806	0.034		Sanford, *Ap. Jour.* **68**, 46, 1928
155	+43°2135	33.7 +42 52	8.4	K2	12.9167	13549.34	154.0	0.08	28.8	+15.3	5.090	0.0316		Sanford, *Ap. Jour.* **61**, 325, 1924

No.	Name	α, δ	Mag	Sp	P	T	ω	e	K	γ	a sin i	f(m)		Reference
156	Boss 3098	42 .8 + 20 46	4.54	F8	71.70	8088.405	270.81	0.008	26.54	+ 0.17	26.170	0.139		Cannon, R.A.S.C. 4, 458, 1910
157	+17° 2402	44 .1 + 16 48	5.95	A2	2.7818	13521.231	61.45	0.018	30.97	−24.21	1.1845	0.009	8.2	Petrie, D.A.O. 3, 331, 1926
158	95 Leo	50 .5 + 16 12	5.49	A2	6.6254	14940.615	4.1	0.02	57.6	−20.4	5.250	0.131	4.4	Struve, Morgan, Ap. Jour. 66, 135, 1927
159	Boss 3138	55 .7 − 19 06	5.28	B3	2.96310	16378.385	68.8 / 248.8	0.057	120.5 / 225	+ 3	4.900 / 9.150		0.74	Van Arnam, Ap. Jour. 75, 348, 1932
160	θ¹ Cru	58 .0 − 62 45	4.48	A5	24.4828	9453.347	358.87 / 178.87	0.609	46.07 / 56.1	− 2.75	12.301 / 14.978		0.61	Mrs. Moore, P.A.S.P. 43, 163, 1931
161	θ³ Cru	11 59 .2 − 62 36	4.98	B3	3.4280	8747.367		0.00	51.34	+16.12	2.420	0.048		Mrs. Grattan, P.A.S.P. 38, 393, 1926
162	Boss 3180	12 06 .7 + 26 25	5.81	K0	461	12360.79	235.29	0.169	14.25	+21.30	89.032	0.1326		Harper, D.A.O. 4, 303, 1930
163	Boss 3182	07 .5 + 78 10	5.12	A5	1.27100	10685.265		0.00	63.2	+ 0.3	1.104	0.0333		Lee, Ap. Jour. 43, 320, 1916
164	η Vir	14 .8 − 0 07	4.00	A0	71.9	7643.50	185.0	0.40	27.6	+ 2.2	25.750	0.126	0.80	Harper, Ap. Jour. 27, 160, 1908
165	+74° 493	17 .9 + 73 48	8.2	G5	5.41454	12853.120		0.00	64.9 / 74.0	−97.4	4.833 / 5.510		0.70	Sanford, Ap. Jour. 56, 449, 1922
166	α¹ Cru	21 .0 − 62 33	1.58	B1	0.977029	13957.548	100.35	0.322	27.7	−12.2	0.370	0.0014		Neubauer, L.O.B. 15, 190, 1932
167	α² Cru	21 .0 − 62 32	2.09	B1	0.97623	13957.170	132.91	0.06	32.0	+ 0.3	0.429	0.0026		Neubauer, L.O.B. 15, 190, 1932
168	+27° 2138	23 .7 + 26 47	6.48	A3	11.782	14585.282	198.50	0.060	41.27	+ 1.79	6.674	0.0855		Harper, D.A.O. 3, 315, 1926
169	κ Dra	29 .2 + 70 20	3.88	B5p	0.89038	14650.429	284.47	0.186	18.87	−11.43	0.227	0.0006		Hill, D.A.O. 3, 349, 1926
170	Boss 3323	40 .6 + 8 13	5.24	A5	38.3	10573.455	223.35 / 43.35	0.072	40.99 / 80	− 8.89	21.530 / 42.020		4.62 / 2.37	Cannon, D.O. 2, 369, 1915
171	Boss 3354	48 .3 + 83 58	5.81	A0	3.28655	14226.669	211.05 / 31.05	0.041	108.34 / 128.86	− 0.05	5.426 / 6.454		2.47 / 2.08	Plaskett, D.A.O. 3, 255, 1926
172	ε U Ma	12 49 .6 + 56 30	1.68	A0p	4.15 yrs.	7722.0	55.8	0.31	3.5	−12.9	69.360	0.0058	1.79	Ludendorff, A.N. 195, 369, 1913
173	ξ² Cen	13 01 .0 − 49 22	4.40	B3	7.649652	8077.493	308.63	0.353	38.8	+14.3	3.680	0.038	1.66	Neubauer, L.O.B. 15, 107, 1931
174	* RS CVn	06 .0 + 36 28	7.8–8.9	F8	4.797944	13579.344		0.0	91.6 / 99.0	− 8.9	6.040 / 6.530		1.70	Joy, Ap. Jour. 72, 41, 1930
175	ζ¹ U Ma	19 .9 + 55 27	2.40	A2p	20.53644	9477.744	103.96	0.535	69.22 / 68.83	− 9.64	16.400 / 16.400		1.62	Hadley, Det. O. 2, 101, 1915
176	* α Vir	19 .9 − 10 38	1.21	B2	4.01416	7955.846	328 / 148	0.10	126.1 / 207.8	+ 1.6	6.930 / 11.400		9.6 / 5.8	Baker, A.O. 1, 65, 1909
177	Boss 3511	30 .3 + 37 42	4.96	F0	1.61100	7018.020	199.05	0.054	10.06	+ 6.64	0.222	0.0002		Harper, D.O. 4, 223, 1918
178	Boss 3544	40 .0 − 32 33	4.36	F5	9.94480	12737.382	137.7	0.247	6.00	−23.91	0.795	0.0002		Jones, C.A. 10, 57, 1928
179	Boss 3547	40 .3 − 50 56	4.68	K0	437.00	14162.96	58.6	0.134	12.29	− 5.55	73.200	0.0818		Jones, C.A. 10, 61, 1928
180	Boss 3555	42 .1 + 26 12	5.91	F5	36.04	12014.483	258.09 / 78.09	0.490	54.01 / 65.82	+ 6.50	23.333 / 28.435		2.34 / 1.92	Petrie, D.A.O. 3, 335, 1926

* Eclipsing variable.

TABLE II.—ORBITS OF SPECTROSCOPIC BINARY STARS.—(Continued)

	Star	α(1900)δ	Mag.	Sp.	P	T 2,410,000+	ω	e	K	V_0 km/sec	$a \sin i$ million km	$\dfrac{m_1{}^3 \sin^3 i}{(m+m_1)^2}$	$m \sin^3 i$	Authority
181	ν Cen	13h43m.5 − 41°11′	3.53	B2	2d.62516	10301.39	......	0.00	20km.63	+9.05	0.745	0.0024⊙	......	Wilson, L.O.B. **8**, 130, 1914
182	Boss 3586	47.5 − 31 26	4.76	B5	6.927	8733.25	147°.22	0.23	21.4	+5.2	1.984	0.0065	......	Paddock, L.O.B. **9**, 42, 1916
183	ζ Cen	49.3 − 46 48	3.06	B2p	‡‡8.024	2266.81	287	0.5	......	......	......	......	......	Miss Maury, P.A. **29**, 636, 1921
184	η Boo	13 49.9 + 18 54	2.80	G0	497.1	8240.60	315.20	0.236	8.69	−0.234	57.735	0.0311	......	Harper, R.A.S.C. **4**, 191, 1910
185	α Dra	14 01.7 + 64 51	3.64	A0p	51.38	7403.284	19.04	0.384	46.25	−17.03	30.173	0.416	......	Harper, R.A.S.C. **4**, 91, 1910
186	Boss 3635	05.8 + 25 34	4.82	F5	9.6045	7679.523	273	0.169	68.40 / 72.05	+9.80	8.904 / 9.380	......	1.36 / 1.29	Harper, D.O. **1**, 303, 1911
187	Boss 3644	08.5 − 0 22	5.81	F5	2.6960	12744.103	93	0.0	24.34	+17.60	0.902	0.0040	......	Duncan, Ap. Jour. **54**, 226, 1921
188	Boss 3649	09.2 + 78 01	5.00	K0	575.24	13104.38	287.3	0.07	11.57	+9.49	91.300	0.11	......	Young, D.A.O. **4**, 27, 1927
189	+11° 2662	13.7 + 10 58	7.13	A3	7.369	16466.450	317.43	0.199	34.36	−28.99	3.344	0.029	......	Harper, D.A.O. **6**, 75, 1932
190	Boss 3673	13.8 + 35 58	4.83	K0	211.95	10561.18	223.42	0.54	18.02	−25.62	44.000	0.076	......	Young, D.O. **3**, 95, 1915
191	+22° 2731	35.8 + 22 24	6.17	F5	101.	13581.68	134.12	0.101	18.88	var.	26.086	0.0695	......	Harper, R.A.S.C. **20**, 180, 1926
192	39 Boo ftr	46.3 + 49 08	6.7	F5	12.822	12379.490	97.05	0.394	58.31 / 72.19	−28.23	9.450 / 11.700	......	1.27	Harper, D.A.O. **2**, 167, 1922
193	* δ Lib	55.6 − 8 07	4.8–6.2	A0	2.32735	1.89	277.05	0.054	76.5	−45.0	2.450	0.108	1.03	Schlesinger, A.O. **1**, 123, 1910
194	Boss 3827	14 56.0 + 66 20	4.86	Mb	750	12065.0	29.2	0.00	6.67	+6.85	68.800	0.023	......	Young, D.A.O. **4**, 32, 1927
195	* UC⁺B	15 14.1 + 32 01	7.9–9.1	B8	3.4522269	......	......	0	69.5 / 181.9	−7.5	3.295 / 8.635	......	[4.27] / [1.63]	Plaskett, D.A.O. **1**, 187, 1920
196	+33° 2574	15.4 + 32 54	6.14	A2	3.5753	13211.641	24.54	0.079	58.63	−25.85	2.865	0.0741	......	Christie, D.A.O. **4**, 55, 1927
197	ε Lib	18.8 − 9 57	5.08	F0	226.95	4785.116	339.52	0.68	14.00	−9.66	32.037	0.0255	......	Miss Jones, P.A.S.P. **42**, 354, 1930
198	γ U Mi	20.9 + 72 11	3.14	A2	0.108449	13204.73	160.0	0.09	14	−2	0.035	0.0000	......	Struve, P.A. **31**, 90, 1923
199	+47° 2227	25.6 + 47 35	5.96	A0	1.0085	13112.161	......	0.00	11.37	−17.04	0.158	0.0002	......	Christie, D.A.O. **3**, 310, 1926
200	* α CrB	30.5 + 27 03	2.31	A0	17.36	7742.55	312.2	0.387	34.93	+0.36	7.671	0.0602	......	Jordan, A.O. **1**, 85, 1909
201	* TW Dra	32.4 + 64 14	7.8–9.8	A5	2.80654	0.019	90	0.054	65.78	−0.34	2.535	0.0826	......	Plaskett, D.A.O. **1**, 145, 1919
202	ζ CrB btr	35.6 + 36 58	5.07	B8	12.58485	13855.681	90 / 270	0.030	134.82 / 137.71	−29.61	23.310 / 23.820	......	13.35 / 13.06	Plaskett, D.A.O. **3**, 179, 1925
203	Boss 4008	40.9 − 1 30	5.37	B8	38.95	9528.597	208.46	0.773	50.52	−11.63	17.170	0.133	......	Jordan, A.O. **3**, 153, 1915

No.	Star	α, δ (1900)	Mag	Sp	P	T	ω	e	K	γ	a sin i	f(m)	m sin³i	Authority
204	π Sco	52 .8 − 25 50	3.00	B2	1.571	15047.023	90 / 270	0.05	138 / 180	− 3.0	11.360 / 17.800		2.96 / 2.27	Struve, Elvey, Ap. Jour. 66, 217, 1927
205	β¹ Sco	15 59 .6 − 19 32	2.90	B1	6.8283	9163.923	20.09 / 200.09	0.270	125.66 / 197	−11.0	9.900 / 3.568		13.0 / 8.3	Daniel, Schlesinger, A.O. 2, 127, 1912
206	θ Dra	16 00 .0 + 58 50	4.11	F8	3.0708	5368.962	126.112	0.014	23.47	− 8.36	2.238	0.0041		Curtis, L.O.B. 4, 156, 1907
207	+8° 3134	00 .8 + 8 22	6.14	A2	8.855	1846.704	265.41	0.376	31.62	−21.54	6.571	0.023		Campbell, D.A.O. 1, 315, 1921
208	+11° 2910	01 .2 + 10 57	8.5	G5	4.28503	12418.052	82.49	0.089	38.1 / 60.12	−60.6	7.516 / 1.320		0.94	Sanford, Ap. Jour. 53, 210, 1921
209	σ CrB btr	10 .9 + 34 07	5.76	G0	7.974	13216.694	90.0 / 270.0	0.081	68.77 / 7.41	−10.63	20.380 / 0.953		1.07	Harper, D.A.O. 3, 231, 1925
210	ζ Tr A	16 17 .6 − 69 52	4.93	G0	12.9762	8103.642	274.54	0.060	38.72	+ 7.58	60.280	0.0244		Jones, C.A. 10, 64, 1928
211	ι Tr A	18 .7 − 63 50	5.30	F0	39.88796	13236.454	87.24	0.280	16.28	− 5.59	8.180	0.0005		Jones, C.A. 10, 68, 1928
212	Boss 4177	19 .3 + 7 10	5.72	A0	4.951	11773.086	355.92	0.511	12.78	−34.36	13.280	0.213		Harper, D.A.O. 4, 179, 1928
213	β Her	25 .9 + 21 42	2.81	K0	410.575	5500.374	24.6	0.550	62.41	−25.52	3.114	0.0014		Plummer, L.O.B. 5, 25, 1908
214	+17° 3053	30 .9 + 17 15	6.27	A0	10.56	12422.236	4.12	0.430	101.36	− 9.88	3.426	0.0519	2.19	Young, D.A.O. 1, 233, 1920
215	Boss 4247	37 .6 + 27 07	5.91	F2	2.3076	13923.856	184.12	0	97.4	−12.6	4.363	0.024	1.35 / 1.11 / 0.99	Sanford, Ap. Jour. 64, 184, 1926
216	μ¹ Sco	45 .1 − 37 53	3.09	B3p	†11.44627	2375.571	190	0.05	108.7	− 3.67	12.625	0.03		Miss Maury, P.A. 29, 22, 1921
217	+13° 3258	50 .7 + 13 47	6.16	F2	11.848	16576.200	267.65	0.308	28.50	−22.59	17.346	0.1337		Harper, D.A.O. 6, 88, 1932
218	Boss 4322	55 .2 + 65 17	4.82	F5	51.710	4813.75	329.32	0.128	17.96	−11.40		0.038		Harper, D.O. 4, 243, 1918
219	ε U Mi	56 .2 + 82 12	4.40	G5	39.482	8005.75	359.46	0.011	31.95	−24.03		0.1395	1.6	Plaskett, R.A.S.C. 4, 460, 1910
220	ε Her	16 56 .5 + 31 04	3.92	A0	4.0235	8086.253	180 / 0	0.023	70.39 / 112.1	+ 3.51	3.890 / 6.200		1.0	Baker, A.O. 2, 21, 1910
221	+12° 3161	17 06 .1 + 12 35	6.46	A0	23.245	11780.290	129.85	0.427	27.67	−37.2	7.997			Harper, D.A.O. 1, 197, 1920
222	α² Her	10 .1 + 14 30	5.39	(F9)	51.590	12468.581	27.89	0.028	29.64	−11.5	2.103			Sanford, Ap. Jour. 53, 212, 1921
223	* U Oph	11 .4 + 1 19	6.0-6.8	B8	1.6773476	8026.703		0.00	179.8 / 204.6		4.147 / 4.718		[5.31] / [4.66]	Plaskett, D.A.O. 1, 138, 1919
224	* u Her	13 .6 + 33 12	4.6-5.4	B3	2.05102	8125.80	66.15 / 246.15	0.053	99.50 / 253	−21.16	2.800 / 7.120		[7.5] / [2.9]	Baker, A.O. 1, 77, 1909
225	* TX Her	15 .4 + 42 00	8.1-9.0	A5	2.059786	0.042		0.0	121.01 / 140.16	− 6.38	3.427 / 3.971		[2.04] / [1.77]	Plaskett, D.A.O. 1, 207, 1920

* Eclipsing variable.
‡ Relative orbit.

TABLE II.—Orbits of Spectroscopic Binary Stars.—(Continued)

	Star	α(1900) δ	Mag.	Sp.	P	T 2,410,000+	ω	e	K km/sec	V_0 km/sec	$a \sin i$ million km	$\dfrac{m^3 \sin^3 i}{(m+m_1)^2}$	$m \sin^3 i$	Authority
226	Boss 4423	17h21m.3 − 5°00′	4.61	F0	26d.2742	8411.524	14°.48 / 194.48	0.491	47km.49 / 50.67	+0.44	14.950 / 15.950	.... /	0.88 / 0.82	Parker, D.O. 2, 331, 1915
227	+34° 2971	23.2 +34 47	5.9	B9	5.9182	13585.527	35.74	0.031	25.09	−22.73	2.041	0.0097⊙	....	Christie, D.A.O. 3, 307, 1925
228	+12° 3341	27.6 +12 00	6.18	B9	6.7984	12878.154	116.26	0.069	50.18	−12.79	4.680	0.0886	....	Campbell, D.A.O. 2, 159, 1922
229	ξ Ser	31.9 −15 20	3.64	A5	2.292285	9209.618		0	19.35	−42.77	0.610	0.0017	....	Young, L.O.B. 6, 161, 1911
230	ω Dra	37.5 +68 48	4.87	F5	5.27968	7415.491	333.76	0.011	36.26	−13.68	2.632	0.0261	....	Turner, L.O.B. 4, 163, 1907
231	+14° 3329	39.8 +14 27	6.13	A3p	3.894	14701.985	74.29 / 254.29	0.04	96.56 / 108.14	−32.39	5.148 / 5.786	....	1.83 / 1.63	Petrie, D.A.O. 4, 81, 1928
232	Boss 4507	44.4 +47 39	6.34	A0	2.82424	12106.713	30	0.017	60.15	−27.30	2.336	0.06	....	Harper, D.A.O. 1, 125, 1919
233	Boss 4520	49.7 −32 27	6.62	Oe5	12.0040	14279.497	23.2	0.065	192.4	−41.8	31.700	8.84	....	Humason, Nicholson, Ap. Jour. 67, 341, 1928
234	• Z Her	17 53.6 +15 09	7.1–7.9	F5p	3.992775			0.00	88.2 / 101.8	−46.5	4.800 / 5.600	....	1.5 / 1.3	Adams, Joy, Ap. Jour. 49, 192, 1919
235	Boss 4602	18 07.5 +79 59	6.18	F5	10.5217	11764.648	256.76 / 76.76	0.314	46.16 / 51.50	+2.93	6.341 / 7.074	....	0.46 / 0.41	Boothroyd, D.A.O. 1, 245, 1920
236	μ Sgr	07.8 −21 05	4.01	B8p	180.2	7495.64	79.13	0.447	66.82	−8.23	148.110	4.0	....	Kohl, A.N. 219, 213, 1923
237	Boss 4622	13.0 +56 34	6.41	F0	2.0476	12147.630	195.10 / 15.10	0.039	105.09 / 108.12	−8.51	2.957 / 3.042	....	1.04 / 1.01	Harper, D.A.O. 1, 307, 1921
238	ξ Pav	14.0 −61 32	4.25	K2	2214	8076.27	187.2	0.264	17.92	+12.40	526.000	1.188	....	Jones, C.A. 10, 72, 1928
239	Boss 4629	15.1 +24 24	5.49	K5	478	13540.65	234.47	0.398	16.07	−14.36	96.904	0.16	....	Harper, D.A.O. 3, 198, 1925
240	Boss 4643	17.1 +29 48	5.54	A2	5.51460	9551.742		0.00	70.1 / 101.7	−20.2	5.320 / 7.710	....	1.72 / 1.18	Daniel, Miss Jenkins, A.O. 3, 147, 1914
241	Boss 4669	22.1 +29 46	5.71	A2	9.6120	12048.711	326.43	0.468	28.49	+7.54	3.330	0.016	....	Young, D.A.O. 1, 131, 1919
242	χ Dra	22.9 +72 41	3.69	F8	280.683	13565.521	126.03	0.419	17.17	+33.64	60.170	0.1104	....	Crawford, L.O.B. 13, 176, 1928
243	• RX Her	26.0 +12 32	7.0–7.6	A0	1.7785740	9658.588		0.00	130.6 / 146.5	−24.9	3.194 / 3.583	....	2.08 / 1.85	Sanford, Ap. Jour. 68, 51, 1928
244	+65° 1276	31.0 +65 22	6.31	A3	14.3450	14710.897	295.93 / 115.93	0.210	68.29 / 72.01	−10.34	13.173 / 13.885	....	1.97 / 1.87	Petrie, D.A.O. 4, 85, 1928
245	ζ¹ Lyr	41.3 +37 30	4.29	A3	4.29991	8109.722		0.00	51.24	−25.97	3.030	0.0601	....	Jordan, A.O. 1, 115, 1909

No.	Star	Position	Mag.	Sp.	P	T	ω	e	K	γ	a sin i	f(m)		Reference
246	β Sct	41.9 − 4 51	4.47	G0	894	12480.9	33.9	0.35	16.65	−21.9	178.000	0.33	1.48	Young, D.A.O. **4**, 35, 1927
247	+49° 2871	44.9 + 49 19	7.18	F2, A	3.76468	12159.769		0.00	97.7 / 98.3	−18.8	5.058 / 5.089		1.47	Sanford, Ap. Jour. **53**, 215, 1921
248	• β¹ Lyr	46.4 + 33 15	3.4–4.1	B8p, B2p	12.922	8.541	325.05	0.014	183.71	−19.02	32.639	8.32		Rossiter, Ap. Jour. **60**, 15, 1924
249	Boss 4779	48.0 + 21 18	5.33	B9	6.3624	14589.683	195.53	0.116	17.68	−19.63	1.537	0.0358	0.95	Meyer, L.O.B. **13**, 49, 1927
250	Boss 4788	49.6 + 75 19	5.37	A0	4.1175	10293.519	107.6 / 287.6	0.012	79.12 / 83.90	− 8.79	4.480 / 4.751		0.90	Harper, R.A.S.C. **13**, 36, 1919
251	o Dra	49.7 + 59 16	4.78	K0	138.420	9258.16	274.31	0.114	23.46	−19.52	28.030	0.183		Young, D.A.O. **1**, 263, 1920
252	δ¹ Lyr	50.2 + 36 51	5.51	B3	88.112	9220.727	204.55	0.28	33.68	−25.85	39.220	0.309		Jordan, A.O. **3**, 119, 1914
253	Boss 4797	50.5 + 22 32	4.56	G0, A3	245.3	9805.0	169.5	0.12	16.0	−23.2	53.580	0.102		Wilson, L.O.B. **7**, 106, 1913
254	+20° 4022	57.0 + 20 42	6.55	B3	15.9526	14698.747	262.24	0.159	55.08	−10.29	11.930	0.266	7.10	Millman, D.A.O. **4**, 97, 1928
255	−10° 4926	18 57.1 − 10 52	6.68	B5	1.840084	15074.648	156.16 / 336.16	0.033	150.58 / 241.18	−12.86	3.827 / 6.129		4.43	Pearce, D.A.O. **4**, 75, 1927
256	Boss 4864	19 02.3 + 10 55	5.10	B8	1.30226	8157.502		0.00	27.59	−18.65	0.494	0.0028		Jordan, A.O. **3**, 77, 1914
257	Boss 4870	03.0 + 41 16	6.15	B3	1.03088	11735.647	20.02	0.015	12.12	−21.19	0.172	0.0002		Boothroyd, D.A.O. **2**, 173, 1922
258	+16° 3758	04.2 + 16 42	6.46	F5	4.812	13630.622	239.16	0.073	86.03 / 86.04	+ 8.80	5.677 / 5.678		1.26	Harper, R.A.S.C. **20**, 15, 1926
259	Boss 4876	04.4 + 38 46	7.48	A3	1.54039	12128.084	14.26	0.008	88.69	−29.79	1.8785	0.112	1.26	Harper, D.A.O. **6**, 7, 1930
260	• RS Vul	13.4 + 22 16	7.4–8.1	B8	4.477325	1.903	236.26 / 56.26	0.053	54.98 / 175.9	−22.04	3.388 / 10.842		[5.26] / [1.64]	Plaskett, D.A.O. **1**, 141, 1919
261	• U Sge	14.4 + 19 26	6.8–9.4	B9	3.38056	1.596	260	0.035	67.9	−15.1	3.155		1.18	Joy, Ap. Jour. **71**, 336, 1930
262	+37° 3413	15.5 + 37 16	6.19	A0	10.3932	13570.622	198.68	0.520	60.26	−14.86	7.356		0.84	Harper, D.A.O. **4**, 183, 1928
263	υ Sgr	16.0 − 16 08	4.58	B8p	137.939	9648.72	18.68	0.087	84.0	+12.1	10.254	1.582		Wilson, L.O.B. **8**, 132, 1914
264	• Z Vul	17.5 + 25 23	7.3–8.8	B3	2.45492		28.6	0.0	48.15 / 96.35	−15.08	91.010		[5.25] / [2.37]	Plaskett, D.A.O. **1**, 251, 1920
265	Boss 4947	19.8 + 16 45	6.03	A0	7.390	10943.233	332.6	0.05	213.74 / 52.95 / 73.8	+11.0	5.370 / 7.490		0.91 / 0.65	Young, D.O. **4**, 55, 1917
266	+55° 2215	29.2 + 55 31	6.52	G6	108.5707	13375.760	87.0	0.054	22.1 / 163.52 / 199	− 5.2	33.040	0.1222	5.3 / 4.4	Sanford, Ap. Jour. **61**, 326, 1924
267	• σ Aql	34.3 + 5 10	5.17	B3	1.95022	10054.331		0.0		− 5.00	4.380 / 5.340			Jordan, A.O. **3**, 189, 1915
268	Boss 5026	36.4 + 54 44	5.86	F5	7.6383	12201.398	46.74 / 226.74	0.527	89.81 / 91.12	−15.59	8.017 / 8.134		1.85	Harper, D.A.O. **1**, 157, 1919
269	+13° 4108	36.5 + 13 35	5.84	B3	2.4968	13963.599	95.7	0.056	47.31	−14.21	1.620	0.0273	1.83	Hill, D.A.O. **6**, 11, 1930
270	• Boss 5070	47.2 + 40 21	5.62	B2	12.427	9636.226	120.08	0.199	94.40	− 6.18	15.808	1.02		Harper, D.A.O. **1**, 257, 1920

• Eclipsing variable.

TABLE II.—ORBITS OF SPECTROSCOPIC BINARY STARS.—(Continued)

	Star	α(1900) δ	Mag.	Sp.	P	T 2,410,000+	ω	e	K	V₀ km/sec	a sin i million km	$\dfrac{m_1^3 \sin^3 i}{(m + m_1)^2}$	m sin³ i	Authority
271	ψ Aql	19h 51m 5 + 11°09′	5.29	A2	3.3204 d	13324.045	56°0	0.055	38.25	−27.63	1.7448	0.0192⊙	.....	Harper, D.A.O. 2, 179, 1922
272	θ¹ Sgr	53.2 − 35 33	4.39	B3	2.10514	1140.645		0.0	15.9	+0.9	0.460	0.0009	.....	Wilson, Huffer, P.A. 29, 86, 1921
273	BDS 9818 btr	19 56.6 + 10 28	7.5	F3	4.4698	13802.192	294.5	0.10	41.3	−43.0	2.526	0.0032	.....	Sanford, Ap. Jour. 61, 330, 1924
274	+35° 3970	20 03.6 + 35 26	7.12	B0	8.33425	14039.940	0.50 / 180.50	0.264	156.97 / 168.5	−5.44	17.351 / 18.626		13.85 / 12.90	Plaskett, D.A.O. 3, 258, 1926
275	θ Aql	06.1 − 1 07	3.37	A0	17.1245	8261.914	14.9 / 194.9	0.681	46.0 / 63.0	−30.5	7.930 / 10.860		0.52 / 0.38	Baker, A.O. 2, 41, 1910
276	Boss 5173	06.4 + 26 36	5.46	A2	9.316	10304.628	103.15 / 283.15	0.012	78.49 / 86.31	−13.04	10.054 / 11.055		2.27 / 2.06	Harper, D.O. 4, 199, 1918
277	Boss 5192	11.2 + 23 12	5.38	G5	251.0	13415.850	121.0	0.042	26.99	−23.75	93.072	0.5112	.....	Harper, D.A.O. 3, 201, 1924
278	Boss 5200	12.3 + 47 24	4.16	K0, A3	1170 / 390	10700.39 / 10515.821	281.05	0.182 / 0	16.64 / 5.86	−14.35	263.250	0.53	.....	Cannon, D.O. 4, 151, 1918
279	β Cap	15.4 − 15 06	3.25	G0, A0	1378.49	6031.49	122.76	0.437	22.44	−19.02	382.500	1.177	.....	Jones, C.A. 10, 76, 1928
280	+45° 3139	15.6 + 46 00	6.28	B1	2.98474	13951.678	103.17 / 283.17	0.098	115.54 / 142.61	−8.93	4.719 / 5.825		2.90 / 2.35	Plaskett, D.A.O. 4, 103, 1928
281	α Pav	17.7 − 57 03	2.12	B3	11.753	6379.90	224.80	0.01	7.25	+2.0	1.170	0.0005	.....	Curtis, L.O.B. 4, 154, 1907
282	+25° 4299	31.8 + 25 34	6.29	A2	11.0630	16492.698	57.3	0.29	59.5	−19.0	8.678	0.212	.....	Shajn, Pul. Cir. 1, 15, 1932
283	ι Del	33.0 + 11 02	5.43	A2	10.9960	12095.816	60.81	0.252	26.72	−5.50	3.910	0.020	.....	Harper, D.A.O. 1, 153, 1919
284	Boss 5294	33.2 − 1 27	4.51	K0	205.0	12311.55	321.43	0.128	9.78	6.09	27.347	0.0194	.....	Harper, D.A.O. 3, 345, 1926
285	• Y Cyg	48.1 + 34 17	7.1–7.9	B2	2.996332		var.	0.13	244.9 / 241.4	var.	10.010 / 9.862		[17.4] / [17.6]	Redman, D.A.O. 4, 341, 1931
286	Boss 5375	49.7 + 44 00	4.68	B3	2.8546	8554.770	45 / 225	0.137	110.4 / 118.8	−16.2	4.200 / 4.620		1.79 / 1.67	Baker, A.O. 2, 35, 1910
287	+44° 3639	20 53.1 + 44 33	6.01	Oe5	48.608	12892.226	66.75	0.0088	42.22	−5.78	28.076	0.374	.....	Plaskett, D.A.O. 2, 183, 1922
288	Boss 5442	21 04.4 + 29 48	5.57	A0	3.3137	12521.230		0.0	26	−26.8	1.185	0.0060	.....	Young, D.A.O. 1, 319, 1921
289	σ Cyg	13.5 + 38 59	4.28	A0p	11.043	11069.27	119.1	0.40	1.98	−3.80	0.276	0.000007	.....	Henroteau, Det. O. 3, 39, 1917
290	+57° 2309	14.6 + 58 11	6.41	B3	5.41364 / 225.44	13635.140 / 13803.98	58.5 / 16.6	0.114 / 0.226	40.0 / 21.9	var. / −17.2	2.960 / 66.130	0.0353 / 0.2273	.....	Sanford, P.A.S.P. 38, 282, 1926

No.	Star	R.A. / Dec.	Mag.	Sp.	P	T	ω	e	K	V₀	a sin i	f(m)	m sin³ i	Authority
291	+32° 4134	17.1 + 32 11	6.03	A0	20.30	14363.558	219.67 / 39.67	0.441	45.71 / 78.95	− 3.98	10.278 / 17.753		1.87 / 1.08	Harper, *D.A.O.* **3**, 319, 1926
292	+39° 4529	17.2 + 39 55	6.46	F8	3.24343	11801.549	357.55	0.0223	62.23	+ 0.16	2.773	0.0811		Plaskett, *D.A.O.* **1**, 113, 1919
293	+18° 4794	21.8 + 18 58	6.06	A3	21.724	13302.555	......	0.0	41.45	−12.42	12.382	0.1607		Harper, *D.A.O.* **4**, 167, 1927
294	+27° 4107	30.9 + 27 46	6.35	F0	12.21	13710.068	46.79 / 226.79	0.318	51.95 / 65.24	−43.17	8.2698 / 10.3852		0.97 / 0.77	Harper, *D.A.O.* **3**, 241, 1925
295	Boss 5565	35.9 + 57 02	5.64	Oe5	3.71063	12889.413	57.36	0.1879	75.29	− 7.99	3.7733	0.155		Plaskett, *D.A.O.* **4**, 108, 1928
296	Boss 5566	36.1 − 14 30	5.28	G5	13.17275	13689.424	172.48	0.195	23.32	var.	4.130	0.0164		Jones, *C.A.* **10**, 81, 1928
297	Boss 5575	37.8 − 20 04	6.17	A3	6.3702	15486.567	......	0	82.1 / 86.3	−25.5	7.191 / 7.559		1.618 / 1.540	Sanford, *Ap. Jour.* **74**, 205, 1931
298	Boss 5579	38.4 + 40 37	5.48	A0	1.72897	11774.161	256.0 / 76.0	0.033	109.70 / 110.35	−25.47	2.6068 / 2.6221		0.96 / 0.95	Harper, *D.A.O.* **3**, 324, 1926
299	Boss 5591	39.9 + 28 19	6.90	A5	3.74860	12175.1577	262.66 / 82.66	0.189	92.1 / 93.2	+ 4.2	4.662 / 4.728		1.19 / 1.17	Sanford, *Ap. Jour.* **53**, 218, 1921
300	κ Peg Aa	40.1 + 25 11	4.27	F5	5.9715	......	var.	0.034	41.5	var.	3.408	0.0443		Henroteau, *L.O.B.* **9**, 120, 1918
301	δ Cap	41.5 − 16 35	2.98	A5	1.02275	11451.86	149.06	0.019	65.67	− 5.82	0.926	0.0301		Crump, *Ap. Jour.* **54**, 127, 1921
302	Boss 5629	48.8 + 55 20	5.54	B3	17.3263	14415.682	269.9	0.224	108.3 / 165.8	− 6.5	25.150 / 38.500		20.8 / 13.6	Pearce, *R.A.S.C.* **26**, 345, 1932
303	• RT Lac	57.4 + 43 24	8.8–9.8	G5	5.073921	8204.444	......	0.0	62.5 / 116.0	−47.0 / −47.0	4.360 / 8.090		1.9 / 1.0	Joy, *Ap. Jour.* **74**, 101, 1931
304	Boss 5671	21 59.7 − 1 24	5.23	A3	7.8325	11804.702	180	0.004	6.94	+20.30	0.748	0.0003		Miss Farnsworth, Miss Jones, *L.O.B.* **16**, 46, 1932
305	Boss 5683	22 01.9 + 82 23	7.37	F5	1.1522143	13213.363	......	0	105.6 / 112.4	−17.0	3.470†		0.65 / 0.61	Sanford, *Ap. Jour.* **65**, 295, 1927
306	+47° 3692	02.0 + 47 45	6.16	B3	2.1721	12138.172	251.81	0.0	127.7	−17.76	3.810	0.47		Young, *D.A.O.* **1**, 195, 1920
307	ι Peg	02.4 + 24 51	3.96	F5	10.21312	4820.966	48.5	0.008	47.99	− 4.12	6.740	0.117		Curtis, *L.O.B.* **2**, 169, 1904
308	α Tuc	11.7 − 60 45	2.91	K2	4197.7	8666.4	180	0.385	7.23	+42.24	385.100	0.1295		Jones, *M.N.* **83**, 657, 1928
309	Boss 5764	16.9 + 46 02	4.66	B5	2.6164	8193.30	......	0.015	80.3 / 98.8	− 9.0	2.890 / 3.550		0.87 / 0.71	Baker, *A.O.* **1**, 92, 1909
310	Boss 5534	31.7 + 49 33	6.20	B3	10.9114	14340.542	67.54 / 247.54	0.253	83.27 / 129.44	−15.28	12.088 / 18.789		6.01 / 3.87	Hill, *D.A.O.* **3**, 358, 1926

• Eclipsing variable.

† (a₁ + a₂) sin i.

TABLE II.—ORBITS OF SPECTROSCOPIC BINARY STARS.—(Continued)

	Star	α(1900) δ	Mag.	Sp.	P	T 2,410,000+	ω	e	K	V_0 km/sec	a sin i million km	$\dfrac{m_1{}^3 \sin^3 i}{(m+m_1)^2}$	m sin³ i	Authority
311	Boss 5846	22ʰ34ᵐ8 − 9°53′	6.74	G0	21ᵈ6997	15172.797	213°1	0.38	56ᵏᵐ5	−39.3	15.599	......	1.47	Sanford, Ap. Jour. 74, 209, 1931
312	η Peg	38.3 + 29 42	3.10	G0	818.0	5288.7	33.1	0.155	60.3	+ 4.31	15.648	......	1.38	Crawford, L.O.B. 1, 27, 1901
313	* + 64° 1717	44.2 + 64 32	6.83	B3	‡1.77476	14076.621	5.60 / 106.3	0.034	14.20 / 225.3	−20.6	157.800	0.234⊙	11.4 / 9.8	Pearce, D.A.O. 3, 171, 1925
314	Boss 5900	48.2 + 16 19	5.72	K0	24.65	12240.992	286.3	0	261.2	−12.84	11.254	0.094	......	Harper, D.A.O. 1, 203, 1920
315	Boss 5913	22 51.8 + 41 04	5.54	B3	12.3106	14063.894	7.8	0.10	33.20 / 22.2	6.9	3.650	0.0138	......	Struve, Bobrovnikoff, Ap. Jour. 62, 142, 1925
316	+ 45° 4147	23 02.7 + 45 33	6.56	B5	3.3372	12151.272	125.67	0.233	87.70	−15.13	3.910	0.215	4.8	Young, D.A.O. 1, 239, 1920
317	+ 58° 2546	03.0 + 59 13	6.28	B3	7.25105	11825.038	71.6 / 251.6	0.376	87.9 / 146.7	− 4.6	8.121 / 13.550	......	2.9	Pearce, R.A.S.C. 26, 345, 1932
318	π Cep	04.7 + 74 51	4.56	G5	556.2	4126.33	5.70	0.281	23.02	−19.63	168.970	0.6228	......	Harper, D.A.O. 3, 204, 1925
319	ι Gru	04.7 − 45 47	4.10	K0	409.614	6115.569	240.76	0.656	13.62	− 4.17	57.900	0.0462	......	Jones, C.A. 10, 89, 1928
320	* Boss 5996	13.7 + 41 14	5.90	A3	3.2195	11059.912	40.57	0.036	73.56	− 4.87	3.240	0.133	......	Young, D.O. 4, 83, 1917
321	* AR Cas	25.4 + 58 00	(5.0–6.0)	B3	6.067	8223.762	3.35	0.224	59.06	−14.78	4.920	0.1203	......	Baker, A.O. 2, 25, 1910
322	Boss 6070	32.6 + 16 17	6.18	A0	11.2298	11916.943	236.38	0.037	26.70	−27.38	4.120	0.011	......	Smith, D.A.O. 3, 163, 1925
323	λ And	32.7 + 45 55	4.00	K0	20.546	6683.46	301.0	0.086	7.07	+ 7.43	1.990	0.0007	......	Burns, L.O.B. 4, 87, 1906
324	+ 27° 4642	49.9 + 28 06	7.30	K0	6.7217	12220.740	18.6	0.059	38.5	−19.8	3.552	0.0125	......	Sanford, Ap. Jour. 53, 221, 1921
325	Boss 6142	50.5 + 56 53	6.05	B0	13.435	10800.634	339.56 / 159.56	0.105	115.5 / 167	−26.7	21.200 / 30.700	......	18.5 / 12.7	Young, D.O. 3, 373, 1916
326	Boss 6148	23 52.1 + 55 09	5.69	F5	12.155	12162.601	213.45 / 33.45	0.278	71.52 / 72.97	+11.98	11.4823 / 11.7155	......	1.70 / 1.67	Harper, D.A.O. 2, 263, 1923

* Eclipsing variable.
‡ Published data corrected by letter.

NAME INDEX

A

Adams, W. S., 228, 239, 242, 248
Airy, G., 17
Alter, D., 121, 244
Anderson, J. A., 68, 250
André, C., 123
Argelander, F. W. A., 254
Åstrand, J. J., 80
Auwers, A., 118, 237, 238, 243

B

Baize, P., 40, 244
Baker, R. H., 182
Banachiewicz, T., 202
Barnard, E. E., 23, 47, 60, 240, 241
Barr, J. M., 213
Barton, S. G., 67
Bell, L., 270
Belopolsky, A., 134, 248, 254
Bergstrand, O., 244
Berman, L., 247, 248
Bernewitz, E., 97
Bessel, F. W., 13, 19, 118, 119n., 225, 243
Bishop, G., 17
Bleksley, A. E. H., 278
Bode, J. E., 3, 4
Bohlin, K., 215
Bond, G. P., 1, 64, 237
Boothroyd, S. L., 22
Bos, W. H. van den, 37, 39, 60n., 71, 78n., 79, 90, 112, 119, 204, 209n., 240, 246, 247, 260
Bosler, J., 62
Boss, L., 226, 227, 239
Bradley, J., 1, 2, 14, 243
Brashear, J. A., 37
Brill, A., 234
Brisbane, T. M., 35

Brown, E. W., 278n.
Burnham, S. W., 10, 17, 19–22, 24, 25, 32–35, 53, 59, 238, 240, 241

C

Campbell, W. W., 29, 46n., 135, 145, 150, 206, 210, 219, 249
Cannon, Annie J., 130, 267
Chamberlin, T. C., 275
Chandler, S. C., 182, 254
Chang, Y. C., 216
Clark, A., 17, 20, 23
Clark, A. G., 23, 118, 225, 237
Cogshall, W. A., 22
Comstock, G. C., 72, 111, 117, 120, 124, 228, 231
Cornu, M. A., 142, 149
Crawford, R. T., 114, 115
Crossley, E., 32
Curtis, H. D., 29, 159, 162, 165, 180, 248
Curtiss, R. H., 146, 150, 180, 254, 255

D

Danjon, M. A., 256n.
Darwin, G. H., 277, 280
Dawes, W. R., 17, 53, 57, 63, 72
Dawson, B. H., 37, 124, 244
De Sitter, W., 124
Dembowski, Ercole, 18, 19, 53, 72
Ditscheiner, L., 145
Doberck, W., 124, 203, 205, 206, 215, 235
Doig, P., 270n.
Donner, H. F., 38
Doolittle, Eric, 33, 34, 241
Doppler, Ch., 125

303

SUBJECT INDEX

A

Algol, 253
Ångström unit defined, 129

B

Binary stars, definition of, ix
  density of, 231
  distribution of, by spectral class,
    267–269
  invisible companions in systems
    of, 118, 225
  masses of, 216
  multiple systems of, 224, 232, 245,
    274
  number of known orbits of, 203–
    205
  parallaxes of, from orbits and
    radial velocities, 224
  relations between period, and
    eccentricity in orbits of, 205,
    213
    and spectral class in orbits of,
    210
  systems of special interest, 235
  tables, of the known orbits of,
    283, 288
  of masses of, 220
  theories of the origin of, capture
    theory, 275
    fission theory, 277
    general statement of problem
      of, 273
    separate nuclei theory, 278
    summary of, 280
    (*See also* Double stars; Eclipsing
      binary stars; Spectroscopic
      binary stars; Visual binary
      stars)

C

Cancri, Tau, 232
Capella, 249
Castor, 248
Centauri, Alpha, 235
Cepheid variable stars, 30
Color contrast in double stars, 16,
  270
61 *Cygni*, 243

D

Doppler-Fizeau principle, 126
Double stars, Burnham's discoveries
  and measures, 20, 25
  color contrast in, 16, 270
  conventions for measures of, 15, 41
  correction for proper motion in, 73
  diaphragms used in measuring, 59
  distribution of, by angular dis-
    tances, and magnitudes, etc.,
    261
    in right ascension and declina-
      tion, 260
  early discoveries of, 1
  early orbit methods for, 71, 72
  early speculations on character of,
    2
  errors of measure of, 60
  eyepieces for measuring, 59
  first collection of, 3
  first photograph of, 1, 64
  general catalogues of, 32, 39
  Herschel's discoveries and theo-
    ries, 4
  Herschel (J) and South's work on,
    9
  interferometer measures of, 67
  Lick Observatory survey for dis-
    covery of, 24, 257